# THE EARTH AND THE STARS

TOTAL SOLAR ECLIPSE, JAN. 24, 1925. (Slocum.)

# THE EARTH AND THE STARS

BY

## C. G. ABBOT, D.Sc.

ASSISTANT SECRETARY, SMITHSONIAN INSTITUTION; DIRECTOR,
SMITHSONIAN ASTROPHYSICAL OBSERVATORY; MEMBER,
NATIONAL ACADEMY OF SCIENCES

*SECOND PRINTING*

*ILLUSTRATED*

NEW YORK
D. VAN NOSTRAND COMPANY
EIGHT WARREN STREET
1926

# PREFACE

To those who wish to acquire by easy reading a general survey of the universe they dwell in, it is hoped that this book may be helpful. The wonderful progress of the last quarter-century has brought about a most happy and fruitful marriage of astronomy with physics. From the structure of the atom to the structure of the universe, we seem to follow a definite thread of reason. Many observations which formerly were interesting and curious, but apparently isolated, now seem to fit beautifully into a general scheme. It has been the aim of the author to present the most salient of the facts in simple words, and in such relations as will display our present views of why and how the celestial host came to be as it is.

This book is for non-technical readers, and not for the professional astronomer. Ten times its size would not cover so wide a range of subjects thoroughly enough for him. Yet if some astronomer happens to take it up, the author hopes that this little volume may not prove unpleasing.

To his friends Dr. W. S. Adams and Dr. S. A. Mitchell, who have criticised the text, and to the many friends who have contributed beautiful and telling illustrations, the author tenders grateful thanks.

CHARLES G. ABBOT

July, 1925

v

# CONTENTS

# LIST OF ILLUSTRATIONS

## PLATES

# TEXT FIGURES

# The Earth and the Stars

## Chapter I

## THE HEAVENLY BODIES AND THEIR GREATEST ENIGMA

It was a famous American astronomer, the late Professor Simon Newcomb, who recommended everybody to go alone on one of those clear, sparkling, moonless nights to a hill in the country where there is a wide horizon. Arrived at such a place he should lie down on the ground and watch the slow majestic march of the stars as one by one they rise, cross the sky, and set. Suppose it is October and, well-wrapped against the nip of the night air, we follow his advice. Soon after sunset, we take our place to watch the sky, unaided by other instruments than our eyes, like the Magi who followed the star of Bethlehem.

Let us look first towards the western sky, before its stars are set. The twilight still shows a dusky sunset glow far down next the horizon. In October of each of the years 1925 to 1929, and in the sixth year after each of these, the little planet Mercury, our sun's nearest neighbor, is evening star, and on clear nights can be seen for a half hour or more after sunset, very near the spot on the western horizon where the sun went down. Similarly in October of the years 1925, 1928, 1930, 1931 and on the eighth year after each of these, the planet Venus, our nearest neighbor after the moon, is evening star. Being farther from the sun than Mercury, she often reaches a much higher standing in the western sky after sunset, and may sometimes be followed for almost three hours before she sets. Venus is often very bright, indeed the brightest of all the heavenly bodies except the sun and moon. If one is upon a lofty mountain in very clear, moonless weather, Venus may sometimes be seen setting like a little emerald, making a beautiful example of the "green ray" which we shall mention in a later chapter.

Every October in the years 1923 to 1927, the great planet Jupiter is visible in the evening hours, and in the years 1923 to 1933 Saturn also. If we had a telescope we should see the wonderful rings of Saturn, perhaps the most beautiful of all celestial sights. Mars, the fiery red planet, is evening star in October of the years 1929, 1931, and every second year thereafter till 1939. All of these five bright planets, and Uranus and Neptune also, which can hardly be distinguished without a telescope because they are far away and faint, follow nearly the path of the sun, so that one sees them set not very far from where the sun went down. Although we loosely speak of them as morning or evening stars, the planets are not stars at all. They are attached to the family of our sun, and shine by reflecting his light. Stars, on the contrary, are other suns, immensely distant and shine by their own light. Planets appear to wander about among the stars. Stars retain their relative places with slight change from year to year.

It makes a great difference in the face of the starry sky how far to the north or the south one lives. The Southern Cross, for instance, is never seen in the United States, nor the Great Dipper in Patagonia. For people in the United States and southern Europe, the October evening sky presents its brighter stars about as follows: In the northwest the glowing Arcturus is about to set, while in the southwest the duskier red Antares in the constellation of the Scorpion is also nearly setting. Somewhat west of the zenith stands the brilliant white star Vega, and towards the east and south from Vega, in the embrace of the Milky Way, lies the slightly fainter white star Altair. Further east, somewhat further north than Vega, and in brightness half-way between Altair and the pole star, is Deneb, another white one. A very brilliant far-northern star is the yellowish Capella, seen a good way to the northeast of Deneb. Of all the bright northern stars, Capella is most like our sun.

Towards the southeast and not well seen early in the October evening lies a field of bright gems. Aldebaran, which is the red star in the V-shaped group, rises earliest of them, and has gotten well up in the eastern sky. Southeast of him lies the great group of Orion whose central figure is like a square with the giant red star, Betelgeuse to the north, and the giant blue star Rigel to the south of it. Further south and later rising is the white Sirius, brightest of all the stars of the entire heavens. Rising still later, and about as far north as Betelgeuse, comes Procyon, slightly yellowish of tinge. Rising soon after Procyon but further north, comes the reddish Pollux, the brighter of the twins Castor and Pollux. Last of all of the first magnitude stars of our northern October sky to rise is Regulus, in the constellation of the Lion, which comes up a little north of east at about two o'clock in the morning on October 15.

Had we traveled in the southern Hemisphere, for instance in South Australia or New Zealand, Deneb and Capella must have been dropped from our list of bright stars, along with the pole star, as too northerly for observation. But the yellow Alpha Centauri, the nearest of all the stars and very like our sun, could replace Capella. In the early evening it would lie in the southwest. Its blue companion, Beta Centauri, would lie still nearer the horizon and further south. Nearly over-head would be the white star Fomalhaut, as bright as Deneb. The brilliant blue Achernar would be directly south at midnight, and following it five hours later, a little further north, would come Canopus, next to Sirius the brightest star of all. The Orion stars would have moved to the northeastern quarter. We should see at this time of the year the two bright bluish stars, Alpha Crucis and Beta Crucis, of the constellation Southern Cross, far down near the southwest horizon in the evening and in the southeast several hours before sunrise. In October, Spica, alone of all the first magnitude stars, would be too near the sun and lost in the morning or evening twilight.

These twenty-one brightest stars and the five brightest planets which we have named should be well known to everybody. A table will be found in the Appendix which gives various facts about them.

Stretching diagonally across the sky from northeast to southwest, and passing almost directly overhead in the October evenings, lies the Milky Way. Like the bright stars, it marches from east to west throughout the night, but some parts of it are always in view, for it is a belt that completely encircles the heavens.

As we watch the stars moving through the night, we see that they move by less and less distances and more and more aslant to the horizon, as we look farther and farther north, till presently we find some that neither rise nor set, but describe large circles in the northern sky. Looking towards the center of these circles, we find the stars moving less and less swiftly, till finally, at the pole star the eye can scarcely see motion at all, unless we guide our view very accurately by some fixed objects in a line, such as stones or houses.

So the sun and all the stars move across our sky from east to west or from west to east according as they are south or north of the pole star. The reason for it is that our round earth is itself rotating eastwardly, one rotation in twenty-four hours, about its axis which points nearly towards the pole star. Of course we know that the earth has no real solid axis, with bearings, like a bicycle wheel. It rests upon nothing, and spins thereon without ever losing its place! We shall think more about this paradox in a later Chapter.

As we watch the stars, going by over our heads, they seem innumerable. But every one of them that the eye can see has long ago been numbered and given a place, each with its identifications and many descriptive annotations, in the astronomical catalogues. The naked eye stars that can be seen in one view of the heavens are, in fact, hardly more numerous than the people in a large full theatre. All of them that the sharpest eye can see unaided in both the northern and southern hemispheres, and in the dark and daylight sides of the earth combined, hardly exceed five thousand.

But it is far otherwise when we search the sky with a giant telescope and photography. For the Milky Way, that looks like a dim cloud, resolves itself into a perfect host of individual stars. It has been computed, for of course no one's life-time would be long enough to examine them every one, that all of the stars which could be photographed with our largest instruments would be nearly as many as the human inhabitants of our earth, or perhaps a thousand millions. Occasionally, as we watch, we see what appear to be little stars dart out from among their neighbors, rush a long way through the sky and disappear, sometimes leaving behind a short-lived train of light. These shooting stars, or meteors, are not really stars at all, but are little cold bits of dust or metal which belong, at least temporarily, not among the stars, but among the planets. They are attached to the family of our sun, and happen, in their courses, to overtake or be overtaken by our earth's atmosphere. Rushing through the air with enormous speeds, they speedily become white hot, and burn up like iron heated too hot in the blacksmith's forge. Most of them are quite consumed in the upper air, but some very large ones reach the earth. Admiral Peary even found one of several tons weight on one of his Greenland Expeditions, and brought it to the American Museum in New York. Here, like a wild animal of the jungle caged in a zoölogical garden, this captured free tenant of boundless outer space is housed up to amuse and instruct the people.

Thousands of years have passed since men first looked upon the stars. Yet we know that their order has apparently changed but little in all that time. Probably there would be little of change of any kind among them that the sharpest naked eye observer could note, if, like the legendary Wandering Jew, he had lived from the time of Christ until now. Stars that were brightest then are brightest now, as we know on the best of grounds.

It is true that once every few years there comes to view what astronomers call a new star. Thus in February, 1901, there blazed up in the northern constellation of Perseus a star, till then obscure, which for a few days rivaled all but the very brightest of our list of the twenty-one. But it soon faded and is now visible only to fair-sized telescopes. Again, in June, 1918, a new star arose near Altair, in the constellation Aquila, which briefly surpassed all but Sirius in brightness. But this also has faded to dimness. It is a curious thought that these new stars of the twentieth century are really so far away that their light, our swiftest messenger, traveling 186,000 miles each second, had been on the way some centuries. These stars had really flashed forth and faded back to insignificance perhaps before Cromwell was Lord Protector of England.

Since it is only the most harmonious relations which survive the shock and wear and tear of time unchanged, it is not surprising that imaginative and poetic natures, contemplating the enduring splendor of the matchless heavens, should have fallen upon the beautiful conception of the "harmony of the spheres." The thought is expressed by some one on a visit to the Alpine heights of Chamonix, as follows:

"Shine! shine! ye stars in splendor.
Rule o'er the Alpine night.
Awake the soul's deep longing
For worlds than this more bright.

While on this lofty mountain
We seem to Heaven more near;
We seem to hear the chorus
Of every rolling sphere.

For though in solemn stillness
The planets circle round,
And though the constellations
Give neither voice nor sound,

The listening soul, enraptured,
The thoughtful eye can see
How like our Heavenly homeland
This world of ours may be."

But it is time that our nocturnal expedition should be ended. We have, let us hope, awakened in ourselves so great an interest in this myriad of wonders that we call the heavenly host, that we shall wish to scan more closely those secrets which the earth, the moon, the sun, the planets, the stars, and all the other heavenly bodies have yielded up to patient investigation of astronomers.

We shall hardly leave our lonely hill of observation, however, without having one other great thought rush into our minds. It is this: Among this myriad of objects which are within the visible creation, is there not, besides our world, some other, or perhaps many other abodes of thoughtful life similar to ours? This is the great enigma of Astronomy. Our study must show how far our science can go to give us a reasonable answer to this question.

Were there but beings like ourselves on other worlds, and could there be some wireless communication established between us and them, what a breathless interest we should have in learning from them of their forms of society, their governments, their religions, the scenes with which they are surrounded, and, in a word, the whole conditions of races of intelligent beings developed independently from ourselves!

## Chapter II

### SOME FAMOUS ASTRONOMERS AND FAMOUS INSTRUMENTS

As we look up at the starry heavens, they present merely a multitude of gleams, diamond-like gleams to be sure, on an azure ground. The fascinating aim of modern astronomy is to give life to this flat picture. The older observers took the census of the sky. Modern astronomers dwell more on applying the latest discoveries in physics and chemistry to determine what the stars are and why.

In ancient times, the clever Greeks worked out the mathematical sciences of geometry and trigonometry, by which we measure inaccessible things through angles, in order to solve in part the problems of the size of the earth and the motions of the sun, moon and stars. One of the greatest of them was Hipparchus who worked about 150 to 125 B.C. He catalogued 1080 stars, founded the science of trigonometry, fixed positions on the earth by latitude and longitude, determined the length of the year, the periods of revolution of the five great planets around the sun, and the obliquity of the ecliptic, that is the inclination of the earth's equator to its plane of revolution about the sun. He found the eccentricity of the earth's orbit, or in other words how far it is from being circular; measured the distance of the moon roughly, and discovered the precession of the equinoxes, or that the sun's place among the stars, at times of equal day and night constantly tends eastward. This last discovery of his waited two thousand years for its explanation.

Nearly three centuries went by from Hipparchus to Ptolemy of Alexandria, who flourished 127 to 151 A.D. He was less a great observer than Hipparchus, but he collected all knowledge in the famous work which the Arabs called "Almagest." He describes the earth as a sphere in the center of the heavens, which he assumes are very far away compared to the size of the earth. "Though

7

some say the earth turns on its axis, and truly this simplifies theory, yet," says Ptolemy, "it is ridiculous." The heavens, he points out, have two principal motions. One carries them around the earth uniformly from east to west each day, the other is peculiar to some stars only (he means the planets, of course) and is contrary to the first and about different axes. Ptolemy gives mathematical tables useful for trigonometry which he computed by an elegant method, and goes on with a great number of facts such as the obliquity of the ecliptic, the length of day and height of the sun at different times and places. Recognizing the earth as the center of things and immovable, he was at pains to work out an elaborate theory of epicycles and eccentrics to explain the apparent motions of the sun, moon and planets. He discusses the eclipse observations of the Chaldeans and his own, and sums up the knowledge of how to calculate eclipses. Ptolemy gives a catalogue of over a thousand of the fixed stars, with their positions, arrangement in constellations, and brightness.

Ptolemy's "Almagest" ruled the astronomical thought of the next thousand years and more, till there came the century of the geniuses. Where else can we find within a single century another such group of men of accomplishment as this! Gutenberg (1398-1468) who invented printing; Columbus (1446-1506) who discovered a new world; Copernicus (1473-1543) who reconceived the place of the earth in the universe; Leonardo da Vinci (1452-1519), Michelangelo (1475-1564), Titian (1477-1576), and Raphael (1483-1520), a quartet whose achievements it is unnecessary to rehearse, and Martin Luther (1483-1546) the apostle of the Reformation.

Copernicus, a physician and priest of a small place in Poland, spent his life in ministering to the poor and thinking of great things. He conceived that the rising and setting of the sun and stars are the consequence of a daily rotation of our earth upon an axis inclined toward the polar star, and that the earth and the great planets, Mercury, Venus, Mars, Jupiter, and Saturn (all that were known in his day) revolve about the sun. So great a derogation as this of the majesty of the earth, and consequently of man, its chief citizen, seemed impious in the eyes of most of Copernicus' contemporaries and successors for a century and more; so that we find the immortal Galileo (1564-1642) suffering persecution in his old age for holding to this heresy.

But, after the long dormancy of the middle ages, events now moved rapidly. The planetary observations of Tycho Brahe and his pupil Kepler, who together flourished from 1570 to 1630, were expressed by the latter in the three famous laws that bear his name. Kepler's laws are these: (1) The earth and other planets revolve about the sun in ellipses with the sun in one of the foci. (2) Lines joining the centers of planets and the sun[1] sweep over equal areas in equal times. (3) The squares of the periods of revolution are proportional to the cubes of the mean distances of the planets. When he had fully verified these three laws, Kepler declared in a burst of enthusiasm: "What I prophesied twenty-two years ago . . . what I promised my friends . . . what sixteen years ago I urged as a thing to be sought, that for which I joined Tycho Brahe . . . for which I have devoted the best part of my life to astronomical contemplations, at length I have brought to light . . . It is now eighteen months since I got the first glimpse of light, three months since the dawn, very few days since the unveiled sun, most admirable to gaze on, burst out on me. Nothing holds me! I will indulge my sacred fury . . . If you forgive me, I rejoice; if you are angry, I can bear it; the die is cast, the book is written . . . it may well wait a century for a reader, as God has waited six thousand years for an interpreter of his works."

Right here, on the threshold between the old and the new, between the eye and the telescope, between the downfall of Ptolemy and the triumph of Copernicus, let us pause to consider the instruments which were available to astronomers from Hipparchus to Kepler.

In the first place they used the most wonderful of all astronomical instruments, the human eye. It is, indeed, a part of every optical instrument which was ever designed, and so is absolutely indispensable. The naked eye alone reveals much. In the first place, consider what a range of brightness the eye perceives. One may look at the sun, though to be sure it is not safe to look long. The Belgian

[1] Usually called the radius vector.

physicist, Plateau, desiring to study the "after images" that would be produced, gazed steadily at the sun for twenty seconds and in consequence lost his sight. But every one has glanced at the sun, so it may be set as the upper limit of brightness. At the other end of the scale may stand sixth magnitude stars, though by remaining in perfect darkness for a considerable time the sensitiveness of the eye passes beyond this limit. The brightness of the sun is more than a million-million ($10^{12}$) times that of sixth magnitude stars, and yet our eyes range over this whole enormous gamut.

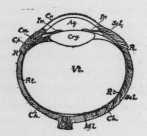

FIG. 1.  DIAGRAM OF THE HUMAN EYE.

*Cr*, cornea; *Aq*, aqueous humor; *Scl*, sclerotic coat; *Cry*, crystalline lens; *Ir*, iris; *Cm*, *Cp*, muscles for accommodation to light intensity and focus; *Vt*, vitreous humor; *Ch*, choroid coat; *Rt*, retina; *Op*, optic nerve.

Without the eye we should know nothing of color. Suppose the violet, the rose, the lily, the crocus, the grass of the meadow and the sunset glow were all a colorless gray, differing only in brightness. We can hardly imagine what loss of quality this void of beauty would produce in human character.

The eye is a very complete instrument. In many ways it resembles a camera for photography. First comes a shutter, the eye lids, armed with eyelashes to keep out the dust. Next is the instrument itself, which like a telescope must point towards different directions, and so is given a universal mounting by being shaped as a ball, moving in a lubricated socket, and pulled about by cords operated on signals from the brain. For distinctness, objects must be focused without giving color blurring at the edges of the images, the so-called "chromatic aberration." So the eye is provided with a compound lens, made up of a concavo-convex part, the aqueous humor, and a double convex part, the crystalline lens. But accomplishing what man cannot readily devise, Nature has provided means to focus on different objects by merely lengthening or shortening the focal length of the combination, not by moving the lens in and out, as in a camera, but by altering the curvature and thickness of the lens. In order to help accommodate the eye to the enormous range of brightness we have described, there is a diaphragm, the iris, which automatically alters its aperture, the pupil, from nearly 3/8 inch diameter in the blackest of dungeons to about 1/32 inch in bright sunlight. This simple expedient, found also in the camera, alters the sensitiveness of the eye nearly 150 fold.

Still serving as a model for the camera, the eye has its sensitive surface, the retina, to receive the images focused by the lens. This retina is indeed a marvel. Its front surface is made up of little rods and cones pointing forward towards the lens, and receiving at their tops the image formed. These rods and cones are no more than 1/1,000 inch long and 1/10,000 inch in diameter. They number something like ten millions. We are perhaps familiar with the device recently invented for transmitting handwriting or pictures from one city to another by telegraph. In that device, the picture falls on separate points which are electrically connected to corresponding points on the distant image. It is not so in the eye. The rods and cones on which the image falls are separated, by several curious layers of branching tendrils and cells, from the layer of some half a million nerves which conveys the sensation of sight to the brain. Just how the wonderful connection is effected in a manner to preserve the distinctness of sight, no man either knows or can imitate.

The ancient astronomers had very little in the way of instrumental aids to the eye. Without telescopes, they had to be content with devices somewhat like gun-sights for fixing accurately the directions of the celestial objects. These were mounted with reference to circles divided to degrees, as in the armilla and the astrolabe. With such instruments, the Greek astronomers Eratosthenes and Hipparchus, and the Egyptian Ptolemy made many discoveries and valuable measurements. Columbus' voyages were navigated with the astrolabe, and Tycho Brahe and Kepler also made with it the observations which proved Kepler's laws.

Great was the step involved in the invention of the telescope by Lippershey of Magdeburg about the year 1600. Immediately the new instrument became popular in Holland. Galileo in Italy (1564-1642), hearing of it, reinvented it for himself; and constructing several telescopes with his own hands, made one in 1610 which magnified 33 diameters and multiplied enormously the number of the stars.

With this famous instrument, he observed the sun-spots, noted the rotation of the sun, described the contour of the moon's surface, with its mountains, valleys and plains, discovered Jupiter's satellites and their revolution, observed the moonlike changing crescent of Venus, and described the rings of Saturn.

Galileo's telescope was like a modern opera glass, with a convex lens in front, a concave one behind. We mentioned that the human

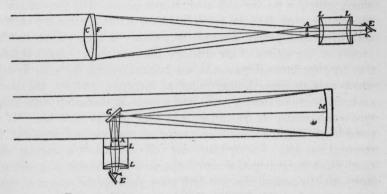

FIG. 2.   REFRACTING AND REFLECTING TELESCOPES.

In the refractor the rays pass through the lens *CF* (made up of two kinds of glass to avoid the color effects called chromatic aberration) and form a real image at *A* which the eye, *E*, examines with the eyepiece *LL*.   In the (Newtonian) reflector the rays are reflected back by the concave mirror, *M*, to the plane mirror, *G*, and thence out at the side where they come to focus and produce a real image at *A* which is observed by the eye, *E*, through the eyepiece *LL*.

eye has a compound lens which is adapted to give colorless images. The inventors of the modern achromatic lens, in which color blurring is avoided by introducing several kinds of glass, were led to its discovery by considering this property of the eye.   With the simple lenses of telescopes of Galileo's time and much later, men soon found that it was useless to increase the power beyond Galileo's limit of 33 without greatly increasing the focal length.   Thus it came about that telescopes of an hundred, some even of six hundred feet in length, were constructed.   There was no tube to such instruments, and no clockwork to drive them, so that the difficulty of using them was immense.   Moreover, the object glasses were very small, for it was then impossible to make glass disks of more than a few inches diameter free from striae. These defects led the great Sir Isaac Newton (1642-1727) to prefer the reflecting, or mirror telescope, over the refracting or lens telescope, and he devised the form of reflector which is still called the Newtonian.[1]

It would be futile to attempt here even a bare mention of all the works of Sir Isaac Newton, but we must not fail to note one of them which indeed is the basis of modern astronomy. His famous law of gravitation — all particles in the universe act as if attracted each to each by a force proportional to the product of their masses and inversely as the square of the distance between them — holds equally true for experimental masses in the laboratory, for the solar system which extends three billion miles to Neptune, and for the stars, enormously more distant still, which include thousands and thousands of systems in revolution according to Newton's law. It is possible to weigh distant stars, some of them indeed invisible, in terms of our sun. For by observing carefully the little angular motions which by gravitation they impart to their visible companions, Newton's law makes even the dark stars yield up the secrets of their times of revolution and their masses.

Kepler's three laws, which rested originally on careful computations based on his own and Tycho Brahe's planetary observations, come directly, by the principles of mechanics, out of Newton's law.[2]

It is curious to know that Newton, in his cautious habit of proving all things, withheld from publishing his law after it had been well tested on the planets because it seemed to fail of exact application in the case of the moon. In his early work, he had used the then commonly accepted estimate of 60 miles for a degree of latitude on

[1] A mirror treats all rays alike, of whatever color, but has a smaller field of good definition than a lens. Lenses bend rays differently, the violet more than the red, so that strictly speaking a lens can focus only one color at a time. By combining two or more lenses of different kinds of glass, this color trouble can be greatly helped. Lenses have the advantage of giving good definition over larger angles than mirrors of equal focus and diameter.

[2] Kepler observed: 1, that planets go round the sun in ellipses; 2, that the imaginary bond which holds the planet to the sun sweeps over equal areas in equal times; 3, that the time of a complete planetary revolution squared, varies as the cube of its solar distance. These results are all contained in Newton's great law.

the earth's surface. This made the earth's radius about one-sixth too small. But when the new measurement of Picard, the French astronomer, yielded a larger value, Newton found to his delight that the moon's distance and the earth's radius harmonized entirely with his law of gravitation.

We have noted that Hipparchus developed the theory of trigonometry, the science of angles, and that Ptolemy worked out some of its important tables for application to the form of the earth and the motions of the planets. Newton, in his more advanced problems, similarly found the mathematics of his time inadequate, and invented what he called "fluxions," but now we call the "calculus," or the science of infinitesimal changes, to enable him to solve some of them. Even with Newton's additions, the mathematics of his time were so very far below their present state that his genius could not entirely overcome the difficulties of applying the law of attraction to the motions of the moon and planets. Nevertheless, he was able to make tremendous progress even in the difficult theory of the moon's motion, a subject which has engrossed the attention of the ablest mathematicians to the present day. Another of Newton's triumphs was his explanation of the precession of the equinoxes, that constant westward march of the sun's place among the stars at the times of equal day and night, which had been a complete enigma for two thousand years. He pointed out that it was due to the protuberance of the earth's equator, on which the attractions of the sun and moon produce this puzzling effect. He investigated the shape of the earth, and the cause of the tides. Not confined to mathematical astronomy, Newton experimented and meditated profoundly on the nature of light, the spectrum, and the colors of thin plates. These colors we see displayed on rainy days where oil has dripped into the street, and they also come and go in soap-bubbles.

The grandeur of his accomplishments can hardly be understood by one not a mathematician, but the great Laplace says of Newton's famous work, the "Principia": "The number and generality of his discoveries relative to the system of the world . . . the multitude of original and profound views which have been the germ of the most brilliant theories of geometers . . . will assure the Principia a preëminence above all the other productions of the human intellect."

So absorbed was Newton in his investigations, that at times he acted unconsciously, taking no cognizance of the ordinary concerns of life. Frequently on rising he would be seized by some new conception and remain for hours seated on his bedside in complete abstraction. Others had to remind him even to take nourishment. Yet he said "I know not what the world will think of my labors, but to myself it seems to me that I have been but as a child playing on the seashore; now finding some pebble rather more polished, and now some shell more agreeably variegated than another, while the immense ocean of truth extended itself unexplained before me."

Sir Isaac Newton was buried in Westminster Abbey with royal honors. His pall was bourne by six peers of the realm. Upon his monument is inscribed, in Latin, "Let mortals congratulate themselves that so great an ornament of the human race has existed."

Though great progress had been made in the astronomy of the solar system, that of the stars remained backward till long after the time of Newton. Stellar knowledge comprised practically only these items: (1) The stars have "proper motions." That is to say, they change their relative positions perceptibly in long periods of time. (2) They are so remote that all attempts to measure their distances failed. (3) Some of them shine with periodically variable light. At this stage arose two great men: James Bradley (1693-1762) Astronomer Royal of England from 1742 to 1761; and Sir William Herschel (1738-1822) sometimes called the Founder of Sidereal Astronomy.

Bradley's exact observations of the places of stars laid the indispensable foundation for many of the discoveries of the nineteenth and twentieth centuries. His precious measurements of places for 3222 stars, reduced systematically by Bessel about 1813, provide trustworthy information of the state of the heavens in 1755. When compared with modern observations, they reveal for these stars the angular motions which have taken place in the past century and a half. But Bradley's great effort was to measure how far away the stars are.  In this he was unsuccessful, but in attempting it he discovered the "aberration of light" and the "nutation of the earth's axis," both of which are not only highly interesting in themselves, but absolutely essential to be allowed for in all exact star positions.  We shall explain them more fully later.  Here we need only say that the aberration of light is the small displacement which a distant luminary shows on account of

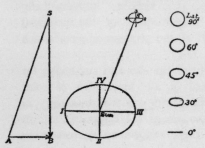

FIG. 3.  THE ABERRATION OF LIGHT.

the advance of the observer, who travels with the earth on which he stands, while the light is on the way.  Nutation is a small modification of the precession of the equinoxes, caused by the moon's changing place in its orbit.

If *AB* is the motion of the earth and *SB* the motion of star-light, the star appears to shine in the direction *SA*. The effect is to cause the star to appear to move in little ellipses as the earth revolves about the sun. The earth positions *I, II, III IV*, correspond to apparent star positions *1, 2, 3, 4*. The shape of the ellipse varies with the observer's latitude, as indicated.

The genius of Sir William Herschel was of another sort. Son of a band-player in Hannover, he made music his profession for many years, and attained great success with it at the English watering place of Bath.  But his mind was ever drawn to the mystery and grandeur of the starry heavens. Wishing to possess a good-sized telescope, he undertook to make one, and lenses being impracticable for him to make, he mastered the art of casting metals and grinding and polishing optical mirrors.  It is said that he made no less than 430 of these metallic mirrors.  He sometimes spent sixteen hours at a stretch on grinding or polishing, without stopping for food except to eat morsels which his devoted sister, Caroline Herschel (herself later the recipient of the gold medal of the Royal Astronomical Society) put into his mouth.  The most famous of Herschel's telescopes was 4 feet in diameter, but he did not use it so much as some of less size.

Herschel was the great explorer of the heavens.  He readily

perceived that the number of the stars is so great that it is out of the question for mortals to ennumerate them, much less to examine each one separately.  But it is highly desirable to study the distribution of the curious objects like nebulæ, double stars, and star clusters which lie among them.  So Herschel undertook his famous "star gauges," counting the stars in selected fields as samples of the whole.  In these studies he counted the stars in 3400 gauge-fields, discovered 806 double stars, 2500 nebulæ, systematically measured the brightness, called "magnitudes," of the principal stars, and made numerous drawings of the stranger objects which he discovered.

He spent much time on the study of the sun and sun-spots, for he perceived clearly the importance of all knowledge of solar phenomena.  In one of his papers he points out that humanity in general is as closely dependent on the sun as the Egyptians are on the overflow of the Nile, so that there can be no subject more deserving of our study.  He goes on to say:

"If the Egyptians could avail themselves of a good Nilometer, what should hinder us from drawing as profitable consequences from solar observations?  [Not only can] we measure from time to time the light actually received from the sun but telescopes may lead us to a discovery of the causes which dispose the sun to emit more or less copiously . . . If we should even fail in this respect, we may at least succeed in becoming acquainted with certain symptoms or indications from which some judgment might be formed of the temperature of the seasons we are likely to have."

After describing in much detail various surface appearances of the sun and the changes in them, he gave some statistics, which he admitted were by no means convincing, in the attempt to find some relation between the prevalence of sun-spots and the price of wheat.

Herschel's arduous time-consuming labors and investigations were carried on at first merely as a side issue to his music.  But when, on March 13, 1781, he discovered the planet Uranus, and thus added another major member to the Sun's family, he sprang almost at once into such fame as an astronomer that the King made him a yearly grant of £200, and thereafter he withdrew from his musical profession, and devoted himself altogether to astronomy.  Sir

William Herschel was first President of the Royal Astronomical Society and his son, Sir John Herschel, its first Foreign Secretary. His epitaph claims for him that "he burst the barriers of heaven."

Though in order of time we ought first to speak of Laplace, of Bessel and of Fraunhofer, we will go right on with the Herschel line, and speak of Sir John Herschel (1792–1871) who worthily upheld the glory of his father's name. He also made his own telescope of 18 inches diameter, and remeasured with it a great number of his father's double stars. In this way, he noted the changes of their places which confirmed their mutual revolution, and in one case found that more than the entire orbit had been completed since discovery. Not long after this, Savary of Paris showed that the measures on one of the doubles fell in closely with Newton's law of gravitation and so extended its sway throughout the universe. Sir John Herschel confirmed his father's discoveries of nebulæ, added many new nebulæ and clusters, and found, besides, more than 3,000 new double stars.

These studies lay in the northern sky. He felt the need of making similar surveys of the southern heavens, and made a famous expedition to the Cape of Good Hope (1834–1838). He made counts of 2299 gauge-fields, examined the remarkable "Magellanic Clouds," so rich in nebulæ and clusters, which he catalogued, measured over 2,000 double stars and nearly 2,000 nebulæ. How extraordinary are the results of such devotion as the Herschels', father and son, in those days before photography, when all the measuring had to be done at the telescope, and the telescope had no driving clock to keep it fixed upon its star!

And now we must turn back to Newton's great successor, the Marquis de Laplace (1749–1827). In the century between these two great geniuses, who observed the heavens as fruitfully with the mathematics as the Herschels observed them with the telescope, their chosen instrument, mathematical analysis, had received almost as great increase of power as had the telescope. Such masters as Leibnitz, Newton's contemporary and codiscoverer of the infinitesimal calculus, Euler, Clairault, d'Alembert, Lagrange, and Legendre had fashioned it and applied it with ever growing power to the problems of the motions of the sun, moon, and planets. And now

PLATE 1. A PERSIAN ASTROLABE.

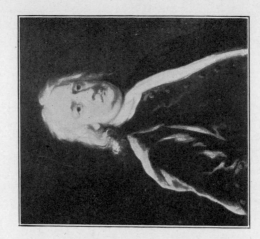

PLATE 2, FIG. 2. SIR ISAAC NEWTON.
(From portrait at the Royal Society.)

PLATE 2, FIG. 1. GALILEO GALILEI.
Inventor, observer, philosopher.

arose Laplace, whose masterpiece, the "Méchanique céleste," brought together and amplified all that his predecessors and contemporaries had discovered and himself conceived.

Going up to Paris as a youth of eighteen, like the celebrated d'Artagnan of Dumas' "Trois Mousquetaires," Laplace carried a letter of recommendation. It was addressed to the great mathematician d'Alembert. But the master paid the letter no attention. Then Laplace wrote him so profound a letter of his own on the principles of mechanics that the enthused d'Alembert responded: "You needed no introduction; you have recommended yourself!" Thereafter, he was Laplace's zealous supporter.

Then began a mathematical duel between Laplace and his great rival Lagrange on the inequalities of the motions of Jupiter and Saturn. The controversy brought out the most superlative brilliance on both sides, and led to the discovery of the causes of some of the most obscure peculiarities of planetary motion, as well as of the most fundamental principles which it obeys.

After this, Laplace devoted himself to his great treatise the "Méchanique céleste," second only as a work of genius to Newton's "Principia." It has been called "the 18th century Almagest," because like Ptolemy's masterpiece, it was the compendium of its subject. The five great volumes stretched out in their publication over the period 1799 to 1825. Even to experts it is not easy, partly on account of the brevity of its style. Laplace was accustomed to omit long passages of demonstration, saying merely "whence it is easy to see." But his colleague, Biot, remarks that sometimes Laplace himself could recover the omitted portion only by an hour's hard labor.

Before the publication of any part of the "Méchanique céleste," Laplace, in 1796, published a part of the pith of it more simply in "Exposition du système du monde." Here occurs the first expression of his famous "Nebular Hypothesis" of the origin of our solar system by condensation and division of a nebula which he assumed once filled the space to beyond the orbits of the outer planets.

Like Newton, Laplace gave attention to a wide range of subjects. The theory of probability, the foundations of the mathematical theories of heat, electricity and magnetism, the discussion of figures of equilibrium of rotating fluids, the gravitational attractions of bodies of different forms, and many other profound subjects were illuminated by the work of Laplace.

And now we may turn to several names that give glory to German astronomical science. First is Friedrich Wilhelm Bessel (1784–1846). At first a clerk in a Bremen mercantile house, but wishing to travel and seeing a possible opening as supercargo, he studied languages, geography, picked up all sorts of information on the habits of distant peoples, and learned something of navigation. From navigation, he was led on to astronomy and mathematics. He made for himself a sextant, and, observing, with the aid of a common clock, amused himself with determining the longitude of Bremen. This fixed his career. Coming upon some old observations of Halley's comet, Bessel deduced from them so good an orbit as to charm the celebrated Olbers, who caused the work to be published. Still Bessel remained in the counting-house, but filled his leisure hours by mastering the calculus and the "Méchanique céleste," till Olbers secured for him the post of assistant in the observatory at Lilienthal with a salary of one hundred thalers a year. Olbers long after declared it was the greatest service he ever rendered astronomy when he induced Bessel to make it his profession. After four years, he was selected by the Prussian Government to be in charge of the new Observatory of Königsberg, where he remained for thirty-two years, until his death.

His first great service to astronomy was to make patient, painstaking, exact reductions of the star places observed by such men as Bradley, applying the minute corrections for refraction, precession, aberration, nutation, and others which are indispensable to the detection of the small "proper motions" of the stars. Star rays are bent or "refracted" by our atmosphere; star places change owing to the westward march or "precession" of the sun's place when days and nights are equal; they are affected by the relative motion of the earth and light which we call "aberration"; and by the moon's gravitational influence on "precession" which we call "nutation." All these effects have to be removed before the star places become standard. Bessel's methods of reduction became classic, and were followed everywhere. It was, however, time to re-observe accurate places for the stars of Bradley and Piazzi, and to add to their number, and this Bessel undertook, 1821-1833. His lists numbered 50, 000. In these observations he was aided by Argelander, whom he drew away from the counting-house even as Olbers had drawn himself. This Argelander was the same who observed and published, about the year 1860, the great "Bonn Durchmusterung" and corresponding "Atlas" in which are found places and brightness of over 324,000 stars, including all in the northern heavens to the 9th magnitude, or some twenty times fainter than the eye can see.

Argelander's work made his Bonn telescope one of the famous instruments of the world. The "Durchmusterung," together with B. A. Gould's extension of it to the south pole of the heavens, is even yet, after the lapse of more than half a century, indispensable. But this famous telescope of Argelander's is only a simple little one about 3 inches in diameter, which shows that it is the man more than his instrument that counts.

So Bessel discovered Argelander. But he did something no less famous, for he was the first to publish the distance of a star. When Copernicus maintained that the earth revolves about the sun each year, he required us to believe that such changes as the earth's motion from one side to another of its orbit (a displacement of 180,000,000 miles) make no sensible change in star brightness. But still more than this, the stars are either all equidistant or else so immensely distant that this 180,000,000 miles change of the observer's standpoint does not appear to make the nearer stars cross over the further ones. As everybody knows, the nearer trees of a forest do seem to cross over the further ones when we ride swiftly by in an auto. But even Bradley, with his skill, could not detect such changes among the stars. Herschel, indeed, had seen that if there could be found a close double star, one of whose members was near, the other far away, it would be easy to try this test. But his doubles proved to be physically connected systems mutually in revolution about one another, and therefore at practically equal distances.

The earlier attempts to measure distance had been made on bright stars, because it was thought that they must probably be the nearer ones. Bessel chose a new principle, and selected the star 61 Cygni which had *moved furthest of any* since Piazzi's measurements of 1792.

It was plain that the nearer a star the larger would appear to be its "proper motion," or angular displacement compared to neighboring stars. And so Bessel, from 1837 to 1840, measured from time to time the position of 61 Cygni among its neighbors. As early as the end of 1838, he was so sure that he ventured to publish the angular displacement of the star due to the earth's revolution. His final value of the "parallax"[1] is 0.3483 seconds of arc. This means that if from a station on 61 Cygni we could observe the earth's orbit around the sun, the radius of it, 93,900,-000 miles long, would fill just a little over one-third of a second of arc, or about the width of a telegraph wire seen at the distance of two miles.

Though Bessel was the first to publish a star parallax, Thomas Henderson had anticipated him in observing one, and published but two months after Bessel the parallax value of 1 second of arc for the brilliant southern star Alpha Centauri. Later measurements have reduced his value to 0.75 seconds, but it is still the largest parallax and therefore represents the least star distance known.[2] But light, traveling 186,000 miles a second, requires over four years to come from Alpha Centauri to the earth.

On July 21, 1801, the Elector Maximilian Joseph happened to witness a sad accident when two alley houses in Munich tumbled down, and buried their occupants alive. Only one person was saved, and he a lad named Joseph Fraunhofer. The elector, moved by his distress, gave the boy eighteen ducats which the young Fraunhofer spent, part for books, part for a glass-polishing machine, and the remainder to purchase his freedom from the looking-glass maker to whom he was apprenticed.

Joseph Fraunhofer (1787-1826), though his life was lamentably short, was the father of the modern great refracting telescope, and of the still more fruitful modern spectroscope. From the time, in 1806, when he entered the optical department of von Reichenbach

[1] The parallax of a star is the angle which the radius of the earth's orbit around the sun would subtend if viewed from the star.

[2] Possibly excepting one. Alpha Centauri has a little companion star revolving about it. This companion is said to be now on our side of the primary star, and therefore a bit nearer than Alpha Centauri. On this account the little star is called Proxima Centauri.

and Utschneider, he devoted himself to the improvement of the achromatic refracting telescope. He developed the theory of lenses and the art of glass making so far that in 1817 he perfected an object glass of finest quality, 9-½ inches in diameter. In those times, this was regarded as gigantic, for even in 1839, as Sir John Herschel tells us, a lens 7-½ inches in diameter, and perfect only to 6, was unique in the history of English glass making. Fraunhofer's 9-½ inch lens was secured by Struve for the Russian Government and installed, in 1824, as the "great Dorpat refractor." This famous instrument was used by Struve with the greatest success for the exact measurement of the angular separation and position of double stars. In these measurements Struve attained such celebrity that it is said another European astronomer expressed the opinion that there was nothing more to do in that line of astronomy. He thought the art was "closed," as the patent men say! Needless to state he was mistaken, as we shall see later.

It was Fraunhofer, too, who made the Königsberg heliometer, or divided-object-glass telescope, with which Bessel determined the parallax of 61 Cygni. But notwithstanding these triumphs of the optician, it is rather the spectroscopist Fraunhofer whom we are still more apt to remember. Newton, Wollaston, and others had done something in this branch of science, but Fraunhofer introduced the narrow slit to limit the entering beam of light which is indispensable to a suitable separation of the rays of the colors and shades of color found in the spectrum. When he had done so, he perceived with great distinctness many dark lines in the sun's spectrum. Wollaston indeed had observed some of them, but Fraunhofer was able to detect about 600 solar lines, to some of which he assigned the letters of the alphabet which we still employ. Among them are the heavy lines A, B and C in the red, D in the orange-yellow, E in the green, F in the blue, G in the indigo, and H and K in the violet. But we honor their discoverer still more by calling all dark spectrum lines, whether seen in sun- or star-light, "Fraunhofer lines." It was not, however, until after Kirchoff's immortal discovery of 1859 that the illumination of Fraunhofer's dark lines began to dawn. From then till now they have been the master key which has unlocked, one by one, the secret storehouses of knowledge of the universe. We shall follow this wonderful story in later chapters, but in order to understand the work of Ångström, Janssen, Lockyer, Huggins, Young, Langley, Rowland, and Pickering, whose names are imperishably associated with "The New Astronomy," or "Astrophysics," we must tell briefly what it was that Kirchoff found.

It was this: Every pure chemical element when heated to sufficient incandescence is a source of light which may be separated into elementary rays in the spectroscope. Unlike the hot stick of the ordinary electric arc lamp it gives out narrow bright rays in the spectrum, separated by wide dark spaces. With some elements, like iron, these are very numerous, while with others, like sodium, they are very few. But they fall almost precisely where Fraunhofer's dark lines do, and, still more suggestive, they may be "reversed," or changed from bright to dark lines if a hotter incandescent substance, like the calcium light which gives a continuous bright spectrum, is caused to shine through them. Here was proof positive that Fraunhofer's lines are produced by the existence of the ordinary chemical elements in the sun and stars. Fraunhofer's $D$ line, for instance, is due to sodium. Astronomers no longer need wish that some angel would bring down star samples for analysis. The stars tell their own composition by their light.

The entrancing story of the spectroscope awaits and allures us. We must hasten through with our partial list of great position astronomers and their works and instruments. The Herschels' greatest reflecting telescopes were eclipsed in size by the famous six-foot reflector of the Earl of Rosse (1800-1867). Sitting in Parliament as a representative Irish peer; President of the Royal Society, 1849 to 1854; President of the British Association, 1843; Vice Chancellor of Dublin University; a genial host and well-loved feudal lord of his tenantry — who would suppose that such a man would busy himself with the construction of the greatest telescope of his time?

James Short, at Edinburgh, had been the pioneer, and the elder Herschel, following after, had attained astonishing results in mirror making. But the secrets of these men died with them. Lord Rosse had to rediscover the proper proportions of copper and tin for the speculum metal, work out the processes of casting, grinding, and polishing, and he did this and constructed and operated his great telescope with the aid of the Irish peasants of his estate whom he trained to this strange work. After successfully making smaller ones, his giant reflector of six feet diameter, fifty-four feet in focus, was finished, ready for observing, in February, 1845. It was mainly used for the study and drawing of the nebulæ. Many objects which had appeared nebulous to Herschel were found to be star clusters. But a new and highly important type was the spiral nebula, whose nature and relation to the stars is even yet not fully understood, though the spiral nebula forms are so remarkable and suggestive that we begin to look upon them as progenitors of star clusters.

Up to the time of Lord Rosse, four of the greatest aids to the modern telescope were not available. They are: Electricity, photography, exact driving mechanism, and mechanical revolving domes. The modern astronomer, sitting at his post, with eye following the guiding star, has his object kept almost exactly on cross-hairs by the automatic action of the self-winding clock-work, leaving him only the finest adjustments to be made, merely by pressing one or another of the electric buttons in his hand. Electric motors many yards away, responding instantly, obey his will, whether to shift the position of the star image, ever so slightly, to revolve the dome or move its shutter, or to raise or lower the platform on which the observer sits. And meanwhile the photographic plate, unwearied, constantly records an ever-gaining impression of the light which tells the secrets of the distant star. Observations which required the older astronomers to gaze hour after hour into the telescope itself, now are obtained in greater richness and accuracy, at convenience, by merely measuring in daylight the photographic records secured in a tenth or a hundredth of the time that the eye observations formerly required.

It will be well to close what we have to say about the telescope by describing two of the greatest modern instruments, the thirty-six-inch Lick refractor and the one-hundred-inch Mount Wilson reflector.

James Lick was an eccentric and wealthy Californian, who

had settled there just before those known as the "forty-niners" rushed into California in the days of its gold discovery. Queer stories are told of him. In his younger days he had been rejected in love by the father of his intended, who was a wealthy miller, because of his poverty. Lick vowed sometime to build a mill which should put to shame the one of his intended father-in-law, and so he did near San Jose, California, at a cost of $200,000. The interior was finished in highly polished California woods, so that it was the curiosity of the region till, unfortunately, it was burned.

As he approached old age, among many other great philanthropies, Lick formed the plan to perpetuate his memory by obtaining the most powerful telescope in the world. He appointed, in 1874, trustees, to whom he made over his whole fortune of $3,000,000 for philanthropy, and to carry out his purpose. They consulted the then foremost American astronomers, and by their advice fixed upon a great refractor, although it was out of the question to obtain one vying in size with Lord Rosse's reflector. Doubtless they reconciled their advice to Mr. Lick's desire by the consideration that with the four great aids we have just spoken of available, and with the larger field of good optical definition in which a refractor has the advantage, the proposed instrument would certainly fulfill the condition of being the most powerful telescope in the world.

The glass disks were made by the firm of Mantois in France. They were ground and polished by the firm of Alvan Clark and Sons, of Cambridge, Massachusetts, at that time the unrivalled big-lens makers of the world. The mounting, clockwork, and dome were by Warner and Swasey, of Cleveland, Ohio, since then the manufacturers of the similar parts for the great telescopes of the Yerkes and Dominion observatories. In the Lick telescope dome, for the first time, they introduced the rising floor, so that all the accessories to observing go up along with the observer as the telescope's position requires.

It was felt not less important to select the proper site than to choose the best makers, for many of the finest telescopes of the world are placed where clouds and poor vision cut down shamefully the number of nights available for high class observation. Professor Burnham, of Chicago, the great double star observer, tested the proposed site on Mount Hamilton, California, by observation with his own telescope. He found forty-two first-class nights and only seven that could be classed as low as medium during his stay. Nothing like such excellence of conditions had ever been united in a site for a great telescope before.

All these things took their time, and, sadly enough, James Lick died more than ten years before his great gift came into operation in 1888. His remains rest beneath the pier of the giant telescope.

There can be no question of its enormous success. With this instrument, Barnard discovered the fifth satellite of Jupiter which few men have seen, Aitken made his great series of observations of the closest of double stars, and Campbell did the classic spectroscopic work which will ever be associated with his name.

From the first, the great Lick telescope has been free to the public for one evening each week. Campbell tells a humorous story about it, which has a good moral. "One of the visitors upon descending from the observing chair, much interested, questioned the astronomer: 'Did you say those stars are all suns?' 'Yes, sir.' 'Did you say that those stars are really larger than our sun, on the average?' 'Yes, sir.' 'Can you give me an idea how large our sun is?' 'Well, if it were a hollow shell, of its present size, you could pour more than a million earths into it, and there would still be much unoccupied space between the earth balls.' 'You say there are possibly or probably planets revolving around many of the cluster stars?' 'Yes, sir.' 'And many of those planets may be inhabited?' 'Yes, sir.' 'Well, then, I think it does not matter very much whether Roosevelt or Taft is nominated next week at the Chicago Convention.'"

The hundred-inch reflector on Mount Wilson we owe also to the enthusiastic gifts of wealthy men. Mr. J. D. Hooker, a resident of Los Angeles, became extremely interested in the five-foot silver-on-glass reflector of the Mount Wilson Observatory. Seeing it frequently throughout its period of construction and erection on the mountain, under the design and supervision of Mr. G. W. Ritchey, he gave a sum of money to secure a larger disk of glass for the mammoth reflector of the world. There were nowhere, even in France, facilities to cast so enormous a block of glass, yet it was attempted at the Saint Gobain glass works, which only a few years later were destroyed by the German invasion. Not being able to cast the great disk in one melting, a second lot was melted and poured upon the first before it cooled. The two lots did not thoroughly combine, so that the line of demarcation was obvious. For some years the compound disk remained in the observatory optical shop at Pasadena, while attempts were made at Saint Gobain, but unsuccessfully, to cast a better one. At length, when the failure was clear, the earlier disk was tested, and the blemish of its interior proved not to injure it for the purpose intended. But meanwhile, Mr. Hooker passed away. The subsequent preparation of the monster mirror and its mounting and dome were carried out by funds provided by Andrew Carnegie, the great steel manufacturer, through the Carnegie Institution of Washington.

Fully seven years the telescope and its smaller accessories were in building at the shops of the Mount Wilson Observatory in Pasadena, mainly according to designs of Mr. F. G. Pease. Meanwhile, the enormous excavation, and the pier of concrete almost rivaling the monster works of the old Egyptians, were being done, under Mr. George Jones, on Mount Wilson. Even the road up the mountain had to be widened and improved in preparation to transport the monster that was to come. The dome and larger telescope structures were at the same time being constructed by the Fore River Ship Building Company in Massachusetts, and were brought round Cape Horn and landed at the port of Los Angeles. The auto truck, without which the turns and doublings of the steep road could scarcely have been negotiated, and surely not with the long teams of oxen or horses of the old days, conveyed the immense parts to their final mountain home.

The mirror alone weighs fully four tons. With the large iron structures necessary to give it freedom of motion to follow any desired star, and to focus the starlight at the top of the tube 40 feet away, all this moving part, including mirror tube and mounting, amounts to no less than 100 tons. The problem of giving it perfect freedom in motion was solved by floating the moving part as if on a pair of ships and straddling between two miniature oceans of mercury.  For at the upper and lower ends of the main polar axis are two great hollow cylinders, 10 feet or more in diameter.  These are enclosed by boxing which admits a film of quicksilver about a quarter inch thick on every side.  As quicksilver weighs over thirteen times as much as water, these two little ships on their quicksilver seas are able to take the whole weight of the telescope off of its defining bearings.  Like a canoe which rolls at slightest touch, this flotation bearing gives almost ideal freedom.

The telescope turns to follow the stars by means of a clock with a governor, something like a steam engine governor, whose two great balls rise and fall by trifling amounts, but in the mean keep the driving rate exact.  This clock turns a screw which gears with a wheel, 17 feet in diameter, whose teeth are ground and polished to almost optical accuracy.  Electric motors at all sorts of unexpected places enable the telescope to be moved quickly or slowly, up or down, right or left, or to slightly accelerate or retard the clock.

Provisions for all kinds of observing are there.  One may sit upon a platform high up in the dome, after the Newtonian plan, or the rays may be brought down again and reflected out at the north side, close by the great mirror.  Or by another scheme, called the Coudé, they are reflected southward, right down the hollow axis, and come to focus just at the south edge of the dome, as if they came from a mirror of 250 feet focal length.  Photography, visual observing, heat measurements, spectrum photography, all are provided for under these several kinds of arrangements.

The telescope is housed in a dome over a hundred feet in height and diameter.  Two immense shutters are run out by electric motors to right and left, and leave the telescope free to look out upon the stars from the zenith nearly to the horizon.  The whole upper half of the dome revolves by electric trolleys on accurately ground tracks.  The motion is so smooth that an observer standing on the dome floor cannot believe that it is himself and not the giant telescope that is in motion, unless he looks out upon the motionless stars or trees outside.

Though the demands of the great war invaded even the peaceful domain of astronomy, and laid hold of the astronomers and the observatory shop for warlike investigations, so that the telescope was delayed in its completion several years, already the Hundred-Inch Reflector has justified every hope, and has an enviable record of accomplishment that gives promise of wondrous things for the future.

As we stated above, the Marquis de Laplace summed up all the knowledge of the motions of the solar system in the great "Méchanique céleste." But such knowledge did not halt, even with him. While Laplace was yet in the height of his powers, on the first evening of the nineteenth century, January 1, 1801, Piazzi discovered the minor planet Ceres. He continued to observe it till February 11 when a dangerous illness prevented him from going on. Not long after, the little planet became lost in twilight, and perhaps would long have remained lost, except for the brilliant work of the mathematician, Gauss, of Brunswick. He invented a new method of computing orbits, devised the system of getting the best result from observations called the "method of least squares," and from Piazzi's short series of position measures, actually predicted the location of Ceres for November so closely that the planet was readily picked up again.

Within a few months, Olbers discovered another little planet or "asteroid" which he called Pallas, and within five years more two others, Juno and Vesta, were found, all belonging to a family whose orbits lie between those of Mars and Jupiter. As time has gone on, nearly a thousand of these little planets have been discovered, so that it is difficult to name them, much more to work out their orbits so as to identify them. One of them, Eros, will deserve special mention later on, but perhaps their greatest value has been that they led Gauss into the line of study which culminated in his great work, "Theoria Motus," a worthy successor to the "Principia" and "Méchanique céleste."

One additional mathematical triumph remained for the astronomy of the first half of the nineteenth century. It was the independent determination by J. C. Adams and U. J. J. Leverrier that the outstanding inequality of the orbit of Uranus could be attributed to the attraction of a major planet lying in a certain region of the heavens. This brought about the discovery of the planet Neptune, September 23, 1846. What a tribute to the human brain that, without a sight of Uranus, and merely by employing some tables of dry figures, it could call up from the depths of space another and greater planet, till then unseen, to take his place in the sun's family! Within three weeks there was also found with Neptune a moon, so that it became possible to fix accurately his mass. As it proved, Neptune is the third most massive of all the planets.

It is our moon's motion which has given most trouble to the mathematical astronomers. Merely to print the algebraic terms representing the moon's motion requires a small quarto volume, and to compute tables from them so as to give accurately the moon's position over a long term of years is the work almost of a lifetime. This task of investigating the motion of the moon was undertaken by Peter Andreas Hansen, Director of the Ducal Observatory of Schleswig-Holstein. His daughter, Mrs. Bayard Taylor, tells in her delightful book[1] how, early in their married life, Hansen attended his sixteen-year old bride to a ball. She was dancing in her wedding gown of white satin, with a wreath of forget-me-nots in her hair, when suddenly she missed her husband. No one could tell her what had become of him. In her fear for him, she ran alone in her white satin slippers all the way from town up the steep height of the Seeberg, and found her bridegroom at his desk, deep in a problem. The idea had struck him in the midst of the dance, and, oblivious of everything, he had rushed home to put it on paper.

Hansen's "Tables of the Sun and Moon" were printed about 1860 by the English Government, which also awarded him a prize of £1000 for them. Of Hansen, Prof. Newcomb, in 1898, says: "He may now fairly be considered the greatest master of celestial mechanics since Laplace."

Even Hansen, however, did not quite succeed in smoothing out all the puzzles in the moon's motion, and something was left for our countrymen, Simon Newcomb and G. W. Hill, so well known for their labors at the Nautical Almanac Office in Washington. Finally, within a decade, Professor E. W. Brown of Yale has carried Hill's methods to greater perfection, and, as it is believed, has finally laid the problem of the moon's motion to rest for many years to come.

[1] "On Two Continents." Doubleday, Page, Co. 1905.

Professor Newcomb (1835-1909) was a remarkable character. Lionlike in appearance, selfmade to be the leading American astronomer of his time, a prolific writer, with a delightful quiet humor, his "Reminiscences of an Astronomer"[1] are among the most enjoyable of biographies. He tells a story, substantially as follows, of a gravitation crank who came one day asking to see Professor Newcomb. Said Newcomb, "I am he, what do you wish?" The visitor said he had called to tell him that he did not believe in Sir Isaac Newton's theory of gravitation. "Jump out of that window and be convinced, then," said Newcomb. That was not what the visitor meant, he did not believe gravitation extended to the moon. "But were you ever there to see?" asked Newcomb. "Of course not," replied the man. "Well, I never was either," answered Newcomb, "and I fear we cannot agree."

The invention of spectroscopic chemical analysis by Kirchoff, and its application to the sun by A. J. Ångström, about 1860, raised up a new type of astronomers. To J. Janssen and Sir Norman Lockyer belongs independently the honor of discovering the element helium spectroscopically in the sun, in the year 1868. It was nearly thirty years before this chemical element was detected on the earth, and only recently that it has been found in large quantities. The history of helium is indeed a romance in itself. Discovered in the sun and 30 years later on the earth, it combines with no other chemicals whatever. Next lightest of all gases, its freezing temperature approximates absolute zero of cold. Lately found in certain gas wells in large quantities, helium being impossible to burn, makes balloons safe from fire.

Besides Kirchoff and Ångström, Janssen and Lockyer, Sir William and Lady Huggins, who made numerous and interesting discoveries in the spectra of the stars and nebulæ at their private observatory of Tulse Hill near London, the pioneers of the new astronomy of the spectroscope are: Professor C. A. Young of Princeton, who discovered the yet unidentified "green ray" of the solar corona, who was the first to see a great storm on the sun associated with a powerful magnetic disturbance on the earth, and who wrote many choice books on astronomical subjects; Professor

[1] Houghton, Mifflin & Co., 1903.

S. P. Langley, late Secretary of the Smithsonian Institution, a master at visual telescopic work, who was the first to study extensively the solar and lunar spectra by the heat they produce, and who thereby traced out the invisible rays of the sun to wave-lengths fully ten times greater than those of the deepest red; Professor H. A. Rowland of Baltimore, whose improvement of the accuracy of the screw led on to the ruling of very accurate reflecting gratings — polished metal surfaces ruled with a diamond to many thousand equally spaced lines per inch — with which wonderful instruments he himself made an epoch-making map of the solar spectrum, identified about fifty chemical elements in the sun, and made possible the solar and stellar work of a quarter-century; Professor E. C. Pickering, of Harvard College Observatory, who created the photographic library of the sky, wherein is daily re-corded the brightness, spectrum, and places of thousands of stars, so that if at any time a new celestial object is discovered, the Harvard plates will furnish its previous history for many years.

We shall have occasion later to refer to other works of these and other remarkable astronomers. The purpose of this chapter is served if it gives the reader a bird's-eye view of astronomical history up to the beginning of the twentieth century, and some slight appreciation of those noble characters who, pursuing Truth for her own sake, have perceived her as the goddess of all countries alike, so that under her banners there can be no war.

## Chapter III

### THE LITTLE AND THE GREAT

WHEN we erect a building, we have to think very early about the bricks. So, before we raise our astronomical edifice, let us consider the structure of the matter composing the heavenly bodies. Far away as the planets and stars are, separated from us and from each other by incomprehensibly great distances, whose smallest units are millions of miles, and whose ordinary measurements may well be expressed in light-years,[1] yet we know that they are all made up of the same chemical elements found on our earth. We shall take up the proof of this statement a little later.

Within the last few years, it has been found that we can go farther even than this in resolving their composition. All the chemical elements, nearly a hundred in number, such as hydrogen, iron, oxygen and the rest, which used to be thought quite independent in very essence, one from another, are in fact made up of only two kinds of stuff. These two fundamentals are called electrons and protons. They exist as single particles of equal but opposite electric charges. All electrons are more like one another than carpet tacks, and all protons more like one another than wire nails, but a proton weighs about 1800 times as much as an electron. Hydrogen atoms have one of each, but oxygen atoms have 16 electrons and 16 protons. Heavy atoms, like those of mercury or lead, contain very many of each but may be made up in several ways to give the same chemical properties. In other words, there are several kinds of lead and also several kinds of mercury, indistinguishable to the chemist except in atomic weight. In all other respects the varieties behave alike.

We need not go farther, at the moment, into this curious bypath,

---

[1] A light-year is the distance light travels in a year, about 6,000,000,000,000 miles.

PLATE 3, Fig. 2. FRIEDRICH WILHELM BESSEL.
Pioneer in measuring star-distances.

PLATE 3, Fig. 1. JOSEPH FRAUNHOFER.
The father of modern spectroscopy.

PLATE 4, Fig. 2. SIR WILLIAM HUGGINS.
(From portrait at the Royal Society.)
A pioneer in Astrophysics.

PLATE 4, Fig. 1. SIR JOHN HERSCHEL.
(From photo by J. M. Cameron.)
The great son and successor of a famous
astronomical father.

PLATE 5. THE 36-INCH REFRACTOR OF LICK OBSERVATORY.

PLATE 6. THE 100-INCH TELESCOPE OF MT. WILSON OBSERVATORY.
The world's greatest telescope.

however, because what we are emphasizing now is the great fact that all things on earth and elsewhere, whether gases, liquids, or solids — things as different as our own bodies and the ground we tread on, for instance — are made up of these same two kinds of building materials, electrons and protons. If we pass to the sun, over 90,000,000 miles away, it is the same. Hydrogen, oxygen, iron, and many other chemicals are there to be sure, but all are made of electrons and protons.

The case of helium illustrates strikingly the identity of the materials all over the universe. Discovered in the sun, next recognized in the stars, finally found on the earth, it became at last well known, and is much used for scientific and technical purposes. But helium, like all the rest of the elements, is built of electrons and protons, four of each. So the bricks of our edifice are everywhere of the same two kinds.

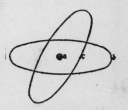

FIG. 4. BOHR'S CONCEPTION OF THE HELIUM ATOM.

The nucleus, $a$, consists of four protons and two bound electrons. In the two circular orbits, which are conceived to be inclined at 120°, revolve the two outer electrons $b$ and $c$.

Let us form some notion of the size of our bricks. If we take the period at the end of the last sentence as our unit, then we must place 50,000,000,000 electrons in line to stretch across its diameter. Protons, though heavier, are still more minute. It is of no use to fill this page with a number large enough to indicate how many electrons and protons it takes to make up our sun, 800,000 miles in diameter! Even more hopeless it would be to convey an idea of the numbers of them in some of the stars, which, despite that they look so little, are many of them much larger than the sun.

Where mere numbers fail to convey an idea of the infinitesimalness of the atomic structure, a curious illustration which we owe to Aston may help us.

Aston held up a glass of water, saying, in substance: Suppose we could label every molecule of this water so that we could distinguish these molecules from all others. Then we might pour this water into the ocean and wait until evaporation, winds, rains, rivers and waves had thoroughly mixed these molecules with all the other water molecules on the earth. When this process shall have been completed, let us fill another glass with water. How many of our original marked molecules would it probably contain? None at all you will perhaps say. But the answer is 2,000! For in one glass of water there are 2000 times as many molecules as there are glasses of water in the ocean! How extraordinary! Yet we must note that Aston is speaking not of protons and electrons, but of the molecules, ten thousand-fold bigger.

We shall wish to show how intimate a connection the electrons have with light. Before doing so, let us stop for a few moments to think of some very little and very great dimensions directly associated with light itself. This is by no means aside from our subject, for everything that we know about the heavenly bodies comes to us by studying their light.

The energy of light appears to be propagated in waves or vibrations. Ten years ago we should have said "light is a form of vibration," without any qualification. But light is now thought to come forth from its sources, such as hot bodies like the sun and stars, not continuously, like a wave, but by successive bits called "quanta." However, the subject is somewhat speculative as yet, and the quantum theory must still harmonize to a great extent with the vibration theory. Probably the two views are like the two ends of the same rope, and supplement each other; so we shall retain here the older view which was developed during the whole nineteenth century to great refinement, so as to explain all of the facts then known.

The vibrations of light-waves are far shorter than those produced by flinging a stone into a still pond. Instead of wavelengths of inches, like water waves, we must take 500 waves of yellow light placed end to end to extend across the diameter of the period which ends this sentence. Of violet light it would require 750, and of red light 450 for the same stretch. So the waves of light, though short, are tremendously long compared to the diameters of electrons.

But when we come to the numbers of light-vibrations in a second, we begin to get back our appreciation of small things. For since light travels 186,000 miles in a second, it takes 500,000,000,000,000 vibrations of yellow light, end to end, each second to make up this enormous distance.

It might easily seem to one unfamiliar with the subject that such numbers must be only rough approximations. But this is not so. Experiments on the subject are among the most precise in all the range of physics. The velocity of light is known to an accuracy of one part in 10,000, and the wave-lengths of definite rays of light are known to an accuracy of one part in 6,000,000.

Light, as everybody knows who has seen a rainbow, is of many colors. These colors blend together by almost imperceptible shades, although we roughly speak of the seven colors, violet, indigo, blue, green, yellow, orange, and red. As nobody can know much about modern astronomy unless he understands something about the band of color called the spectrum, let us devote a short space now to a description of it. Some readers can have access to a spectroscope, but others may, if they please, make one in the following manner which will give them much pleasure.

Either obtain three microscope-slide glasses, or dissolve the film from a photographic lantern-slide plate and cut it into three equal strips. Using sealing wax, fasten the three strips of glass together at the corners so as to make of them a hollow triangular prism. Set this down on one of its triangular ends upon a piece of glass and seal it onto the glass with wax. Care must be taken to make all of these six joints water-tight. Fill the prism with water.

If, now, the room is darkened and a beam of sunlight is reflected into the prism by means of a small mirror, a beautiful display of rainbow colors is produced. If two observers work together, one can reflect the sunbeam into the prism pretty steadily, and the other can move the prism and watch the effects. At once it appears that the light is deflected through quite an angle by the prism, and that the violet end of the spectrum is deflected more than the red. By turning the prism slightly, a certain position of it can be found such that the deflection is a minimum. Rotating the prism in either direction from this position increases the deflection.

Now let the sunlight be restricted by a very narrow vertical slit. The spectrum will of course be fainter. But by setting up a spectacle lens, or reading glass, beyond the prism, the band of light becomes much purer; that is, the red, yellow, green, blue, and so forth, stand out very definitely, each by itself, on a sheet of white paper held at the proper distance. If the glass of the prism is very flat and free from defects, if the slit is very narrow, if the room is well darkened, and if the white paper is moved toward and away from the lens to get the very sharpest focus, there may be seen several dark lines crossing the band of colors at right angles. These will be easiest seen in the green, blue and indigo, but it will be difficult to make the experiment well enough to show them. There are, to be sure, other liquids, as oil of cassia and oil of cinnamon, which can be purchased of the druggist, and which, if substituted for water in the prism, will give a much longer band of colors wherein the dark lines will be more pronounced.

Lest the reader may fail to see with a home-made spectroscope the dark lines in the sun's spectrum, we give in Plate 7, Fig. 2, a reproduction from a photograph taken at the Mount Wilson Solar Observatory showing the region of the blue and green as observed in a fine instrument. We mentioned at the beginning of this chapter that it is possible to show that our familiar elements, hydrogen, oxygen, iron, and many others, occur in the sun and stars. To show how this is done, we reproduce with the portion of the sun's spectrum, the spectrum of the light of an electric arc having iron poles, in short the spectrum of iron produced in the laboratory. It is made up evidently of bright lines of different intensities. But we see that for every one of them there is a dark line in the solar spectrum, and with nearly similar gradations of intensities. In ancient days, certain prehistoric animals walking in mud flats left footprints which have become fossilized. Those fossils, exhibited in our museums, give us exact ideas of these curious creatures that no man has ever seen. We do not see the feet of the creatures, but a reversal of them, having hollows in place of toes, with ridges instead of spaces between. It is very like the case of the spectrum. For as we see line for line faithfully reproduced, only reversed, dark for light, we can have no hesitation in saying that iron exists in the sun, although it is impossible for us to go there to see. It is in this way that not only iron but the other elements indicate their presence in the spectra of the sun and the stars.

But the spectrum can show more. It registers the velocity at which a star is approaching or receding from the earth. For it is easy to see that if a star is approaching us rapidly, sending out light vibrations all the time, we shall receive more of these each second than we should if the star remained at a fixed distance. But the only difference between red and violet light is in the number of its vibrations which reach us per second. Violet has nearly twice as many as red. If we could take a red light and move it towards us fast enough, it would be violet. Hence it is that all of the spectrum lines of a star which is approaching us are shifted slightly towards the violet, and those of a star which is receding are shifted towards the red. An illustration of this effect is shown in Plate 7, Fig. 3, from a photograph of the spectrum of the star Mu Orionis made at the Yerkes Observatory. It is easy to see that the star-spectrum lines are all to the right of corresponding ones of the comparison spectra above and below. Hence, we know that this star is receding from us. There are several other valuable indications given by spectrum lines relating to pressures, temperatures, and magnetic fields existing in the sun and stars, and they even afford evidence as to whether a star is big or little, young or old. But avoiding too many technical details at one time, we shall pass over these items for the present, and return to the subject which we promised to mention, that of the relation between electrons and light.

In the first place, we must specify more particularly than we have done how the electrons and protons are arranged in an atom. The protons and approximately half of the electrons reside in a central nucleus. Remembering that protons are about 1800 times as heavy as electrons, it is obvious that nearly all of the atomic weight is in the nucleus. We mentioned above that some of the chemical elements have several kinds of atoms, all similar in chemical behavior but of different atomic weights. We may remark here, in explanation, that this merely means to add or subtract one or more protons and an equal number of electrons in the nucleus. Being in equal numbers, these additions or subtractions satisfy each other electrically, and exert no influence to modify the chemical behavior of such an atom. An example is chlorine, which has two varieties

of atoms, one kind of atomic weight 35, the other 37.  As there are
about three times as many of the lighter as of the heavier kind in
every mass of chlorine, the observed atomic weight is 35.45.

So much for the composition of the atomic nucleus.  As it has
about twice as many positive charges (protons) as negative charges
(electrons) the nucleus is positively charged with electricity.  In
hydrogen atoms, the positive nuclear charge is one unit, that of helium two units, that of oxygen eight units, and generally the positive
charge of a nucleus is approximately half of the atomic weight of
the element.  This unbalanced positive charge is able to attract an
equal negative charge of electrons.  These bodies arrange themselves
in rings, orbits, or some such-like configuration outside of the nucleus.  The hydrogen atom has one, helium two, oxygen eight, and
so on, of these orbital or outside electrons.  It is the number of
these which gives the atom its chemical character.  Indeed, the numbers of outside electrons per atom is now called "the atomic number."  These numbers run upwards, one by one, from hydrogen, 1,
helium, 2, lithium, 3, and so on, up to uranium, 92, which has the
highest atomic number.  A few gaps in the series exist, showing that
there are probably nearly a half dozen chemical elements in existence
as yet undiscovered.

Now we come to the relation of this atomic structure to light.
The outside electrons make excursions, when urged by heat or electrical stimulus.  Thus electrons may be driven away from their
atoms and go free for a time.  When this happens the substance is
"ionized," as we say.  Such is the condition of the rare gas in the
bulbs used in wireless.  When an electron passes from one ring or
orbit to another ring or orbit, a definite "quantum" of light either
is given out or extinguished.  We say that light is emitted or absorbed in these cases respectively.  Whether emitted or absorbed
depends on whether the electron in the new condition has less energy
of position and motion or more.  This is the quantum theory of the
origin of light.  But still we believe the passage of light across the
apparently empty spaces between the heavenly bodies is accomplished
by wave motion and wave motion requires a medium.  That medium is called the luminiferous ether.  It cannot be seen or weighed
or otherwise perceived.  Nothing indicates it except by the imperi-

ous requirement the mind recognizes that where waves pass there must be a medium to convey them. This may seem a slender peg to hang the ether upon, but as yet physicists have not been able to avoid the conception.

We must take leave in our minds of our old idea of a solid body as being a space quite filled up with matter. Every atom, even in a solid, is separated from its neighbors. Besides that, every atom within itself encloses a quantity of free space as overwhelmingly larger than the total volume occupied by its electrons and protons as the great solar system, extending out to Neptune, is larger than the combined volumes of the sun and planets. A solid, then, is quite as little crowded with matter as a room is filled with the little motes of dust that dance in the sunbeam.

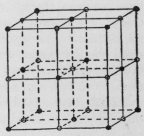

FIG. 5. The arrangement of the atoms, as it is in a crystal of common salt and many other similar substances. If the blackened circles represent sodium atoms, the open circles will represent the chlorine atoms in common salt. Equal distances separate all the atoms from their neighbors. In other types of crystals a different and more complex symmetry prevails.

We have fixed our thoughts on the smallest things in nature, the electrons and protons which make up all matter, and the wave-lengths of light which convey to us all the knowledge that we possess relating to the heavenly bodies. We have seen that the atoms are somewhat like our solar system, with a nucleus which we may liken to the sun, since it contains practically all the mass of the system; that the atoms also contain a group of outside electrons which we may liken to the planets, since they reside at different distances from the central nucleus, since they are held together by the attraction of that nucleus, and since they occupy and disport themselves in a region of space which, though inexpressibly tiny as compared with our ordinary measures, is yet immense compared with the dimensions of these outside electrons themselves. We have seen that in some way not fully understood, the wave-trains of light originate discontinuously in bits of light energy, called "quanta," when electrons are shaken out of one orbit or configuration in the atoms into another with a loss of electronic energy. Such disturbances of atomic configuration may be caused by heat, and also by electric stimulation. By means of the wave-trains of light which are thus originated, the heavenly bodies touch each other, as we may say, across distances whose immensity defies words to express. It would take ten journeys round our world to reach the moon; four hundred journeys to the moon to reach the sun, twenty-eight journeys to the sun to reach the planet Neptune; ten thousand journeys to Neptune to reach the nearest star; and ten thousand journeys to the nearest star would certainly not carry us to the bounds of the universe of stars. All of this prodigious expanse of space is alive with interesting objects from which we continually receive light messages which tell a wealth of knowledge about the celestial denizens. Modern astronomy is the interpretation of these messages.

## Chapter IV

### OUR EARTH AND HER NEIGHBOR, THE MOON

THE strangest thing about the earth is the people upon it. Not that we are all strange people, but we do not positively know that there is another single orb in the heavens that boasts of any living inhabitants. Surely none of the visible stars, or the sun, are habitable, for they are all so hot that nothing could live there any more than in a blast furnace. As for the moon, it is a lifeless world despite Locke's "Great Moon Hoax," printed eighty years ago in the New York Sun, at which we shall glance later. Only Venus, among the planets, seems a promising abode for life like ours, but it is too cloudy for us ever to see its surface. The rest of the planets surely seem very inhospitable. Of course, there may be among the stars many habitable worlds too far away to discover, but at least living neighbors, if we have any, do not force themselves on our attention.

So the earth stands out because of its life, in air, on land, and in the waters. This leads us at once to think for a little of the conditions which make it habitable. One is temperature. All life depends on vegetation, and all vegetation languishes outside the temperature range $+ 55°$ to $- 10°$ Centigrade ($+ 132°$ to $14°$ Fahrenheit). These look like wide limits expressed in these terms, but let us refer them to the fundamental or absolute scale, which starts at absolute zero where molecular motion stops. We then express them as $328°$ to $263°$ Absolute Centigrade ($591°$ to $473°$ Absolute Fahrenheit). Looked at in this way, we see that luxuriant vegetable life, and therefore all kinds of life on earth, demands that the temperature shall not vary over 11 per cent either way from $296°$ Absolute Centigrade.

What prevents it? The sun, the air, and the water. If the sun shone as it does now, but on a cloudless earth without atmos-

43

phere, the earth's surface temperature would go to boiling by day and below frozen quicksilver by night in the United States as it does on the moon. Our equable climate is produced by the tempering effect of air, and the water vapor and clouds which it always contains.

A nice balancing of influences is in play. At prevailing temperatures, the earth radiates as much energy as it receives from the sun. We see sunlight, of course, which warms us. The sun has other powerful rays extending with great intensity beyond the red end of the spectrum to wave-lengths twice as great as the deepest red ones. Far beyond these, and wholly invisible to our eyes, are those powerful rays of the earth, the loss of which cools us. Their intensest wave-lengths are from ten to fifty times the wavelength of deep red. But these rays, through which the earth's surface is constantly cooling itself by sending them out in every direction, are cut off completely by thick clouds, and very largely by water vapor in the air.

In high-level deserts where clouds and moisture are well-nigh absent, the cooling by the earth's radiation is enormously greater than in the cloudy humid tropics, and there are, therefore, great temperature extremes between night and day, summer and winter, in such deserts. Everywhere the earth's actual temperature results from a balance between such of the incoming warmth-bringing sun rays as are able to pass the clouds and humidity, and the outgoing warmth-dissipating earth rays which escape through and from the atmosphere to space.

In the next place, all life depends on the red, blue, and violet sun rays. For plants, which are food for other life, do not grow in darkness. There is an unknown process going on whenever sun rays of either of these three colors fall upon a plant-leaf, by means of which the plant takes in carbonic-acid gas from the air and builds it into the chemicals of life. Not only are these sun rays indispensable to all life on earth, but so, too, is carbonic-acid gas, which makes up only 1/25 of one per cent by weight of the earth's atmosphere.

In the next place, all life depends on water. Every living tissue, even bone, contains a large percentage of water, varying from

20 per cent in some kinds of bone to 95 per cent, or more, in some kinds of vegetation. Curiously enough, this indispensable liquid, water, is the only common liquid which exists naturally on the earth at the livable range of temperature, without being a product of life agencies. And this unique agency, whose properties are extraordinary among liquids, exists in perfectly prodigal profusion on the earth. For while the atmosphere weighs 5,000,000,000,000,-000 tons, the water of the world weighs no less than 250 times as much.

All life depends on the extraordinary and unique chemical properties of carbon. Chemistry is, indeed, divided into two branches. Inorganic chemistry, the briefer branch, deals with *all the other* chemical elements except carbon. Organic chemistry is already far the more bulky of the two branches. Yet men are hardly more than beginning to explore its field, which deals solely with the compounds of carbon. It gets its name, organic, because it was once thought that all these compounds could be produced only by the agency of organic beings. But there is, at any rate, no other chemical element capable of combining in such a multitude of complex forms as are indispensable to the mystery we call life.

Finally, all animal life depends on the existence of free oxygen. Air is one-fifth oxygen diluted with four-fifths nitrogen, and containing some other gases in relatively trifling proportions. The oxygen which we inhale sustains a slow fireless combustion inside our bodies. It is this which keeps us alive and warm.

Thus, we see that it is no ordinary happening that life exists on our earth. Without the remarkable combination of conditions we have examined, we should perish. Some of them depend on the earth's size, and some on its rotation and distance from the sun. So we pass instantly from biology to astronomy.

About the beginning of this century, Professor Johnstone Stoney showed that for every planet there are some gases which must escape, others which must be retained, depending on the planet's mass, volume, and temperature. We all know how temperature affects water. The hotter it grows, the faster it evaporates, because some of the molecules, moving faster than the average, keep escaping from its surface. When hot enough, all the water molecules move so fast that none remains, and the water becomes entirely steam.

In the atmosphere, something a little analogous goes on. Gravity tends to keep the gases down, but their flying molecules tend to escape. Very light molecules like hydrogen do escape. Probably there would be no hydrogen remaining uncombined in the earth's

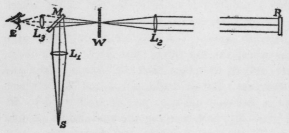

atmosphere, if it were not being slowly supplied, all the time, by chemical processes.

On the moon, gravity is so much less, because the moon has only $1/80.5$ the mass of the earth, that all of our common atmospheric gases, as well as carbon dioxide and water vapor, long ago escaped.

FIG. 6.   TOOTHED-WHEEL METHOD FOR VELOCITY OF LIGHT.

From the bright source, $S$, a beam is focused by the lens $L_1$, and the thinly silvered mirror, $M$, upon the rim of the toothed wheel, $W$. Thence the light diverges to the lens $L_2$, which sends a parallel beam to the distant mirror, $R$, from which it returns through $L_2$, $W$, and $M$, and is focused by the lens, $L_3$, at the observer's eye. At great speeds, the teeth of the wheel, $W$, give alternately light and darkness, according as the returning beam strikes a tooth or a space. Knowing the speed of the wheel and the distance traveled, the velocity of light is calculated.

This is why the moon is dead. So much for the influence of size and mass. But if the moon's atmosphere had always been exceedingly cold, as cold as it would have been if lying as far from the sun as Neptune, probably carbon dioxide, water, oxygen, and nitrogen would still be retained, because the molecules would not go fast enough to defy gravity to hold them. So much for temperature influence on the composition of the atmosphere.

Since the presence of the oceans and the air, both indispensable to life, depends on certain conditions of temperature and gravity, we naturally inquire about the things that make these conditions — the sun's heat and distance from us, the earth's diameter and mass. Let

us postpone the inquiry about the sun's heat till we come to consider what the sun is, and take up now the other three questions.
There are quite a number of good ways to measure the sun's distance from the earth. Most direct are those which depend on the velocity of light. This quantity has been measured very accurately by Michelson, Cornu, Fizeau, and others. Imagine a toothed wheel rapidly revolving, and a beam of light brought to focus just where it would meet either a tooth or a space in the rim of the wheel. Then let the ray pass out several miles to a mirror which reflects it straight back to the teeth again. You will see at once that at a certain speed of the wheel the ray would pass between two teeth, go out to the mirror, and on its return meet the adjacent tooth and be cut off, giving darkness. But at double this speed of the wheel, the ray would slip by between the next pair of teeth. So by increasing the speed gradually, and counting the alternations of light and darkness, one could get many teeth to pass, and obtain a high degree of accuracy in the measure of the time required by light to go out to the mirror and return.

Those interested may consult books of reference on light, and learn of other methods, but they all agree closely in giving the velocity of light as 299,860 kilometers (186,330 miles) per second. This being known, we have the sun's distance if we can measure the time required for light to come to us from the sun. We saw in Chapter II that Galileo discovered the four moons of Jupiter with his telescope. These moons are frequently eclipsed by Jupiter's being between them and the sun in part of their revolutions about him. As we watch these eclipses from the earth, they do not follow at perfectly regular intervals, because Jupiter and the earth are at different distances apart in their orbits from time to time. Thus light has farther to go to us from Jupiter's moons when Jupiter is directly beyond the sun than when he is directly beyond the earth. The difference is just the diameter of the earth's orbit. Thus by observing the times of the eclipses of Jupiter's satellites, and combining with the velocity of light, we find the double distance of the sun.

Professor Sampson has done the latest work by this method, and his results give for the sun's distance 149,510,000 kilometers (92,900,-000 miles). There are at least five other independent methods, some of them of greater accuracy than this. Most astronomers would prefer a value of the sun's distance about 149,400,000 kilometers (92,800,000 miles). This is the result of what amounts to a triangulation, like a surveyor's, on the minor planet Eros, one of that numerous group of which Ceres was the earliest discovered. Eros comes nearer the earth at times than any other planet known, so that, as seen from opposite sides of the earth, it sometimes differs in its place among the stars by as much as 2 minutes of arc. From this angle, and the known diameter of the earth, is ascertained the distance of Eros. But the relative distances of all planets from the sun are known from Kepler's laws, since we know the time of their revolutions. Hence, from the distance of Eros is derived the solar distance of the earth, because we know the map of the solar system, and only need one distance to fix the scale of the whole of it.

It is a curious thing to consider, that if we should accept the sun's distance as computed solely by means of the velocity of light methods (there are several of them), and accept the angular displacement of Eros from opposite sides of the earth as known, we could work backwards from these data and get the earth's diameter without troubling a single surveyor. And the result would be accurate within one part in a thousand, at that.

But there is a much more accurate way to measure the earth, which, however, has cost millions of dollars to carry out. First, the shape of the earth had to be known. Special pendulums are used which are caused to swing in vacuum enclosures for many hours at many points over the earth's surface. The time of vibration at each station gives a measure of the force of gravity there, and this gives a measure of the relative distances of the earth's center from all the pendulum stations. In this way it is proved that the earth is not spherical, but bulges at the equator. The earth's polar diameter is less, in fact, than its mean equatorial diameter by 1 part in 297.

The shape of the earth being known, the actual dimensions are obtained by measuring long arcs of its surface. In doing so, the observers first prepare a "base line" several miles long by laboriously setting end to end special measuring rods on a levelled support, on which the rods are kept at measured and nearly constant tem-

perature throughout the job.  It is possible to find this base length
to one part in a million or better.  Then, by surveying instruments,
they strike out triangles, extending out from hill to hill, until at last
they carry the measurements to thousands of miles.  It is said that
the arc across the United States, 3,000 miles long, is measured to
within a probable error of 85 feet.  Several other long arcs have
been measured in
other countries.  As a
result, the earth's
mean equatorial ra-
dius is said to be
6378.39 kilometers
(3963.34 miles) with
a probable error less
than 1 part in 100,000.

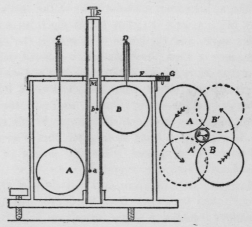

The mass of the
earth is the next most
interesting quantity.
To obtain it, we have
to weigh the earth in
terms of a standard
weight.  Several ways
of doing this have
been used.  The most
striking, perhaps, was
among the first em-
ployed.  In the year
1775, the Astronomer

Fig. 7.  Measuring the Constant of the Force
of Gravity (Boys).

In order to weigh the earth against the large balls,
A, B, the little suspended balls, a, b, whose time of
circular vibration is observed, so as to measure the
earth's attraction for them, are arranged to be attracted first in one direction, then in the other, by
the balls, A, B.

Royal Maskelyne, working under the auspices of the Royal Society
of Great Britain, made the celebrated measurements of the deflection of the vertical, as indicated by a plumb line or a level, by
the attraction of the mountain Schehallion in Scotland.  The idea
was thus to compare the attraction of the mountain to the attraction
of the whole earth, and then, by taking samples and measurements,
to find how many tons the mountain weighed.  But the results were
rather uncertain.  Perhaps the best method is called the method of
Cavendish, and was best employed by C. V. Boys in the year 1894.

Two small balls on opposite ends of a rod, supported at its center by a fine-drawn fiber of quartz crystal, are attracted by large masses suitably placed so that the fiber is twisted through a measured angle. The force of the twisting, in terms of the earth's attraction, is measured by noting the time of swing of the rod, and so the attraction of the large masses for the small ones is compared to the attraction of the earth for them, and thus the mass of the earth is obtained.

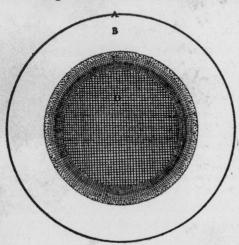

FIG. 8.  THE EARTH'S INTERIOR (after William-son and Adams).

*A* is the outer crust of granitic rocks 35 miles thick. *B* is a layer of silicates of iron and magnesium, about 1,000 miles thick. *C* is a layer in which the silicates gradually change to metallic iron 850 miles thick. *D* is a central core of nickel-iron.

As it comes out, the earth's mass is 5.997 × $10^{24}$ kilograms[1] (1.320 × $10^{25}$ pounds). Compared to an equally-sized globe of water, the earth weighs 5.52 times as much. This also is very interesting, for earth and rocks, such as form all of the solid earth which we can ever explore, weigh, on the average only 2.8 times as much as equal volumes of water. Hence it is plain that down below these materials must be others very much heavier. One could write a romance about tons upon tons of platinum, gold, and silver, hidden away down in the bowels of the earth, to be discovered by some gallant, but poor, boy, with his beautiful and charming sweetheart, who should penetrate these secret places by some new scientific discovery. He would bring away the treasures to do untold good with them among the distressed ones, and to embrace the wonderful opportunities of science, engineering and art on the top of the earth!

[1] Which means 5997 followed by twenty-one ciphers!

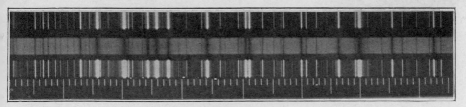

PLATE 7, FIG. 1. THE BRIGHT AND DARK SPECTRUM OF IRON AS OBTAINED IN THE LABORATORY.
The violet region between wave-lengths 3800 and 3900 Angströms.
(Photographed by Anderson, Mt. Wilson Observatory.)

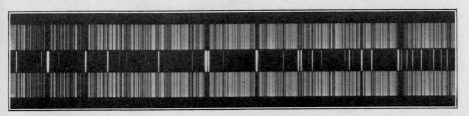

PLATE 7, FIG. 2. EVIDENCE OF IRON IN THE SUN. (Mt. Wilson Observatory.)
The bright line spectra are produced in the laboratory. The dark line spectra above and below are solar. Note that every bright line has its dark solar counterpart. Many other dark solar lines appear also. These are produced by the existence in the sun of other vapors than iron.

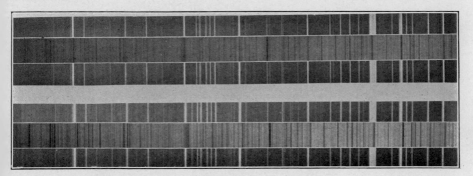

PLATE 7, FIG. 3. SPECTROSCOPIC BINARY MU ORIONIS, SHOWING LARGE DISPLACEMENT OF LINES. (Yerkes Observatory.)
The figure shows the spectrum of this star taken on two different dates. Some of the dark lines in the star's spectrum closely coincide with the comparison lines of titanium. In the upper spectrum the star's lines are only slightly displaced toward the right (toward the red); in the lower spectrum the displacement is in the same direction, but is much larger. This shift of the star's lines is due to the speed of the star in the line of sight, away from the earth (recession), which the measurements on the original show to be 19 kilometers (12 miles) per second on the upper spectrum, and 63 kilometers (39 miles) per second on the lower.

PLATE 8. FOSSIL FOOTPRINTS. (Amherst College Collection.)

The ancient creature (Anomeopus Curvatus) that walked upon a muddy shore has sent his mark to us across the great gulf of time no more convincingly than the chemical elements in distant stars are sending us the evidences of their presence in the spectral rays that bridge over chasms of both time and space equally stupendous.

Calculations and experiments have been made which show that it is quite out of the question to assume that this increased density towards the earth's center comes merely from the enormous compression caused by the weight of the over-head layers. Yet when one considers that the pressure at a thousand miles depth is about 10,000,000 pounds on each square inch, this suggestion does not seem so foolish.

Taking all known facts into consideration, such as the speed of earthquakes, the earth's moment of inertia, along with those we have spoken of, the best opinion is that the earth has a skin of ordinary earth and rock about 60 kilometers (37 miles) thick, then a shell 1600 kilometers (994 miles) thick of compounds of iron, magnesium, and silicon, then a shell 1400 kilometers (869 miles) thick in which iron begins to predominate, and finally a nickel-iron core something like a meteorite in make-up, 6800 kilometers (4225 miles) in diameter. The pressure at the center is something like 50,000,000 pounds per square inch, and the material there is about 10 times as heavy as water. Of course, other substances like platinum, gold, silver, lead, copper, are scattered through the mass, but it is not supposed that they make up a very large proportion of the central core compared to nickel-iron. This view is taken partly on account of the well known composition of meteorites.

So much for the size, weight, and structure of the earth. Now a few words about its indispensable coverings, air and water. About 70 per cent of the earth's surface is submerged in water, and to an average depth of 12,000 feet. The atmosphere stretches up and up, getting rarer and rarer, till at 15 miles above the earth's surface 24/25 of it are left below. Yet there is air sufficient to produce white heat in meteors, as they rush into it, as high up as 100 miles. At the earth's equator, the air is composed in percentage by volume roughly as follows:

| | Nitrogen | Oxygen | Carbonic Acid | Water vapor | Argon | Other gases |
|---|---|---|---|---|---|---|
| Per cent | 76.0 | 20.4 | 0.02 | 2.6 | 0.9 | 0.01 |

The water-vapor load varies from one-tenth per cent to four per cent of the weight of the permanent gases in different times and locations. At higher elevations, water vapor rapidly grows less.

Carbonic acid also diminishes, but not so fast. It is supposed that at very high levels the composition of the atmosphere is utterly changed. Ozone (another form of oxygen) is there, as the spectroscope shows us, and it is supposed that finally helium (that light gas first found in the sun and now used to fill balloons) and other light gases become predominant.

Sometimes people express surprise that scientists claim that the earth's heat comes mainly from the sun. For, say they, the higher up towards the sun one goes on a mountain, or in an airship, the colder it is. The explanation of this paradox is easy. Sun rays heat only that which absorbs them. Perfectly transparent substances, if there were any, would not be warmed at all by transmitting sunlight. Thus a glass window-pane feels cold, though the hand grows warm inside the room when the sunlight falls upon it. So the air, being very transparent, is little warmed by sun rays, and a person on whom the cold air blows at high elevations is chilled also. But screen off the wind, and absorb the sun rays on a blackened receiver, and you will find it grows hotter at high altitudes than it does at sea level, not because it is appreciably nearer the sun — what is a mile among 93,000,000 of them ? — but because some sun rays are lost in passing through the air, even though it is very transparent.

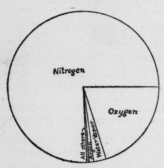

FIG. 9. COMPOSITION OF OUR ATMOSPHERE.

The cross-hatched sector includes carbonic acid gas and a number of rare gases not named.

The changes of temperature from pole to pole of the earth are due to the fact that the earth is nearly spherical. For consider an open frame a yard square to be set up so that it is at right angles to the sunbeam, and at noon on March 21 or September 21 carry it so from pole to pole. At the equator, the shadow of it will be of the same size as the frame, because, the sun being directly overhead, the frame is parallel to the earth's surface. But as we leave the equator in either direction, the earth's surface grows more and more oblique to the frame, and therefore the shadow of it gets bigger and bigger, till at the pole it becomes miles long. All of this time, the frame lets through just the same area of sun rays. Scattered over the larger area on which they fall, it is easy to see why they produce less warming.

It is, of course, the same sort of proposition between noon, morning, and night, only that the atmosphere keeps the heat over night to a considerable degree, so that the extremes are much less than between the equator and the poles, where they have nights six months long. Also, the same sort of considerations show why mountains, broken by ravines, and with their steep slopes having so much exposed surface oblique to the sun's rays, are cooler.

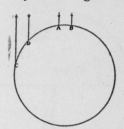

The seasons, which also occur because of change in the obliquity of sun beams, depend on still another factor. Like a gyroscope, the spinning earth keeps its axis nearly in a fixed direction in space, pointing near the north star. But the "ecliptic," or orbit in which the earth revolves about the sun, is inclined about 23-1/2 degrees from the earth's equatorial plane. Remember that the sun is practically unchanged in direction among the stars, no matter where you stand upon the earth. This is because the earth is so small, compared to the immense distance of the sun from us. To move clear from the south pole to the north would only displace the sun among the stars by 17.6 seconds of arc, or about as much as the width of a window seen six miles distant.

FIG. 10. COLD WEATHER AT THE POLES DUE TO THE OBLIQUITY OF SUN RAYS.

Compare the widths *AB* and *CD* over which the warmth of equal bundles of solar rays must be distributed at the equator and near the poles.

Now, as for the seasons: When the sun lies in the plane of the equator, it is neither winter nor summer anywhere, because then he is shining quite impartially upon the earth, and day equals night in length everywhere. But since the plane of the equator is inclined to the plane of the ecliptic, this can only happen twice in a year. It is when the earth, in its revolution, reaches the line of intersection of the two planes. This occurs at the "equinoxes,"

March 21 and September 21. At all times between September and March, the sun is south of the equator and favors the southern hemisphere, while between March and September, he favors the northern hemisphere. We reach the extreme positions at the "solstices," December 21 and June 21.

The earth goes round the sun from west towards east in 365.-2564 days. When this period is done the sun will have returned

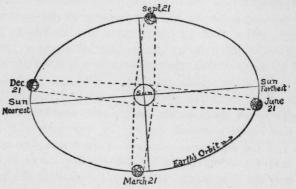

FIG. 11. CAUSE OF THE SEASONS.

The earth's equator is inclined about $23\frac{1}{2}°$ from the plane of its orbit, and the earth's axis always keeps in parallel positions as the earth revolves about the sun. Hence, part of the northern hemisphere is in shadow in the months near December, and part of the southern hemisphere in those near June. At the equinoxes, in March and September both hemispheres are fully illuminated. The sun is nearest in January so that the northern winters are warmer than otherwise they would be.

very closely to the same place among the stars it has now. In twenty-four hours of mean solar time, the earth rotates from west to east upon its axis, but, reckoning by the stars, the day is 23 hours, 56 minutes, 4.09 seconds. This difference of nearly 4 minutes comes from the fact that in making a day's journey on its orbit about the sun, the earth makes $1/365\frac{1}{4}$ of a rotation additional, so that while the sun rises only 365-1/4 times in a year (so to speak) the stars rise 366-1/4 times, if we may say so.

We noticed in Chapter II that though Hipparchus discovered the "precession of the equinoxes," Newton, 2,000 years later, explained it. Let us first state clearly what Hipparchus discovered. When the constellations were first named, the March equinox occurred when the sun was in the direction towards the constellation Aries. But as time went on this direction steadily changed until now the sun is in Pisces at the March equinox. That is to say there has been a "precession" of about 28 degrees towards the west. Newton showed that this was precisely the sort of thing which ought to happen because of the attraction of the sun and moon for the protuberance of the earth's equator. The earth, indeed, can be looked upon as a monstrous gyroscope, and a force which pulls it in one direction starts a "precession" around an axis, so that the real motion which occurs is at right angles to the action of the force which produces it. You may see the same thing in a top, which is a kind of gyroscope. The pull of gravity which tends to tip the top over merely causes it to go round and round a conical figure. In consequence of the "precession" of the equinoxes, the pole of the earth, like the axis of a top, makes a swing among the stars. This takes 25,800 years. While now the pole points within 1-1/4 degrees of the north star, 12,000 years hence it will point close to the bright star Vega.

We saw that the Astronomer Royal, James Bradley, in seeking to detect "parallax," or the apparent motion of stars due to the real motion of the earth around the sun, failed therein but found instead "nutation" and "aberration." Nutation is but a sort of lunar excresence to "precession." For since the gravitational pulls of the sun and moon on the protuberance of the earth's equator together produce precession, it is easy to believe that because the moon moves around the earth 13 times a year, marching very far to the north and south, and also very elliptically in her orbit, her attraction must be variable, and must give a nodding or wavy curve to the general circular march of the pole of the earth attending precession. This wavy motion is "nutation."

Bradley's "aberration" is quite of another sort. It is the result which comes to the apparent position of stars from the velocity of light not being infinitely great compared to the speed of the earth in its orbit. Bradley, indeed, was led to its explanation one day while boating on the river Thames. For he saw that the vane at the masthead pointed to a different quarter, depending on which way the vessel steered, and this without a change in the wind's direction.  The classic illustration is that of the umbrella, which,

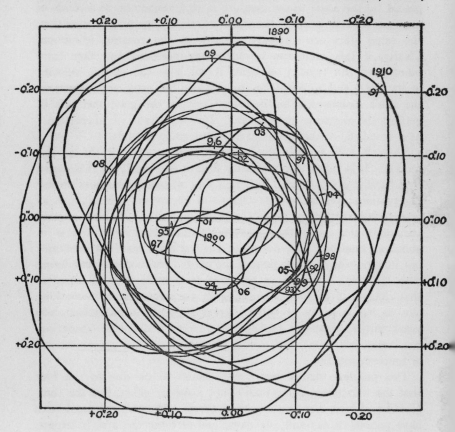

FIG. 12.  Wanderings of the earth's pole from the year 1890 to 1910.  The scale is in seconds of arc.  The extreme diameter of the figure, about 0″.6, corresponds to about 60 feet on the earth's surface.  (After Albrecht.)

while it would shield from a vertical rainfall if held upright over a stationary person, yet must be inclined forward if the holder should run at speed, because the rain would then seem to come obliquely.

Similarly with the stars. As the earth travels its orbit at, roughly, 18.6 miles per second, those stars lying over opposite to the sun's direction in the plane of the ecliptic are apparently displaced by the angle whose measure is 18.6/186000 or 20 seconds of arc. Six months later, as the earth travels in the opposite direction, the same stars are displaced equally in the contrary direction. Clearly, if this angle can be accurately measured and then combined with the velocity of light, it will give the earth's velocity in its orbit, and so enable us to measure the orbit and determine the sun's distance. This is indeed one of the good methods of getting the distance of the sun. The "constant of aberration," as it is called, is usually taken at about 20.47 seconds.

There is still another small vagary connected with the earth's motion. It is called the "variation of latitude," and was discovered by Chandler about 1890. He found that when the best sets of star observations ever made were cleared of all known defects, such as precession, aberration, and the others, there remained certain variations that were of a periodic nature, running a course in about 14 months. The nature of the variation was not constant, but in 1890 was as if the pole of the earth's rotation was wandering over the earth's surface in an orbit from west towards east, so that changes of latitude amounting in the aggregate to something like 30 feet actually occurred. From Bradley's observations, 160 years earlier, Chandler found the same type of polar wandering, but larger in amount, and taking place in little over a year instead of fourteen months.

This puzzling change was finally found to be due to the fact that the wandering of the pole is not a simple effect, but the combination of two, and possibly even three. The two principal ones have periods of 427 and 365 days, and of these the first is largest, but the second is variable in its magnitude. Sometimes the two conspire together and produce larger wanderings, while at other times they interfere and the wanderings are less. They go through the full cycle of these changes in 7 years.

The discovery appeared so important that six observatories were founded, located in the United States, Japan, Russia, and Italy, respectively, all at closely equal latitudes, for making the most accurate possible series of latitude determinations, so as to determine exactly the march of the pole. Their work was continued without interruption from about 1900 until the great war, when Russia fell out, and there has been some delay since in proper reduction and publication of the results, though the observations are still being continued at several stations.

The reason for the existence of the larger component part of the variation of latitude is too abstruse for a book of this kind, involving, as it does, principles of mechanics as applied to the rigidity of the earth, and the relation of the axis of rotation to the axis

FIG. 13. ATMOSPHERIC REFRACTION.

The observer at $O$ is beneath a sea of air $OZ$, which gradually grows less dense from the ground upwards, till at 100 miles elevation the atmospheric rarity rivals the best vacua. When the heavenly bodies are quite appreciably below the sensible horizon, $A\ O\ B$, they may still be seen owing to the curvature called refraction which their rays experience in passing obliquely through the gradually densifying air layers. This is indicated with exaggeration by the rays $OC$, $OD$.

of symmetry of figure. As for the second factor, whose period is a year, one might well expect some such thing, considering the unequal advance and retreat of the winter snow and ice, and other changes which attend the seasons. Without going further into causes, we must be glad that the discovery led to clearing up some puzzling discrepancies in the work of several astronomers, which had hitherto cast some discredit on their reputations for accuracy, and on the excellence of their instruments. Now their work takes a rightful high standing.

One other thing which adds difficulty to accurate astronomical work is atmospheric refraction. We have all seen an oar looking like a broken stick in the still water. Light is like an army which marches along with even front until one wing comes to a difficult stretch of territory and lags behind, so that the average direction of the front swings through an angle. So it is with light from the submerged part of the oar. As it reaches the air-surface, where it travels easier, the light is turned ("refracted" is the technical word) in its course.

This happens, too, in the lens and the prism, and also in the atmosphere. For the air next to the earth is denser than what is above, and light travels slower in it. Hence, the sun's rays at setting are bent around towards the earth, and therefore the sun can be seen after the clock says he should be below the horizon. Thus it is, too, with all stars, but to a less and less extent the nearer they are to the zenith, where the atmospheric refraction becomes zero. The refraction varies with altitude, barometric pressure, temperature, and differs for all different colors of light. Hence, it is very difficult to make a satisfactory allowance. It is very time-consuming, with this, and the other little corrections, to get exact results from star observations.

We have dwelt quite long enough on these various little troubles of exact astronomy, and will now turn to a grander influence which the sun and moon display upon the earth, namely the tides. As everybody knows who has ever lived by the ocean, the water rises and falls twice a day. Every two weeks there is a time when the tide is unusually high and another when it is unusually low. These are called spring and neap tides. As long ago as the times of the ancient Greeks and Romans, they knew that these phenomena were connected with the motion of the moon, but the real explanation began to dawn when Newton discovered the law of gravitation. He discussed the cause of the tides in the "Principia," and determined the tide-generating forces of the sun and moon, but did not account fully satisfactorily for the lag of the tides behind these forces. As observation shows, the spring and neap tides arrive at a port about 1-1/2 days after the full and change of the moon.

Next to Newton, the greatest work on tides was done by Laplace in the "Méchanique céleste," and, after him, among the most fruitful tide students were Lord Kelvin, Sir George H. Darwin, S. S. Hough, and R. A. Harris. The subject is complex beyond all possibility of exposition here, but we may at least see why it is that there are *two* tides formed at opposite ends of the earth's diameter, instead of merely one on the side towards the moon or the sun, whichever we are considering. As the problem is a little too troublesome for easy reading we will relegate it to the Appendix.

When one looks upon the great tidal flows in some rivers and

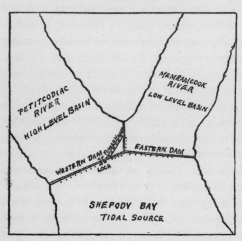

inlets of the ocean, he is struck by the enormous energy displayed, and wonders if it could not be profitably used for power purposes. Tidal plants have been used for several centuries at various places, but none on a large scale. One of the most notable proposals is that at Hopewell, New Brunswick, described in the Journal of the Engineering Institute of Canada, October, 1919.

FIG. 14. HOPEWELL TIDAL POWER PROJECT.

The Petitcodiac River is to act as a tide-filled reservoir, discharging directly into Shepody Bay, or into the Memramcook River, according to the height of the tide. In this way a fairly steady head of water is to be maintained to operate turbines and so furnish power for electric distribution.

Hopewell stands at the head of an arm (Shepody Bay) of the Bay of Fundy, where the low-level neap tide seldom is less than 32 feet, and the high-level spring tide seldom exceeds 42 feet. Two little rivers, the smaller the Memramcook, the larger the Petitcodiac, empty into the bay at this point. The proposal is to run two dams across the arm of the bay just at the junction of these rivers, and to build a third short dam to separate the two rivers completely, so that they would form two independent basins. The eastern dam across the smaller river is to be so high that the tide can no longer enter it, while the western dam is especially constructed to permit the tide to back up into the larger river.

The power plant is to be situated just across the junction of the western dam and the short separator dam, and is to be provided with turbines capable of operating at constant output under a moderate change of head of water.

In operation, the attendants would alter the gates of the dam at intervals predictable years in advance from the tide tables. Thus the flow of water would be either from the big reservoir into the bay, or from the big one to the smaller one, at pleasure, in either case operating the turbines. In this way they are to be kept running under a head which fluctuates only between about 27 and 15 feet, and most of the time much less. The power is to be generated continuously, owing to the large amount of water impounded, and is to be turned into electric power and transmitted throughout Nova Scotia and New Brunswick at costs ranging from 3/4 cents per kilowatt hour, for large power users, up to 4 cents for small lighting service.

We have mentioned in Chapter II what a difficult field the theory of the moon's motion has proved, calling the greatest mathematicians to display in it all their powers. It is therefore very unsuitable to a book of this kind to venture far upon it. Still there are a few general facts that will interest us. First, as everybody knows, the moon presents almost the same face to us all the time. That means that she rotates in the same time that she revolves around the earth, in 27.32 days, as the stars indicate.

The moon shows us more than half her figure, however. This is called "libration" and is of three kinds. First, daily, because the earth is larger than the moon, so that we see beyond her central plane at moon rising and setting. Second, in latitude, because the moon's orbit is inclined, and just as the sun shines beyond the north pole in summer and the south pole in winter, so the earth sees beyond the moon's poles. Third, in longitude, because the moon's motion in her orbit is not precisely uniform.

During the moon's period, her face goes steadily from almost complete duskiness to almost full illumination and back again. Sometimes the sun, moon and earth come almost exactly into line. Then we have eclipses. When the moon is in the middle position she hides the sun, and it is a solar eclipse. When the earth is in the middle position she hides the moon, and it is a lunar eclipse.

During a total lunar eclipse, or when the moon presents only a thin bright crescent, the dusky part of the moon's surface can usually be seen very plainly, though faintly. This is because the earth helps to illuminate the moon, but differently in the two cases. When the moon is totally eclipsed, the sun rays are bent somewhat by refraction in the earth's atmosphere, and thereby reach the moon diffusely, and are reflected back to us.

But at new moon, the lunar inhabitants, if there were any, would see a glorious sight as they gazed on the earth. For, compared to the full moon, the earth would look four times the diameter, and would average nearly three times as bright, so that nearly fifty times as much sunlight would be reflected by the earth to an observer on the moon as is reflected by the full moon to an observer on the earth. The pale light we see at new moon is some of this glorious earth effulgence reflected back to us.

Neither the moon nor the earth sends out any visible rays of its own. But if our eyes were sensitive to rays of ten to twenty times the wave-length of red light, we should see the moon by her own rays, and find her sending several times as intense ones as she reflects from the sun. By examining these lunar rays with the delicate electrical thermometer which he invented and called the bolometer, Langley and his colleague, Very, showed that the sunlit moon approaches boiling temperatures. But when a total lunar eclipse comes on, it takes only a few minutes, they found, for the moon's surface temperature to fall far below freezing, indeed so cold that they could no longer detect her rays. This is one proof that the moon has no such atmosphere as the earth has. But, more decisive, no clouds are ever seen there, and no bending of star rays occurs when the moon passes between stars and us. At such times, called "occultations," the stars are blotted out suddenly, as if they were instantly annihilated. If the moon had an atmosphere, the stars would disappear lingeringly, as the sun does when he sets.

So the moon is a dead barren planet. Nevertheless, soon after Sir John Herschel went on his famous expedition to the Cape of Good Hope to explore the southern heavens, one Richard Adams Locke published a series of articles in the New York Sun of August and September, 1835, purporting to explain why Sir John had gone to the Cape, and what wonderful intelligent beings and curious plants and animals he had observed on the moon. This narrative, called now-a-days the "Moon Hoax," is written in such a serious scientific-sounding style that any but an expert might almost believe it. At the outset, the introduction presents the absurd proposition that the only obstacle to the unlimited magnification of celestial objects, so as to bring them, as it were, to our very observatory doors, is the faintness of the light which results from such enormous magnification. The narrative begins with a conversation between the great physicist, Sir David Brewster, and Sir John Herschel about this lamentable "paucity of light." Presently, "Sir John diffidently inquired whether it would not be possible to effect *a transfusion of artificial light through the focal object of vision!* Sir David, somewhat startled at the originality of the idea, paused awhile, and then hesitatingly referred to the refrangibility of rays, and the angle of incidence. Sir John, grown more confident, adduced the example of the Newtonian Reflector, in which the refrangibility was corrected by the second speculum, and the angle of incidence restored by the third. 'And,' continued he, 'why cannot the illuminated microscope, say the hydro-oxygen, be applied to render distinct, and, if necessary, even to magnify the focal object?' Sir David sprang from his chair in an ecstasy of conviction, and leaping half-way to the ceiling exclaimed, 'Thou art the man!'"

Although this sounds so learned, it is as exquisitely funny to those who know anything of optics as the famous indirectly astronomical rhyme of

> "A Tam o' Shanter dog
> And a plaintive piping frog
> With a cat whose one extravagance was clothes
> Went to see a bounding bug
> Dance a jig upon a rug
> And a beetle balance bottles on his nose."

After perfecting the details, the matter was presented to His Majesty William IV, "who on being informed that the estimated expense was £70,000 naïvely inquired if the costly instrument would conduce to any improvement in navigation. On being informed that it undoubtedly would, the Sailor King promised a *carte blanche* for the amount which might be required."

Then follows these delicious absurdities: "Sir John had submitted his plans" for "an object glass of twenty-four feet in diameter, just six times the size of his venerable father's . . . The material chosen was an amalgamation of two parts of the best crown with one of flint, the use of which, in separate lenses, constituted the great achromatic discovery of Dolland. It has been found, however, by accurate experiments, that the amalgam would as completely triumph over every impediment, both from refrangibility and discoloration, as the separate lenses." The lens "was presumed to be capable of representing objects in our lunar satellite of little more than eighteen inches in diameter, provided its focal image of them could be rendered distinct by the transfusion of artificial light. It was not, however, on the mere illuminating power of the hydro-oxygen microscope, as applied to the focal pictures of this lens that the younger Herschel depended . . . He calculated largely upon the almost illimitable applicability of this instrument as a second magnifier . . . So sanguinely indeed did he calculate upon the advantages of this splendid alliance, that he expressed confidence in his ultimate ability to study even the entomology of the moon, in case she contained insects upon her surface." [ ! ! ! ]

The preparations, the expedition, the mounting, having been described, the telescope is about to be turned for the first time on the moon. "We are assured that when the immortal philosopher, to whom the world is indebted for the thrilling wonders now for the first time made known, had at length adjusted his new and stupendous apparatus with a certainty of success, he solemnly paused several hours before he commenced his observations, that he might prepare his own mind for the discoveries which he knew would fill the minds of myriads of his fellow men with astonishment, and secure his name a bright, if not transcendent conjunction with that of his venerable father to all posterity. And well might he pause! From the first hour that the first human pair opened their eyes to the glories of the blue firmament above them, there has been no accession of human knowledge at all comparable in

sublime interest to that which he has been the honored agent
in supplying . . . Well might he pause . . . He was about to
crown himself with a diadem of knowledge which would give him
a conscious preëminence above every individual of his species . . .
He paused ere he broke the casket which contained it."

At first the observers merely perceived lunar landscapes of
extraordinary magnificence. Crystals shining in glorious colors,
which instead of being small like our jewels were like the enormous
stalactite columns in the great caves of the earth. Gold outcropped
over whole precipices. Presently they came upon lunar forests,
of trees not very different to some of our species, growing near
seas so enchanting that "fairer shores never angels coasted." They
observed great trees like forest oaks, "having broad glossy leaves
like that of the laurel, and tresses of yellow flowers, which hung,
in the open glades, from the branches to the ground." At length
came their first view of animal life, "herds of brown quadrupeds
having all the external characteristics of the bison," but much
smaller, and with "one widely distinctive feature, which we afterwards found common to nearly every lunar quadruped . . . namely
a remarkable fleshy appendage over the eyes, crossing the
whole breadth of the forehead and united to the ears. We could
most distinctly perceive this hairy veil, which was shaped like the
upper front outline of a cap known to the ladies as a Mary Queen
of Scots cap, lifted and lowered by means of the ears. It immediately occurred to the acute mind of Dr. Herschel that this was a
providential contrivance to protect the eyes of the animal from the
great extremes of light and darkness, to which all inhabitants of
our side of the moon are periodically subjected."

So the tale goes on, telling of curious creatures of land and
water, and extraordinary landscapes abounding in gold and precious
stones, until "we were thrilled with astonishment to perceive four
successive flocks of large winged creatures, wholly unlike any kind
of birds . . . which presently alighted . . . walking erect towards
a small wood . . . Certainly they were like human beings, for
their wings had now disappeared, and their attitude in walking
was both erect and dignified . . . We introduced lens $H_2$ which
brought them to the apparent proximity of eighty yards . . . In

general symmetry of body and limbs they were infinitely superior to the orang-outang; so much so, that, but for the long wings, Lieut. Drummond said they would look as well on a parade ground as some of the cockney militia! . . . These creatures were evidently engaged in conversation; their gesticulation . . . appeared impassioned and emphatic . . . Our further observation of the habits of these creatures, who were of both sexes, led to results so remarkable that I prefer they should first be laid before the public in Dr. Herschel's own work, where they . . . are faithfully stated, however incredulously they may be received . . . We scientifically denominated them Verspertilio-homo, or man-bat, and they are doubtless innocent and happy creatures, notwithstanding that some of their amusements would but ill comport with our terrestrial notions of decorum." Here the editor remarks that of course he has obeyed Dr. Grant's private instruction to omit certain highly curious passages, but really there was no occasion to do so, for they would certainly be told by Dr. Herschel "with the certificates of the civil and military authorities of the colony and of several Episcopal, Wesleyan, and other ministers who, under stipulations of temporary secrecy, had become eye-witnesses of the wonders which they were requested to attest."

"The surface of the moon," continues the narrative, "exhibits three oceans of vast breadth and circumference, independently of seven large collections of water, which may be denominated seas. Of inferior waters, discoverable by the higher classes of instruments, and usually called lakes, the number is so great that no attempt has been made to count them." After various wonderful regions had been examined, they found some more inhabitants of far higher culture than those first seen, who had a temple built of polished sapphire with myriad points of scintillating golden light. Some days passed amid these wonderful telescopic adventures, when one morning, shortly after sunrise, the observers were awakened by a cry of fire and, as it proved, through some inadvertence the sun had fallen on their enormous lens, and not only set the observatory on fire, but vitrified portions of its walls into glass, and ruined some of the mirrors. However, the repairs were made in one week, and the observations went on again.

PLATE 9, Fig. 2. THE LUNAR CRATER COPERNICUS
AND SURROUNDING REGION.
(Mt. Wilson Observatory.)
The diameter of this crater is about 50 miles.

PLATE 9, Fig. 1. A PART OF THE MOON'S SURFACE.
(Mt. Wilson Observatory.)

This desolation is matched by few large regions
upon the earth. Some of the craters, as for instance
the one with the dark rim-shadow, seem to be surely
extinct volcanoes. Many of the little ones may possibly have been caused by meteorites falling with no
air cushion upon the naked surface.

PLATE 10.  THE LICK OBSERVATORY.

We may now turn from this agreeable nonsense to a view of the real moon as photographed by the 100-inch telescope of Mount Wilson Observatory. Its surface is highly desolate, abounding in extinct volcanic craters, and level-looking deserts, probably the bottoms of long dried-up seas of past ages, and, like the nitrate and borax deserts of Chile and Bolivia, doubtless covered with a crust of chemical deposits. The atmosphere, if any is now remaining, is inadequate to support life unless of the most primitive cell-like types. There is no evidence that water remains on the moon now, though possibly deep in the ground there still may be moisture. Sir G. H. Darwin suggests that possibly the material which composes the moon separated from the earth owing to a condition of instability associated with the earth's former shape and motion, and that, as a consequence of tidal influence, the month, at first identical with the day, lengthened, the distance separating earth and moon increased, and in course of time (not less, he estimates, than 200,000,000 years) the present arrangement developed. Darwin investigated the subject with great care mathematically, and while nothing so remote from observation is certain, he shows much plausibility for this hypothesis of the origin of the moon.

Having now considered some of the outstanding conditions which prevail on our own home, the earth, and on our nearest neighbor, the moon, we shall go on in the next chapter to speak of the rest of the sun's family, which includes the great planets, their satellites, and "those vermin of the skies," as Weiss of Vienna called them, the minor planets, comets, meteorites, and the zodiacal light.

## CHAPTER V

## THE SUN'S FAMILY, THE SOLAR SYSTEM

To Marshall Davout's men who marched the weary 90 miles from Vienna to the Pratzen Lakes in 48 hours, to join in the battle of Austerlitz, or to the "forty-niners" plodding their dreary journey, week after week, from the Mississippi to the Golden Gate, it would have seemed a mockery to describe our earth as a little planet. But yet, with its diameter of only about 8,000 miles, it is so compared to Jupiter, Saturn, Uranus, and Neptune, with their diameters of 86,500, 70,000, 31,500, and 34,800 miles. Still more is it a puny object compared to the sun, whose diameter is 865,000 miles. The immensity of the sun is indeed overpowering. What the population of New York City is to that of an old-fashioned family, what the length of the Mississippi river is to that of the gutter spout of a roof, what the power of the "Mauretania" is to that of a row-boat, such is the mass of the sun compared to that of the earth. Even the immense planet Jupiter is swung by the sun's attraction over an orbit 3,000,000,000 miles in circumference, and, in retaliation, is only able to swing the sun through an orbit a thousand times smaller. Thus the sun is monarch of the solar system without a peer.

The prime laws of his sway are the three laws of Kepler and that of Newton. (1) The centers of the planets go in orbits which are ellipses with the center of the sun in one of the foci. (2) The line which joins the centers of the sun and planet (the radius vector) sweeps over equal areas in equal times. (3) The square of the period of revolution of a planet is proportional to the cube of its mean distance from the sun. (4) Newton's Law. — Every particle attracts every other with a force proportional to the product of their masses, and inversely to the square of their distance. Kepler's three laws, just stated, can be derived from it. When the separate attractions of all the particles of two separated spheres or spheroids are summed up, they prove to be the same as if the total mass of each was concentrated at a point in its center.

The movements of a planet cannot be determined by considering its relations to the sun alone. All other bodies in space have their attractive influences, small to be sure compared to the sun's, but some of them not to be neglected. It is easy to see how this must complicate the problems which mathematicians have to solve in order to express planetary motion. For the planets continually change their distances and directions from one another, so that their mutual attractive influences are always varying. The greatest masters of celestial mechanics have found the problem of planetary motion insoluble in absolute strictness, and have been obliged to resort to ingenious simplification and approximate methods, which can be repeatedly applied, with ever-growing accuracy of result, till a satisfactory degree of approximation is secured.

One great fact was proved long ago by Laplace. It is that the solar system is stable. One can conceive that, as ages pass, the mutual attractions of the planets might so alter each other's orbits that some catastrophe of collision among them would result. It is this which Laplace was able to show would never happen.

We saw in Chapter III that there is an exact orderliness in the miniature planetary systems which comprise the atoms, and that the successive steps upward in atomic weight result from definite changes of complexity, following exact laws. Nothing so orderly seems to hold with the arrangement of the solar system. If one turns to Appendix C, he sees nothing suggestive of order in the march of increase of distance, or of mass, or of the numbers of attending satellites in the system of the planets. One [curious approximate linkage has been found, called Bode's law, but it breaks down with Neptune. It is this: Write down the series of numbers which, after the second term, are found by multiplying each preceding term by 2:

0    3    6    12    24    48    96    192    384

add 4 to each number as follows:

4    7    10    16    28    52    100    196    388

Compare the distances of the planets from the sun on such a scale that the earth's distance is 10:

| 3.9 | 7.2 | 10.0 | 15.2 | 27.7 | 52.0 | 95.4 | 191.8 | 300.5 |
|-----|-----|------|------|------|------|------|-------|-------|
| Mercury | Venus | Earth | Mars | Ceres | Jupiter | Saturn | Uranus | Neptune |

Up to Uranus the agreement is pretty close.

By aid of Kepler's third law, the known periods of revolution of the planets fix all the distances within the solar system in such a net that, if one of the distances becomes known, all others follow. For instance, the periods of Mercury and Mars are roughly 88 and 687 days, or nearly as 1 to 8. The squares of these numbers being as 1 to 64, and the cube root of 64 being 4, we should expect Mars to be about 4 times as far from the sun as Mercury. The actual distances are 36.0 and 151.5 millions of miles, almost as 1 to 4.

Our earth is not the only planet to have a moon. Most of the major planets, indeed, have more than one, as shown below:

| Planet: | Mercury | Venus | Earth | Mars | Jupiter | Saturn | Uranus | Neptune |
|---------|---------|-------|-------|------|---------|--------|--------|---------|
| Moons: | 0 | 0 | 1 | 2 | 9 | 9 | 4 | 1 |

These moons are a boon to mathematical astronomers, for it is easy to find the mass of a planet which has a satellite.[1]

[1] The rule may be expressed as follows:

Let the combined mass of sun, planet, and satellite be $M$, the combined mass of planet and satellite be $m$, the period of the planet's revolution about the sun, $P$, the period of the satellite's revolution about the planet, $p$, the mean radius of the planet's orbit about the sun, $R$, and the mean radius of the satellite's orbit about the planet, $r$.

By Kepler's law

$$\frac{M}{m} = \frac{p^2}{P^2} \times \frac{R^3}{r^3},$$

whence $\dfrac{M - m}{m} = \dfrac{p^2 R^3}{P^2 r^3} - 1$

where $M - m$ = mass of the sun.

This gives the ratio of the mass of the sun to the combined mass of planet and satellite. To get the mass of the planet alone, one must know the proportion which the satellite's mass bears to that of the planet. There is no simple way to obtain this, but the value now accepted for our moon is $\dfrac{1}{81.53}$, depending on calculations from certain observed inequalities of the motions of the solar system. In the cases of some other planets, their satellites are so insignificant in size that their masses may be neglected.

People often ask what force it is which keeps the planets in motion. This question is natural enough, because in our experience all machines stop running unless power is given to keep driving them. In the solar system, the case is different. There is neither resistance of the air nor friction to overcome. The planets swing along around the sun, age after age, without any expenditure of power at all, for the simple reason that there is absolutely nothing tending to stop them. It did take an enormous quantity of power sometime in the unknown past to put them into this state of motion, but, once done, it requires none whatever to maintain it. No one knows definitely the character of the primeval forces which set the system in motion originally.

Let us now consider a little the physical state of the other seven great planets besides the earth. The major planets fall in two groups of very different types. There are the four smaller ones, Earth, Venus, Mars, Mercury, in order of descending mass, and the four greater ones, Jupiter, Saturn, Neptune and Uranus, similarly arranged. The first group is the inside, the second the outside group. The planets of the first group are all dense, with an average density nearly five times that of water, while the planets of the second group are all rare, with an average density only about 1.1 times that of water. These are very striking facts, which sometime will play a large part in the true theory of the origin of the solar system.

*Mercury.* — This little planet, of only about one-twentieth of the mass of the earth, is so near the sun that it receives almost seven times as intense solar heat as the earth and moon do. Mercury reflects only about 7 per cent of the solar light, while the earth reflects 44 per cent, and Venus 59 per cent. The moon reflects about the same as Mercury. There is no reason to think Mercury has upon it either air or water, so that probably the full glare of the intense solar radiation falls upon its surface. This view agrees with the low reflecting power of the planet. Furthermore, it is believed, though not fully demonstrated, that just as the moon always presents the same face to the earth, so Mercury always presents the same face to the sun. If this is so, there is every reason to believe that the bright face of Mercury has a temperature almost hot enough to melt tin. Bread or biscuits would bake there in the open within a few minutes, and it would take a skillful baker to keep them from burning.  By contrast, the perpetually dark side of the planet must be cold enough to freeze air, so that if there had ever been air and water on the bright side, they must now both be distilled around onto the dark side and congealed there.  Such are the consequences of the assumption that the day and the year of Mercury are of exactly equal length.  Mercury, like Venus and the moon, presents its phases to our view, ranging from crescent to gibbous shapes, depending on whether it lies on this side or the further side of the sun from us.

The orbit of Mercury is the most "eccentric," or elongated, of any in the system of the major planets, and it presents the perplexing feature that the orbit rotates so that the "perihelion," or point of nearest approach to the sun, travels around the sun faster by 43 seconds of arc per century than it should, so far as the attractions of all known members of the solar system would compel it.  For a long time, it was supposed that an unknown planet called "Vulcan" existed between the sun and Mercury, and caused the discrepancy, but this idea is now given up.  This is because many eclipse photographs, which included all stars near the sun to the 9th magnitude, have all failed to reveal "Vulcan."  Seeliger, however, showed that perhaps the matter which sends us the so-called "zodiacal light" may be the disturber of Mercury's orbit.  But many astronomers now accept the theory of "relativity," whose author, Einstein, proved that if "relativity" be true, the perihelion of Mercury should indeed rotate in accord with observation.  One cannot say that this proves "relativity," for it might be that Seeliger's zodiacal light, or some other explanation, is valid.  On the other hand, if there were no outstanding revolution of Mercury's orbit, it would be a severe blow to "relativity."

Venus. — Of all the planets, Venus is most like the earth.  It is the one which comes nearest to us, excepting our moon and some of the little bodies called "asteroids" or minor planets.  Eight-tenths as massive, more highly reflecting, and two-thirds as far from the sun as the earth, Venus seems more fit on many accounts than any other of the planets to support life similar to ours.

There is one obstacle to this view of which we shall have to take account. It rests on the uncertainty as to the time of the planet's rotation. There is no doubt at all about the approximate length of day of Earth, Mars, Jupiter, and Saturn, but with the other planets, including Venus, there are no plain markings to be seen telescopically. We know that the moon only rotates once a revolution. If Venus is of that class, and her day exactly equals her year, there would be a hot side and a frigid side, both unfavorable to living conditions, and combining to distill over the water and atmosphere to be congealed on the dark surface.

The spectroscope has its word to say about this matter. It is easy to measure the rotation of the sun, because the one edge of it is coming towards us and the other receding, so that if the light from the east and west limbs is brought together in a spectroscope to give two bands of spectra superposed, the lines from the metals on the west limb are displaced towards the violet, compared to those arising on the east limb. The same thing has been done by Slipher for Uranus, and though the light does not arise there, but is reflected from the sun, yet the limbs of Uranus reflect solar rays whose spectra show the same sort of displacements of lines, and indicate that the planet rotates in 10 hours 50 minutes "retrograde," that is opposite to the prevailing direction for the other planets.

When this is applied to Venus, as has been done with extreme care by Slipher at the Lowell Observatory, and by St. John and Nicholson at Mt. Wilson Observatory, no decisive evidence of the planet's rotation is found. But the method is not sensitive enough to prove that the day of Venus is equal to its year, which is nearly 225 of our days. All that the spectroscope has yet been able to say is that the rotation of Venus occupies at least 10 days, and may possibly be equal to the revolution period of 225 days.

But this leaves the whole question of its habitability open. The direful consequences of distilling over the atmosphere and water to the dark side would occur only if the day and year were just equal. If the day is long, but not equal to the year, the consequence would not be disastrous to life. There is, moreover, another observation which seems to indicate that the day and year of Venus are not equal. It is this:

The reflecting powers of Venus, Earth, Mars and the moon are, respectively, 59, 44, 15, and 7 per cent. The moon is known not to have an atmosphere, Mars so little that he always shows his surface, while the earth is half cloudy. A fully cloudy planet would reflect 77 per cent, according to Aldrich's measures made from a balloon above a level sea of fog. Accordingly, it is natural to infer that Venus is nearly, but not quite, completely cloudy. If so, her atmosphere and moisture cannot have distilled away to a frigid side never touched by sun rays. But there is still one more difficulty. Slipher, and also St. John and Nicholson, observing carefully with the spectroscope, found no strengthening of water-vapor lines in the light reflected from Venus. If the planet is covered with clouds of water, how can this be? The explanation is, perhaps, that the clouds we see are very high ones, like our own cirrus clouds, which are composed of ice crystals, and that the light does not penetrate deeply enough into Venus' atmosphere to reach much water vapor.

In the year 1924 conclusive indirect evidence of the moderately rapid rotation of Venus was obtained by Pettit and Nicholson. They observed that the *dark side* of the planet is nearly uniform in temperature from west to east, and nearly of the temperature that the earth would appear to be if viewed from another planet. Obviously this could not be so without fairly rapid rotation.

This being the true state of affairs on our sister planet, the conditions seem likely to be nearly as favorable for life there as on our earth. Firstly, the clouds indicate abundant water. Secondly, the temperature should be suitable. For, on account of distance, the intensity of solar radiation should be just about twice what it is with us, but the greater reflecting power reduces the fraction absorbed in the ratio of 7/10, so that the resulting solar heat absorbed on Venus averages about 1.4 times that upon the earth. This would tend to raise the mean temperature of Venus' surface to something like the temperature of our tropics, where life flourishes in greatest luxuriance.

Of course, this is conjectural, but, so far as we can see, conditions on Venus are favorable to life such as we know. But life was never known to start itself. Pasteur's experiments have discountenanced the supposed observed spontaneous generation of life. Its primeval origin is unknown, and the mere existence of favorable conditions is no warrant for the existence of life. We cannot know in the case of Venus by telescopic examination, because apparently we are shut off by an impenetrable veil of clouds. Whether there are intelligent works of engineering there, we may never observe. Unless there should be wireless communication, we probably never shall know whether we have intelligent neighbors on Venus or not.

But it makes the blood stir to imagine what might follow if ever our people could come into fluent communication by wireless with a race brought up completely separate, having their own systems of government, social usages, religions, and surrounded by vegetation and animals entirely unrelated to any here on earth. It would be a revelation far beyond the opening of Japan, or the discoveries of Egyptologists, or the adventures of travellers in the dark continent.

*Mars.* — Only half as great in diameter and one-ninth as massive as the earth, and situated so far away from the sun that the solar heat is reduced to less than half the intensity it has here, obviously the conditions on Mars are very different from ours. According to Professor Johnstone Stoney, it is very doubtful if Mars is massive enough to keep water vapor, if it has any, from escaping. But many persons would think this a mistaken view because there are white polar caps which form and melt away as the two polar regions are alternately tilted from and towards the sun. It may be, however, that these caps are frozen carbonic acid gas, for there is quite a possibility that the poles of Mars get cold enough to make snow of this substance. Still it is equally probable that the polar caps are a sort of hoarfrost of water vapor, for the reasoning of Professor Stoney was not really conclusive against the presence of water on Mars.

The spectroscope has had its say on this question. As we look at the sun's spectrum, we find it crossed by dark lines in the yellow, orange, and red which are well known to be produced by the water vapor in our own atmosphere. At high altitudes and in cold weather, these lines are very faint. Professor W. W. Campbell and colleagues took advantage of this effect of altitude, in 1909, and photographed the spectrum of Mars and of the moon, at equal standing above the horizon, on the same plates. They did this from the summit of Mount Whitney, California, almost as high as Mont Blanc. Here the water-vapor lines were very weak, almost invisible, and the light of Mars gave no stronger ones than that of the moon. Certainly there is no appreciable water vapor on the moon, and there was not enough in a path twice through the atmosphere of Mars to give any observable strengthening of the bands. Later on, in the cold of February, Dr. Campbell, with his colleagues, repeated the spectroscopic test in another and even more decisive way on Mount Hamilton, and again the result was negative. He concluded that there is not as much as a fifth of the water vapor on Mars that there is in cold dry weather in the earth's atmosphere above Mount Hamilton, and this is very little indeed. At the same time he tested for oxygen, and his result was equally negative.

We must conclude, then, that the atmosphere of Mars is very inhospitable for life such as we know it. A further drawback to life there is to be found in the temperature. There is, to be sure, no extensive cloudiness on Mars to compare with our own clouds in keeping out the sun, so that, though the sun's heat is only 4/9 as strong there as upon the earth, there is a larger proportion of it absorbed on the planet than here. The reflecting power is but 15 per cent against 44 per cent for the earth, so that 85 per cent against 56 per cent is useful. Hence the solar heat available to warm Mars is about two-thirds of the intensity of that which warms the earth. This would doubtless suffice to heat the desert soil, directly under the sun on the bright side of the planet, to a surface temperature of about 125° Fahrenheit, or as hot as deserts are upon the earth. But what of the dark side? Deprived of the clouds and the high percentage of humidity which holds back the cooling of the earth at night, the Martian surface temperature, as soon as sunset comes, must cool with great rapidity, and probably falls below zero Fahrenheit every night, even on the Martian equator. Towards the dark pole, it is perhaps cold enough to freeze carbonic acid, or even to liquify air.

The inhospitality of such conditions is apparent. We have, it is true, many evergreen trees, mosses, and other forms of vegetation, which survive here in climates as rigorous as those at the Martian equator, but we cannot believe that Martian life braves out these conditions to be so abundant or advanced in type as some students of the subject would have us suppose.[1]

The evidence which has been brought forward by some for the existence of water, abundant vegetation, and highly intelligent life on Mars rests on drawings and photographs of the planet's surface, which appear to show long straight markings, even double markings, which have been assumed to be great canals constructed by highly intelligent engineers for leading the melting snow water of the polar caps down towards the equator for purposes of irrigation. It is said that the banks of these "canals" show a bursting out of green vegetation at the proper season, as the banks of the river Nile might do if looked upon from the moon.

These views have been hotly defended by men of great ability, especially the late Dr. Percival Lowell. On the other hand, many astronomers of distinction, armed with great telescopes, in highly favorable stations, as for example the late Professor Barnard at Lick Observatory, though they sought eagerly to see all that could be seen on Mars, were totally unable to confirm these evidences of highly intelligent design and extraordinary powers of engineering. To such men, the telescopic view of the surface of Mars shows detail, it is true, but not of this artificial character. Rather it is like the delicate yet vague detail the moon presents to the naked eye, very beautiful and interesting, but absolutely unlike the actual surface of the moon which the telescope reveals. If the planet Mars were near enough to get a good telescopic view of its features, as the moon is, such astronomers as these incline to think the features observed would be not unlike the deserts of the world, with their long ranges of hills, mesas, ravines, and sandy wastes. Very possibly Mars supports life, but very improbably is this life abundant or of high order.

*Jupiter.* — This is the giant planet. Of 10 times the earth's diameter, 317 times her mass, so far from the sun that the solar rays are only about one-thirtieth of their intensity here, blessed with a

[1] These general conclusions as to conditions on Mars are supported by Coblentz' observations of the year 1924 at the Lowell Observatory, which he has reported since this book went to press. See *The Scientific Monthly*, April, 1925.

ten-hour day, composed of a material only a quarter as dense as that of the earth, surrounded by nine moons — surely a human would find extraordinary changes in his outlook if he wakened some morning on Jupiter! Labor unionists there would be adjusting their demands for a three hour day for labor, and be in line with eight-hour practise upon Earth.

There are some very queer things about the rotation of Jupiter. He shows great reddish spots and belts upon his surface. It is by the march of these markings that the period of rotation is measured. It proves variable in the different Jovian latitudes. According to Williams, the rotation periods are as follows:

| Latitude | + 85° to + 28° | + 28° to + 24° | + 24° to + 20° | + 20° to + 10° |
|---|---|---|---|---|
| Length of day | 9 h 55 m 37 s | 9 h 55 m | 9 h 49 m | 9 h 55 m 34 s |
| | + 10° to − 12° | − 12° to − 18° | − 18° to − 37° | − 37° to − 55° |
| | 9 h 50 m 20 s | 9 h 55 m 40 s | 9 h 55 m 18 s | 9 h 55 m 5 s |

These figures, some of them, rest on observations of as many as 60,000 revolutions of the planet. The irregularity of them is rather puzzling. It seems unlikely that it is a solid body that is being observed. And yet it is very hard to understand how a definite object could remain so long in a liquid or gaseous surface as these red spots do. They may be floating islands, it is true, like islands of seaweed, but the subject is certainly very obscure.

It has been thought by some that Jupiter is hot from his own sources, even so hot as to give light of his own. But against this view is the fact that the satellites cast good dark shadows upon the planet's surface when they pass between Jupiter and the sun. Hence Jupiter's light must at least be very feeble, compared to the weak sunlight there. Coblentz and Lampland, too, in recent observations with the thermopile, found evidence of very low surface temperatures for both Jupiter and Saturn.

The eclipses of Jupiter's four larger satellites (often called Galilean, because discovered by Galileo) give a means of determining the sun's distance from the earth, as has been described in Chapter IV. But this method is not the most accurate one. In old times, it was proposed to make use of the positions of these satellites to aid in navigation. For they are so many, and change their places so fast, that their appearance at any time, if compared to the places given in the Nautical Almanac, is sufficient to give a fairly close value of the Greenwich time, and so of longitude at sea. This method cannot compete in our day with a good chronometer.

*Saturn.* — Among all the beautiful and wonderful sights which the heavens afford, the four leading ones, perhaps, are the glories of the rising and setting sun, a total solar eclipse, the aurora with its weirdly dancing polar streamers, and the telescopic view of the planet Saturn. To see that silvery ball, so delicately poised within its wonderful rings, is a sight that never fails to charm, however familiar.

Like Jupiter, Saturn shows spots upon its surface occasionally, though far less conspicuously than Jupiter. From observing them, the time of rotation is known. It is 10 h 14 m at the equator and longer towards the poles, as with Jupiter and also with the sun. This planet is the least dense of any of them, indeed only 0.7 the density of water, and thus little more than half the density of Jupiter. It is as well provided with moons as Jupiter, for each has nine. The ninth satellite, discovered in 1898 by W. H. Pickering, makes its revolution in opposite direction to the others.

Far more remarkable, however, is the wonderful system of rings which has no fellow among all the heavenly bodies. Half the light the planet sends us is reflected by the rings. These are really a multitude of fine particles in procession around the planet. The rings are very thin compared to their total breadth, which amounts to 37,500 miles. Saturn itself is 70,000 miles, and the outer ring 167,-000 miles in diameter. Because the rings are inclined 27° to the orbit of the planet about the sun, and this again is slightly inclined to the earth's orbit, they present themselves to us under very different aspects. Sometimes the rings come almost exactly in line with the earth and practically disappear, but at other times they open out widely and expose all their grandeur. Saturn lies so far away from the sun that it requires nearly 30 years to complete its orbit, so that it marches but little among the stars from month to month, and the changes in the aspect of its rings require the impatient observer to wait a long time. Owing to its great distance, sunlight at Saturn is less than 1/80 of the intensity with us.

*Uranus.* — When Sir William Herschel discovered this planet, in

1781, he saw a round nebulous disk, which he supposed to be a comet, moving slowly among the stars. When its motion proved that it was really a planet, there was at first some disagreement among astronomers in selecting a name. Herschel's loyal preference for "Georgium Sidus," in honor of King George III, was supported officially in England till the year 1850.

Uranus, like the three other greater planets, is nearly of the density of water, and less than one-fourth that of the earth. Situated more than 18 times as far from the sun as the earth is, it receives only about 1/400 as intense sunlight, and requires eighty-one years to make a revolution. The spectroscopic observations of Slipher indicate 10h 50m as the length of Uranus' day. It has four moons, of which the outside one takes a little less than half the period of our moon to encircle its planet, while the inmost one goes round in 2-1/2 days. A curious thing about the satellites of Uranus is that they all go in orbits inclined nearly at right angles to the ecliptic. Thus it happened in 1882 and 1924 that their orbits were seen edgewise, and the satellites seemed to us to swing north and south on each side of the planet. In 1903 and 1945, on the other hand, the orbits of the satellites present their true circular form.

*Neptune.* — A most remarkable thing about this planet is the story of its discovery. John Couch Adams, just graduated from the University of Cambridge, began in 1844 to examine mathematically the problem of the size and position of a planet competent to produce by its attraction the disturbances which had been observed in the orbit of Uranus. By the autumn of 1845, he was ready to present his results for the inspection of the Astronomer Royal, Airy. He called at the Greenwich Observatory, but unfortunately missed seeing the Astronomer Royal because he was at dinner and his butler would not disturb him. So Adams left a paper for him which gave the computed place and elements of the supposed planet. This paper Airy acknowledged, but raised some further question, which for some reason Adams failed for some time to answer, perhaps because he thought that he had received a rather chilly welcome. So nothing towards looking for the planet was done in England for another year.

In the meantime, U. J. J. Leverrier, who had also attacked the problem in France about the same time as Adams in England, published his first results in October, 1845, and June, 1846. In a third paper, published August 31, 1846, Leverrier indicated that the planet would be large enough to show a disk which would distinguish it from a star. By this time, Airy had become more interested, and in July, 1846, recommended to Professor Challis to undertake a search with Adams' positions. This search Challis began in August. But he had no star maps suitable for the purpose, and photography was not perfected, so that he got over the sky but slowly, and he did not immediately map his observations.

So it happened that Dr. Galle of Berlin, Germany, who had received from Leverrier a letter informing him where to look, and who fortunately had available a star chart of the region, recognized the planet on September 23, 1846, and was the actual discoverer. Challis had really seen it 50 days earlier without knowing it. Nor was he the first, for when the orbit became known it was found that Lalande, at Paris, had recorded its place in May, 1795, over 50 years earlier. The mathematical work of Adams and Leverrier, who independently located very closely the unknown Neptune by its perturbing influence across the billions of miles to Uranus, is the feature of this old story which has always raised the admiration of mankind.

Neptune is the outermost known planet, 2,792,000,000 miles from the sun. He requires 165 years to complete his orbit, so that a large part of it is still to be traversed before the planet will return to the place where Lalande was the first man ever to see it. At this immense distance, the sun's rays are only 1/900 the intensity of those that warm our earth, so that unless Neptune has stores of heat of his own, his temperature must be very low. Despite this low temperature and his large mass and gravity, the density of Neptune is only a fifth that of the earth, and not far from that of water.

We have little real knowledge of the physical state of what lies below the visible surfaces of the four great planets, Jupiter, Saturn, Uranus, and Neptune. But, from the low density, we suppose them to be largely gaseous, and from the low intensity of solar radiation at those immense distances, we see that they cannot be of temperatures fit for life unless their own activities provide other sources of heat than sun rays.

*The Minor Planets.* — Between the orbits of Mars and Jupiter lies a large gap of space, in which, according to Bode's law, should lie a planet 2.8 times as far from the sun as our earth. Beginning about the year 1800, astronomers have been filling this gap with little planets, none of them nearly as big as our moon, and ranging from a diameter of 500 miles down to, comparatively speaking, mere rocks of but a few miles in size. In all, nearly a thousand

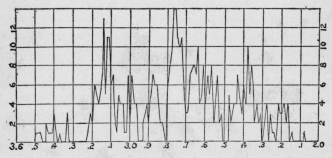

Fig. 15. Numbers of minor planets or asteroids, at solar distances between 2.0 and 3.6 times that of the earth. Note the gaps near 2.49, 2.81, and 3.24, which are points which require (by Kepler's law) 3, 5/2, and 2 times Jupiter's mean angular motion respectively.

have already been discovered, and it seems probable that if we could detect every one, however small, the number would be almost countless. Now-a-days, they are discovered by photography. If a photographic telescope is set to follow the stars exactly, so that they appear as round dots on the photograph, the minor planets will give elongated images, because of their motion, and this leads to their recognition. The difficulty comes in determining whether they have been seen before.

Some of these bodies are variable in their light, which means that one side is more reflecting than the other. This gives a chance to measure the time of rotation for a few of them.

Gauss suggested that these bodies might be fragments of a larger planet which exploded. But it is not now held that this was the

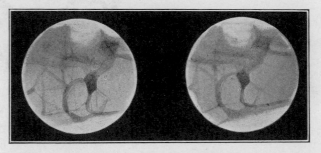

PLATE 11, Fig. 1. MARS.
From drawings made June 17, 1922, one hour apart, by
E. C. Slipher, Lowell Observatory.

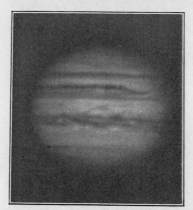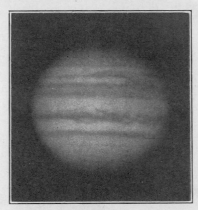

PLATE 11, FIG. 2. JUPITER. (Photos by E. C. Slipher, Lowell Observatory.)
Left, October 19, 1915. Right, December 19, 1917.
The photographs show two different longitudes of the planet. The region of " the great red spot " is seen near the right edge of the left-hand view.

PLATE 11, Fig. 3. SATURN. (Photos by E. C. Slipher, Lowell Observatory.)
Left, February 11, 1916. Right, May 24, 1922.
The bands upon the planet are perhaps of a cloudy nature. The rings are made up of meteoric particles rotating about the planet.

PLATE 12, Fig. 1. HALLEY'S COMET OF 1910. (Photo by Ellerman.)

This famous comet, named for Newton's friend, Halley, who discovered its periodicity, revolves about the sun in about 76 years. Its orbit is very eccentric, so that at farthest it is about as far from the sun as the planet Neptune, and at nearest only about half as far as the earth.

PLATE 12, Fig. 2. THE TUCSON METEORITE.

This curiously shaped mass of nickel-iron weighs nearly 1400 pounds, and fell from the skies no one knows how long ago.

case, because the character of the orbits does not seem to allow mathematically of this hypothesis. It is very interesting to note that the orbits lie in groups as indicated by the mean solar distances. In the accompanying diagram, the heights indicate numbers of planetoids, and horizontal positions indicate distances from the sun compared to the earth's distance. The curious feature has been pointed out that the groups tend to avoid distances in which the angular motion is in exact multiples of Jupiter's motion. Such points are 2.49, 2.81, 3.24, where the mean motion is 3, 5/2, and 2 times that of Jupiter, respectively.

There are a few of these little planets that have nearly the same mean distance as Jupiter, which is a very interesting coincidence. There are several others that lie nearer the sun than any on the diagram. One of these is Eros, which sometimes comes within 15,000,000 miles of the earth, much nearer even than Venus. Such occasions offer the most favorable opportunities for determining the scale of the whole solar system, including the earth's distance from the sun. Unfortunately, the most favorable one occurred in 1883-4 when Eros had not yet been discovered. In 1900-1 the opportunity was fairly favorable. What is generally regarded as the best "solar parallax" value, 8.807 seconds of arc, resulted from the observation then made. Another favorable occasion will come in 1931.

The late Professor James Watson discovered a good many minor planets. He felt such a fatherly interest in them that he made provision in his will for a trust fund, called the Watson Fund, in the custody of the National Academy of Sciences, to be devoted to the promotion of knowledge of the Watson planets, and closely related subjects. Thus, among charitable homes for so many other things, we have something like a refuge for lost planets. There are, indeed, so many minor planets known, and so many being discovered, that the late Professor Weiss of Vienna used to speak of them as "those vermin of the skies." Without occasional reobservation and appropriate rectification of the data of their orbits, many of them would be lost. This has already happened with quite a number of them.

*Comets.* — Many readers will recall the return of Halley's comet in 1910. This wanderer comes close to the sun once in 76 years.

Halley was the friend of Newton who aided in the publication of the "Principia," and who used Newton's principles, then newly framed, to compute the orbit of this famous comet of 1682. Halley identified it with the comet observed by Apian in 1531 and by Kepler in 1607, and fixed its return for 1758-9. Sure enough, it reappeared on Christmas day, 1758. Since then it has been observed in 1835 and 1910. The present author saw it from Mount Wilson, California, in the early morning, just as twilight was beginning to show its first faint glow in the east. The comet's head was just below the horizon, and its tail stretched beyond the zenith like a gigantic searchlight beam. It was thought by some that the tail might interpose between the earth and sun on May 16, 1910, and possibly dim the sun's effulgence. But measurements of the solar radiation showed nothing remarkable.

One of the most brilliant comets of recent times blazed out suddenly in full daylight, on February 28, 1843. It was seen simultaneously in Mexico, the United States, and Southern Europe. On the steamer "Owen Glendower," off the Cape of Good Hope, the passengers were surprised to see a "short, dagger-like object" following the sun towards the western horizon. The head of the comet was then situated only 1°23', or little over twice the sun's diameter, from the center of the sun itself, and observers in Italy were able to trace the tail four or five degrees at midday. On March 3, the tail measured 25°, and on March 11 a second tail, twice as long as the first, shot out in a single day. The Russian, Boguslawski, estimated the length of tail at 581 million miles on March 21, or longer than the radius of Jupiter's orbit.

When the comet went closest to the sun, its center was but 78,000 miles outside the sun's surface. The comet went right round the sun through 180° of its path in 2 hours 11 minutes at the rate of 366 miles a second. Not only so, but the *tail also swept round*, always streaming away from the sun. Had it been *the same tail*, and as long as Boguslawski observed it, the outer end must have traveled over 800 million miles in 131 minutes, or say 100,000 miles a second, approaching near the velocity of light. We know now, as Olbers believed then, that it was *not* the same tail, but new matter driven off from the head continuously by the *pressure* of the light of the sun. Clerke Maxwell proved theoretically, and Lebedew, and Nichols and Hull, afterwards demonstrated experimentally, that light exerts a pressure on small particles, which becomes enormous in such close proximity to the sun as this comet was in March, 1843.

Comets, as the spectroscope indicates, are composed in part of gaseous materials, mainly compounds of carbon, nitrogen, oxygen, and hydrogen. The tail always streams away from the sun, following behind the comet's head during the approach to the sun, but preceding the head when the comet is receding. This behavior toward the sun is like that of a person presented at court, who must never turn his back on his sovereign, but withdraws backwards. They say that General Tom Thumb could not keep pace with the rest in withdrawing from Queen Victoria's presence, and had to turn around and make two or three little runs for it, with his short legs, to catch up. As we have said, this curiosity of cometary behavior is understood now, because the tail is thought to be continually being formed of new material driven off from the head by the pressure of sun rays. It is easy to see that the position of the tail must depend jointly on the velocity of the head, the pressure and velocity of light, and the masses of the individual particles or molecules driven off. Hence, if there be several kinds of particles or molecules available, it is not strange that a comet may present two or even more tails, those materials which are driven faster streaming out more nearly directly away from the sun.

As respects their orbits, comets are sometimes put in two classes, those evidently revolving in closed orbits, so as to be periodic like planets, and those which either are not permanent members of the solar system, or go out so far from the sun that their orbits are impossible to determine. Sometimes a half dozen of these splendid great unheralded comets, possibly never before visitors to the solar system, come in a single century.

The short-period planetary comets, on the other hand, are all inconspicuous, and some of them only telescopic. Two of the most celebrated of them were Encke's and Biela's. Encke's comet was discovered by Pons of Marseilles, November 26, 1818, but investigated by Encke, who found its period to be 1208 days, which is shorter than that of any other comet then known. He traced it back, and identified it with comets seen by various observers prior to 1800. After carefully investigating the perturbations it must suffer from the planets, Encke predicted the time and place of its return, and the event closely followed his prediction. The orbit lies altogether within that of Saturn, and is not extremely elongated. However, at "perihelion," or nearest approach to the sun, it goes inside the orbit of Mercury. This comet has served, by the perturbations it has experienced, to give some evidence on the mass of Mercury, as also that of Jupiter. On several occasions, the nucleus of Encke's comet (and indeed those of other comets) was observed to shrink in size as it neared the sun. It is a curious effect, not perhaps quite understood, but may mean that the larger diameter represents an object shining by its own light too feebly to compete with sunlight on near approach to the sun. Encke's comet, for a number of revolutions, seemed to be falling nearer and nearer the sun, and shortening its period, as if it was encountering resistance to its flight. Later on, however, this tendency was reversed.

Biela's comet, discovered February 27, 1826, had a period of between six and seven years. It also was traced back into the eighteenth century. It returned several times, as predicted, but in 1845, after presenting first a pear-shaped form, it divided into two comets which gradually separated, thus perhaps showing in miniature the history of the earth and moon. On the return in 1852 the double form was recognizable, but the companions were over 1,200,-000 miles apart. Both vanished shortly after their rediscovery, and have never been seen since.

The great planets, Jupiter and Saturn, are powerful disturbers of the comets. Occasionally one of them passes so near one of these great attracting bodies that the cometary orbit is changed altogether, sometimes to give it a planetary character, and sometimes perhaps to throw it out of our system altogether.

Comets are excessively tenuous and small of mass. Very faint stars have many times been observed right through the center of the nucleus of a comet thousands of miles in diameter, without perceptibly dimming the star's light. Lexell's comet approached the earth within 1,500,000 miles on July 1, 1770, and Laplace showed that had its mass been as much as 1/5000 of that of the earth the year must have been lengthened appreciably, yet no such thing occurred.

The following incident is related by La Harpe of Messier, a devoted French observer of the eighteenth century.

"He is a very worthy man, with the simplicity of a baby. Some years ago, he lost his wife, and his attention to her prevented him from discovering a comet he was on the search for, and which Montaigne of Limoges got away from him. He was in despair. When he was condoled with on the loss he had met, he replied, with his head full of the comet, 'Oh, dear! to think that when I had discovered twelve, this Montaigne should have got my thirteenth,' and his eyes filled with tears, till, remembering what it was he ought to be weeping for, he moaned, 'Oh, my poor wife!' but went on crying for his comet."

*Meteors and Meteorites.* — What people speak of as "shooting stars" are not stars at all. They are bits of matter varying in size from dust particles up to bodies of many tons weight, that go coursing around the sun like planets. Some of the orbits which they occupy intersect the orbit of the earth, and thus it happens that we often fall in with them in our journey around the sun. When this happens, the energy of motion of the little body, entering the earth's atmosphere with immense speed, by friction with air is converted into heat. This heat is generally sufficient to melt the outer part of the body. In this condition there is a union between its substance and the oxygen of the atmosphere, so that often the little wanderer is consumed in a blaze of light, and we see a meteor. Often the outer layer cracks off by expansion, and leaves its fragments behind as a meteor-train, lasting bright for several seconds.

If the meteor is very large, it may go entirely through the atmosphere to the earth's surface, and then we speak of it as a meteorite. Thousands of them are now preserved in museums. The largest is one found in Bacubirito in Mexico, estimated to weigh 50 tons. The late Admiral Peary found one in Greenland which weighed 26-1/2 tons. He conveyed it to New York, where it now is deposited in the American Museum of Natural History. Although meteors enter the earth's atmosphere with velocities ranging from 10 to 45 miles a second, their speeds drop to very moderate values after they encounter the resistance of the air. Hence, it is very seldom that a meteorite makes itself a hole in the earth's surface as deep as 10 feet, and in one case a shower of them fell on ice and rebounded without breaking it.

Although the surface of a meteorite becomes very hot at its first entrance into the atmosphere, it is cooled again in the lower air. If it reaches the earth, it is seldom hot enough to char wood, and often is merely a little warm to the touch. Very few fatalities have ever occurred by reason of persons being struck by meteorites. Several close escapes are on record, as when one fell between two carters on a road at Charsonville, throwing the ground up to a height of six feet, and when another broke through the roof of a cottage at Braunau. Human beings occupy so small a part of the earth's surface that the chance of a meteorite hitting one is very, very small.

Meteorites are of three classes. In one, they are composed mainly of metallic iron alloyed with nickel; in the second these substances are mixed with stony matter; and in the third, they consist almost exclusively of stony matter. Altogether, about one-third of the most common chemical elements present on the earth have been found in meteorites, but no unknown ones. It seems probable that our earth is not very different in its make-up, both as regards elements and their proportions, to a mixture of all the meteoric specimens which have been collected.

Some years ago, the readers of "Science" were entertained by several articles on "The Norwood Meteorite." A certain farmer in Norwood, Massachusetts, sent for an astronomer nearby to inspect a meteorite which his hired man had found that morning, still warm, in a hole under a pair of bars which it had apparently broken in its fall. This astronomer examined the object, and reported upon it in two papers read before the American Association for the Advancement of Science. Later the object was exhibited in a cheap museum in Boston for a consideration. Here another scientific man saw it, and in some way secured a bit of it, and found that it was of very strange composition for a meteorite, being, in short, no different from a great many common rocks. He reported this in "Science." The astronomer then made further researches, which he, being a good sport, also published in "Science." He found that the farmer was associated with the museum man, and had himself charred the stone in a brush fire, broken the bars, and interred the warm stone in its grave beneath them. He had sent the innocent hired man on some errand to the spot, and used his excited report to summon the astronomer, whose learned description before the scientific society was all that was needed to make a good thing of the "Norwood meteorite" for the dime-museum exhibit.

Multitudes of meteors fly in space. On dark, clear nights, nearly a dozen may usually be seen in an hour by one observer. Twice as many fall in morning hours as in evening ones, and more than twice as many in the last half of the year as in the first half. These peculiarities, of course, have to do with the direction the meteors go in their orbits, and the direction in which the earth is going with respect to them at different times. Successive meteors are separated on the average by 250 miles, but during the special showers, as that of November, 1833, they come along as frequently as one for each 15 or 20 miles. It is estimated that as many as 20,000,000 meteors big enough to be visible, if it were always dark, clear, night-time, enter the earth's atmosphere every day. If telescopic meteors were included, the estimate would be hundreds of millions every day.

The great showers of meteors come about 33-1/3 years apart, and have been noted in history since the tenth century. They are called the November meteor showers, and they occur to a lesser extent on November 14 of every year. The next great November shower is due about 1932 or 1933. Since they radiate from a point within the Sickle of the star-constellation Leo, they are called the "Leonids."

The explanation is that there is a great stream or ring of meteors, extending all the way around their orbit about the sun, with condensed groups in certain parts of it. As the orbit is elliptical and intersects that of the earth but once, the earth falls into it only once each year. But once in 33-1/3 years the big group is encountered at the intersection.

The Leonids travel 26 miles a second, making a combined speed of approach of over 44 miles a second. It is a curious and significant fact that Tempel's comet revolved in an orbit identical with the Leonids, so that some of them may be the comet gone to smash. Several of the comets have shown disintegration, and it may well be that there is a close relation between comets and meteors.

There are several other times of the year when it is worth while to look specially for meteors, notably for the Andromids of about November 20 to 24, whose principal showers are 6.7 years apart. Their orbit agrees with Biela's comet which was last seen in 1852. These meteors overtake the earth, and so seem to fly but slowly. Another great display is that of several weeks centering about August 10, when the Perseids come on. These seem to be nearly evenly distributed from year to year. Again, there are the April meteors, which radiate from near the bright star Alpha Lyræ (Vega) about April 19 to 21.

*The Zodiacal Light and the Gegenschein.* — If one is in a favorable location, and the best is on a high mountain in or near the tropics, on a cloudless, moonless, night just a little while after sunset twilight ends, in the months January to April, or just before morning twilight begins, in the months September to December, he may see a faint illumination of the sky, stretching up from the direction of the sun towards the zenith. If his eyes are keen, and the conditions are right, he may even see the band of light stretch clear across the sky at midnight. But it is much brighter nearer the sun. This glow is called the "zodiacal light."

Just opposite the sun, at a proper interval of something less than two hours before sunrise, or after sunset, a still more delicate glow may sometimes be seen. It is not larger in diameter than the bowl of the Great Dipper. It is called the "gegenschein" or counter-glow. From its position it evidently relates closely to the zodiacal light.

The spectroscope has shown that these lights are reflected sunlight. But they are not, like twilight, caused by our own atmosphere. They seem to be due to a swarm of meteoric or possibly gaseous particles, encircling the sun in a great lens-shaped swarm extending out beyond the earth's orbit. In a way, it suggests the rings of Saturn, only that the zodiacal swarm is not thin as Saturn's rings are, but even spreads beyond the diameter of the sun. The plane of the lens does not lie exactly in the plane of the earth's orbit, but makes an angle of about 3° therewith.

Now we have called the roll of the sun's family, the solar system: Planets, satellites, minor planets, comets, meteors, zodiacal light, and gegenschein. In the next chapter we must take a "close-up" of the sun himself, see what he is, how big, how hot, how composed, and in a word get acquainted with the immense globe which is at once our nearest star, the ruler of the solar system, and the fountain of influence which supports all life on the earth.

## CHAPTER VI

### OUR STAR, THE SUN

*always*

THINGS are not what they seem. Stars look much like fireflies or like meteors. They are really white hot globes of gas. Many of them are so big that if the earth and sun were transported into one of them, the earth might circle round the sun at present distance, and always be submerged nearly a hundred million miles deep inside of the star. Again, the sun appears no larger than the moon. Really there are on his surface oftentimes sun-spots, too small to be seen with the naked eye, that are yet big enough to swallow up a dozen moons. Finally, the sun looks big enough to cover up all of the stars in the heavens, and bright enough to give a million times as much light as they all. In reality "the sun," as the late Professor Young used to say, "is only a private in the host of heaven." Betelgeuse is about three hundred times the sun's diameter. Rigel gives about 10,000 times the sun's light. It is distance that we have to allow for to correct these false appearances. Though it takes sunlight 8 minutes to come to earth, it takes the light of Rigel 400 years to come, and Rigel is by no means a distant star. There are many of them a hundred times further off.

Our sun is an average star in several ways. No star could have obeyed better the spirit of the advice of Robinson Crusoe's father to stick to the middle class as the happiest. The sun's light is about 10,000 times less than the brightest, and about 10,000 times brighter than the faintest stars thus far observed. Its spectrum is about half way in character between the blue stars and the very red ones. Its mass is just about the average mass of all the known star masses. All that is peculiar about the sun as a star is that we know he has a family of planets, one of them the home of life. But because the sun is such a near star, we know a great deal about him that helps us to know the others.

What is the sun, then? A tremendous globe which, containing almost all the chemical elements that have been found on earth, is so hot that all of them are gaseous. In the foundry, we see iron poured like water in a white-hot stream, but the sun is far hotter than that. We see carbon dazzling hot in the crater of the electric arc light, but the sun is far hotter than that. The sun is so hot that if the carbon stick of the arc lamp was thrust into its depths, the carbon would burst into gas with an explosion. We stand upon the solid earth. There is no solid standing room upon the sun. We may float in boats upon a lake. The sun contains no liquid to float upon. We fly in planes above the earth, but though the sun is gaseous like the atmosphere, no plane could navigate it an instant, because the whole structure of the flying machine, pilot, engine and all, would explode into gas.

But though the sun is all gaseous, it averages 1.4 times heavier than water. This is partly because so large a proportion of the gas probably is of iron and other heavy elements. Still more, however, because the gas is under perfectly enormous compression. At the outer surface the pressure, of course, is very small. For just as in our atmosphere the density falls as we rise, and at a few miles high becomes vacuum-like in rareness, so the sun's gases merge into the vacuum of space. The sun, however, has over 300,000 times the mass of our earth, so that although his radius is an hundred times the earth's, gravity at the surface is about 30 times what it is here. In other words, a man on the sun's surface would weigh two or three tons. Under this enormous attraction the pressure of the solar gas-globe increases rapidly downwards from the surface, so that only a tenth part of the way from surface towards center we may suppose the pressure to reach a thousand atmospheres at least.

On the other hand, there are perfectly enormous forces tending to drive outward the solar gases. First is temperature. Dr. Eddington, whose work on the interior condition of the stars is epoch-making, shows that from 6,000° Absolute Centigrade [1] at the surface, the solar temperature probably rises to the prodigious figure of 18,000,000° at the center. We know very well how steam pressure

[1] Reckoned from the absolute zero, − 273° Centigrade. In Fahrenheit the absolute zero is − 459° and the sun's surface temperature 10,800° Absolute.

rises with temperatures in engines, usually not 70° above boiling. Imagine an engine run by the pressure effect of 18,000,000°!

But there is another disruptive force considerable in the sun, and in some greater stars quite formidable. It is the pressure of light. We saw how remarkably it forces out comets' tails as they near the sun's surface, even, it is said, driving out a tail 500,000,000 miles long from the comet of 1843. But within the sun such light-pressures as the comets meet with would sink into insignificance. Eddington has shown it to be probable that while light-pressure is not nearly as large as the gas-pressure due to temperature for stars of the mass of our sun, or smaller, it becomes the main disruptive agent for greater ones, and actually prevents the existence of any stars of masses more than five times the sun's mass. Greater stars than these would fly asunder under the pressure of their own inner light.

With these staggering figures before us, we can no longer be surprised that the sun's rays are warm, even on the earth, over 90,000,-000 miles away. But in order to get a really vivid impression of what energy the sun rays carry, we should read pages 104 to 108 of Langley's "The New Astronomy."[1] He describes how he made an experiment to compare the rays of the molten steel poured from the Bessemer converter with those of the sun. Into the enormous converter-pot there streamed first some 15,000 pounds of molten iron loaded with half a ton of silicon and carbon. Then a blast of air was forced up through the glowing mass, and the chemical action set up a heat which so far surpassed mere iron-melting temperature that when another 15,000 pounds of molten iron was added it looked like "chocolate poured into a white cup." The cataract of liquid steel was then discharged, shooting showers of scintillations that seemed sunlike in their brilliancy, and spattering the surroundings for an hundred feet with little shooting stars. But there was nothing really sunlike at all in this fierce glare. For when Langley exposed an apparatus which took a balance between the brightness of the surface of the steel and an equal surface of the sun, the sun was found to send out at least 87 times as intense radiation, square foot against square foot, as the dazzling

[1] Houghton, Mifflin & Co., 1896.

steel. This for the total rays, whether visible to the eye or not. But for the light rays only, the sun proved intrinsically not less than 5,000 times the stronger source. And this was near Pittsburgh, where the sun's rays had already lost over half their intensity in the murk of the atmosphere.

So immense is our own distance from the sun, that we get no impression like this of his power from merely holding out our hand to his rays, but only when we try for even an instant to gaze at him. Plateau, the Belgian physicist, dared to look upon the sun for 20 seconds. He lost his sight thereby. However, the sun's heat, too, is enormous. If there was a shell of ice of the same radius as the earth's orbit, enclosing the sun, it would have to be nearly as thick as the Washington monument is high not to be all melted in a single year. It would weigh $4 \times 10^{25}$ (4 followed by 25 ciphers) tons, and the complete melting of it would take as much heat as $4 \times 10^{23}$ (4 followed by 23 ciphers) tons of anthracite coal would furnish. Such is the sun's yearly output of energy.

Of all this heat, the earth and all the planets gather only about 1/200,000,000 part. The rest goes on and on, so far as we know, to infinite distances. But geology shows that plants and animals basked in sun rays about as intense as present ones apparently an hundred-million years or more ago, and that during all the time since then, possibly, even, ever since a thousand million years ago, the sun has kept on flooding his rays throughout the universe about as fast as now. How is it possible that this can be? From what storehouse could energy so inexhaustible be delivered?

The answer was as unknown as the riddle of the Sphinx until a few years ago. To be sure, Helmholtz had pointed out that as the sun cooled he must shrink, and as he shrank, the energy of the fall of his material towards his center must be turned to heat. But it was shown that even if he once extended out to the orbit of Neptune, there could not be derived enough energy in this way to maintain radiation at present rates 25 million years. The great source was still a mystery. Now a gleam of light has come.

As we described in Chapter III, the atoms of all chemical elements are built of two kinds of "bricks" so to speak, the electrons and the protons. We do not find, either in our laboratories or in the gaseous nebulæ of the heavens, the conditions which build complex atoms from simple ones.  In the laboratory, radium and other complex elements disintegrate, but none are formed into greater complexity.  In the nebulæ, only the simpler elements, such as hydrogen, are found.  Somewhere must have been the wonder-making laboratory of Nature, where the intricate structures of electrons and protons, composing the atoms of the metals, were framed together out of these two original and universal constituents.  No place is more probable than the interiors of stars, where temperatures and pressures inexpressibly exalted prevail.  If these are the crucibles of Nature, then it is here that hydrogen must take on complexities and become helium, oxygen, iron, gold, and all the rest.

This may be the source of heat.  For the atomic weights of all the elements but hydrogen are indistinguishable from whole numbers, when separated into their pure constituents, or "isotopes," as Aston has done.  Hydrogen, however, is an exception, with its atomic weight of 1.008.  When four atoms of hydrogen weighing 4.032 become one atom of helium of weight 4.000, the loss of weight represents, according to modern physical conceptions, a store of energy set free.  Possibly similar stores are liberated less copiously when further complexities are introduced in forming heavier atoms.  It is this sub-atomic storehouse to which we now look as the source of the all but inexhaustible radiation of the sun and stars.  An even bolder suggestion is that matter, which is a passive form of energy, is changing into radiation, the active form, at these tremendous temperatures.  If so the stars continually lose mass as they grow older.

At the high temperature (6,000° Absolute Centigrade) prevailing even at the sun's surface, and the far higher ones prevailing near the sun's center, we have said that nothing but gases can exist.  But if this is so, says some reader, how can the edge of the sun look not fuzzy but sharp, as it certainly does?  Ought we not to see right through the gases of the sun as we do through our own atmosphere?

To answer this question we must first refer to the late Lord Rayleigh's explanation of why our sky is blue.  He investigated what happens to light when it enters an atmosphere of particles so small

that even the waves of light are long compared to the diameters of
the particles. Such an atmosphere is ours, for though the dust particles it carries are larger, the molecules of oxygen, nitrogen and
other gases in it are very small indeed compared to wave-lengths.
Lord Rayleigh found that such an atmosphere, and we may as well
say at once any gas, scatters the beam of light in every direction.
The scattering obeys certain perfectly definite laws which connect
its amount to the angle the scattered ray makes with the original
one, and to the wave-length of light. After working out these laws
theoretically, he tested his results practically by observing the intensities of the various colors found in the light of the sky. His
laws were verified. Later on, Schuster, Fowle, King and others
tested them more rigorously against the accurate measurements of
the transmission of sunlight by our atmosphere, which have been
made on Mount Wilson and elsewhere by Smithsonian Institution
observers. The agreement of theory with observation is close.
Fowle calculated the number of molecules in a cubic centimeter of
atmosphere from Rayleigh's formulæ as applied to these observations. His value agreed within 1 per cent of the best results by
wholly different electrical methods.

So the light of the blue sky is sunlight scattered in every direction
by the molecules of the gases of the atmosphere. The amount of
yellow light scattered in passing vertically through the clear atmosphere to the level of Mount Wilson is about 6 per cent, and that of
the blue over 20 per cent. A column of air containing 75 times as
many molecules would scatter 99 per cent, even in the yellow. Now
on the outer layers of the sun such a column would be made up by
the solar gases within a path of 5,000 miles. Hence, practically
speaking, we cannot see more than 5,000 miles deep down into the
solar gases. For all visible rays which arise lower than that must
be completely scattered before they can reach the surface. If this is
so even at the center of the sun's disk, a far thinner layer, say 500
miles, must suffice near the edge of the visible disk, because we see
into it obliquely. But such a layer is little more than 1/1000 part
of the sun's radius. Therefore, we must suppose that all of the fuz-
ziness of the sun's outline must be confined within 1/1000 of his radius. Evidently this is to all practical appearances sharpness of

outline.  Hence, we see that the mere scattering of light by the molecules of the solar gases (atoms, too, will do as well for this purpose) must suffice to give the sun's sharpness of outline.  The recent researches of Lindblad and others seem to indicate that even this sufficient limitation is not the only one, but that actually the absorption of the gases, and not their scattering action, is the chief limiting agent to cut off the depth to which we see.  This must, he thinks, act even quicker than scattering.

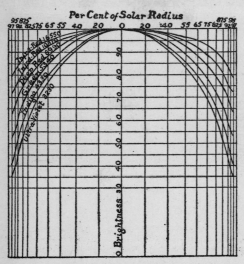

It is a curious consequence of these considerations that the edge of the sun's disk must appear less bright then the center, and that this contrast of edge and center brightness must be greater for violet and ultra-violet rays than for red and infra-red ones.  For, as we have just said, the scattering and absorption also becomes complete in a much thinner layer of solar gases when viewed obliquely, as they are near the sun's

FIG. 16.  Distribution of brightness along a diameter of the solar disk in various spectral colors.  The sun is much fainter, near the edges of its disk, and this contrast of brightness between edge and center is more marked for the violet end of the spectrum.  (From Smithsonian observations.)

edge.  Therefore, we look there on more superficial, and consequently cooler, sources than when we look straight down deep at the sun's center.  Besides, the effect is far greater for short-wave rays than for longer ones, and so the violet and ultra-violet come from the most superficial layers of all, and show most contrast between edge and center.  These results are confirmed by observation as shown in Figure 16.

How can we know what chemicals the sun and stars contain?

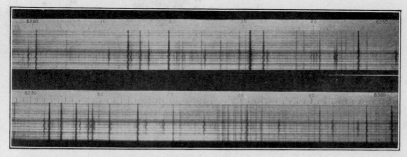

PLATE 13, Fig. 1. PROOF OF MAGNETISM IN SUN-SPOTS.
(Hale, Mt. Wilson Observatory.)

The dark band which runs lengthwise through the centers of these solar spectra is caused by a sun-spot. The many dark lines caused by gaseous absorption show zigzag offsets where they cross the sun-spot. This is the Zeeman effect of magnetism disclosed by polarization apparatus. Many of the fainter lines show no zigzag bendings. These lines are produced by absorption in the earth's atmosphere, not in the sun. Many short lines appear in the sun-spot region alone. Such lines are due mainly to compounds which form in the relatively cool sun-spots, but break up and disappear over the hotter solar surfaces.

PLATE 13, Fig. 2. A GROUP OF BOLOMETRIC APPARATUS.

The Langley bolometer, an electric thermometer sensitive to the millionth of a degree of temperature, is used in connection with a spectroscope, a galvanometer, an exact clockwork and a photographic recorder to produce automatically "bolographs" or curves of the distribution of heat in the rays of the solar spectrum.

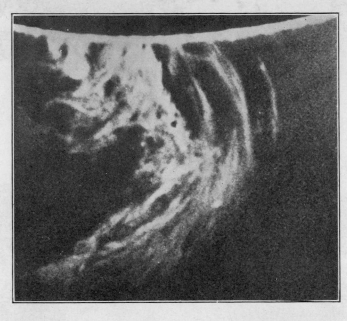

PLATE 14, FIG. 2. A GREAT SOLAR PROMINENCE.
(Mt. Wilson Observatory.)

This photograph is taken spectroscopically, not during an eclipse. It shows one of the immense flamelike protuberances of hydrogen and calcium gases which frequently dash out from the sun's surface. In this case the extreme height is about 150,000 miles above the sun's surface.

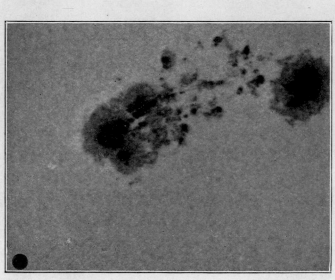

PLATE 14, FIG. 1. A GREAT SUN-SPOT.
Enlarged from a direct photograph.
(Mt. Wilson Observatory.)

It will be noticed that the whole solar surface shows an indistinctly mottled appearance. There are no clouds on the sun. This mottling is due merely to temperature differences which cause differences of brightness of the hot gases which send

As we have said in Chapter II and III, a hot body sends out light, owing to the disturbances by heat of the outer electrons of its atoms. The frequency of the vibrations which the disturbance sets up in the ether fixes the color of the light. The quicker the vibrations, the more the light tends towards the violet, and away from the red end of the spectrum. So each kind of an atom, having its own peculiar structure, sets up a different frequency of vibration, or a group of them. Incandescent iron differs from incandescent magnesium in the color of the several spectrum rays it arouses, and so each chemical element has its own characteristic group of spectrum rays.

But Kirchoff found in 1859 that the characteristic rays of a very hot gas are absorbed if a cooler gas of the same kind lies in the path of the rays. Hence, if some hot substance gives but a continuous bright spectrum without displaying any special characteristic rays, and in front lies a cooler gas, the resulting spectrum, after the rays pass through the gas, will be a bright band crossed by dark lines at the places where the gas alone would give bright ones. Such a case is offered by the sun and stars. Their interior presents so complex a path to the rays which shoot hither and thither, back and forth, in every imaginable direction, that it would give a continuous band of spectrum, if it were not that the cooler gases lying at the surface absorb their special rays, as the light escapes through them to us. So the solar and stellar spectra present bright bands of color crossed by dark lines of all the surface gases which are in position to produce their characteristic absorbing effects.

We have only to compare the dark-line spectra of the sun and stars with the bright-line spectra of the chemical elements, as we may easily produce them in the laboratory, to find, line for line, and in many cases even line-intensity for line-intensity, the evidences of the existence of these elements in sun and stars. The laboratory spectrum we may compare to a photographic positive, the solar and stellar spectra to negatives of the same subject. Yet though the reversal is unmistakable, there are small but highly significant differences in positions and intensities of the spectrum lines which add wonderful chapters to the story.

First, there is the "Doppler effect," so called after Christian Doppler, professor of mathematics at Prague, who pointed out in 1842 that the precise color of a shining body, like the exact pitch of a sounding one, must be changed by velocity of approach or recession. Doubtless all have heard the change of pitch of a locomotive whistle as it passes a crossing, and noticed it higher as it comes, lower as it goes away, because more vibrations reach the ear per second while the locomotive approaches, and less while it recedes. The same sort of thing holds for light, except that since light travels so exceedingly fast, more than 700,000 times as fast as sound, it takes a very high velocity of a luminous body to make any effect of this kind that can be noticed. However, the speed of the sun towards the stars of the constellation Hercules, about 12 miles a second, and the difference of over 2 miles a second between the speed of approach and recession of the sun's western and eastern edges, due to the sun's rotation on its axis, are easily measurable.

In fact, better values of the sun's rotation period are obtained by displacements of the spectrum lines than by watching sun-spots cross the disk. For individual sun-spots do not stay, as a mountain does on earth, exactly in the same places on the sun, but drift about a little both in latitude and longitude. Moreover, the spectroscope has the advantage that it can measure the sun's rotation at all latitudes, whereas the sun-spots only occur rather near the sun's equator. The sun, like Jupiter, exhibits slower rotation towards the poles. The results of Adams show this plainly, but at the same time show decided differences for spectrum lines of simple high-level atoms, like hydrogen and calcium, and for those of heavy, low-lying elements and compounds, like lanthanum and cyanogen.

According to these results the sun's equator travels 14.65° a day and requires 360/14.65 = 24.6 days for a complete rotation, while at other solar latitudes the times of rotation are 26.3 days at 30°, 31.2 days at 60° and 35.3 days at 80°. These values hold for the average solar surface. But the high-level hydrogen and calcium go faster at all latitudes, and besides they show much less slowing up towards the sun's poles. These results are confirmed very closely by other methods of observing the sun's rotation, including observations of the march of sun-spots, faculæ and flocculi across the sun's disk, of which we shall speak later.

Another significant little difference in spectrum lines relates to their intensity. Adams and Gale, working in the laboratory with spectra of metals, found that certain spectrum lines grew stronger, others weaker as the source of light was changed in hotness, beginning with cool flame spectra, passing to low intensity electric arcs, high intensity arcs, spark spectra, and very intense spark spectra. We know now that these differences depend on the average condition of the atoms, as to what proportion of them are so excited as to lose one, two, or more of the outer electrons. In applying their studies, Adams and Gale perceived here a proof that sun-spots are cooler than the rest of the sun, because the cool-source spectrum-line condition prevailed in them. Hale and Adams also proved that the reddish stars, like Arcturus and Aldebaran, are similar in this respect to sun-spots, showing that they, too, are cooler than the general surface of the sun. We shall have occasion to go into these things much more when we come to speak of the stars.

Still another spectrum difference depends on magnetism. The great English physicist, Faraday, tried many experiments to find some connection between magnetism and light. But success was reserved for Zeeman of Holland, who discovered that in strong magnetic fields single spectrum lines are broken into two, or sometimes many, components, separated very distinctly in their spectrum places. The components, moreover, are of "polarized light," and the polarization is dependent on the direction of the magnetism. Hale used this effect of Zeeman's to discover and measure magnetism in the sun. He found that sun-spots go in pairs, of which one presents a north, the other a south magnetic polarity. Sometimes one of the spots is nearly invisible, though magnetically active. Furthermore, Hale found that the polarity of the pairs reversed itself between the northern and southern solar hemispheres, so that if the advance spot was a north pole in the southern hemisphere, it would be the following spot that was a north pole in the northern hemisphere. Still more curious, he found that though one arrangement of polarities persisted through a whole sun-spot cycle of 11.1 years, yet the new spots of the next sun-spot cycle showed the polarity reversed. This makes the full sun-spot cycle 22.2

years to bring everything, magnetic conditions included, back to the original starting-point. We do not yet know the causes of these queer magnetic reversals, but doubtless they have something to do with the unequal rapidity of solar rotation in different latitudes.

Rowland showed many years ago that electrically charged particles in rotation behave like currents of electricity in loops of wire. As everybody knows, a current of electricity in a loop of wire makes of it a magnet. On this, of course, the electric telegraph depends. There are many electrons in a sun-spot. If they are in a whirl, as indeed the spectroscope shows them actually to be, the Rowland principle applies. Hence, probably, arises the magnetism of sun-spots. Hale, Ellerman, and Van Maanen have found a weak magnetic field existing all over the sun's surface, and have been able to locate the sun's magnetic poles, a little removed from the poles of the sun's rotation, reminding us of the case of the earth's magnetism.

Spectrum-lines also give a measure of pressure. Humphreys and Mohler found displacements of spectrum lines depending on the pressure which the gas producing them is sustaining. St. John has recently concluded from careful studies of this indication that the pressures prevailing where solar spectrum lines are produced are but a small fraction, certainly less than $1/10$, of our atmospheric pressure. So the spectrum lines are of very superficial solar production, for as we saw above, the pressure increases enormously as we go down towards the sun's center.

All these are minutiæ of spectroscopic study. But there is another branch of it much more impressionistic (to borrow an art term) in its effects. The rays of sunlight heat whatever absorbs them. On lampblack, they produce nearly maximum heating. Dr. S. P. Langley invented an electrical thermometer which he named the "bolometer" for measuring the heat of the rays of the solar spectrum. The instrument has two hair-like ribbons of platinum, narrower than the strokes of the printed letters on this page, almost as thin as the ink which makes them, and as long as one's finger nail. These tiny metallic ribbons are blackened with lampblack, and one of them is hidden behind a metal plate. As the rays of the solar spectrum fall upon the exposed one, they warm it above the temperature of its hidden neighbor. The tiny temperature difference, even if less than 1/1,000,000 degree, suffices to alter the electric current balance of which the two ribbons form parts, and a little mirror, smaller than a pinhead, is turned by the electromagnetic impulse which the current-change produces. A tiny shaft of sunlight reflected by the mirror moves across a photographic plate, and so records the warming or cooling of the exposed ribbon of the bolometer.

A clockwork moves the solar spectrum over the bolometer ribbon, and moves the photographic plate at the same time. Thus, the warming and cooling of the ribbon is recorded as a jagged line, whose high spots show warm parts, and whose low ones show cool places in the solar spectrum. Such curves are reproduced in Figure 17. The dark spectrum lines of Fraunhofer, being cool, are depressions of the curve, which we call a "solar energy-spectrum curve" or "bolograph."

As Langley and his successors produced these curves, they found heat in the solar spectrum far beyond the ends of the spectrum visible to the eye. Beyond the violet lies the "ultra-violet," also observable by photography. Beyond the red lies the "infra-red," partly observable by special photography with dyed plates. In this infra-red region there are few Fraunhofer solar lines, but great wide deep bands of absorption by the oxygen, water vapor and carbonic acid gas of our own atmosphere.

The chief advantage of this method is not so much for showing details of invisible parts of the solar spectrum, as that it measures accurately the energy of all rays, whether they affect the eye or not. So we get a true picture of the distribution of energy in the spectrum of the sun. Recently the same thing has been done with the stars also.

We all know that as the blacksmith heats his iron, it produces heat at a distance, while not yet glowing red. Presently it becomes dull red, then yellow, finally white hot. If we should examine with the bolometer the spectrum of the rays sent out, we should find them at first only in the infra-red. But as the iron became very hot, the red, yellow, green and blue rays would grow more and more

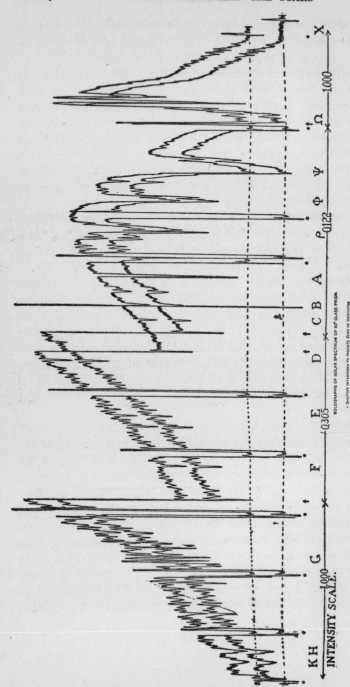

FIG. 17. BOLOGRAPHIC ENERGY CURVES OF THE SOLAR SPECTRUM.

The heat in the different colors and beyond the red where the eye sees nothing is here twice independently measured by the bolometer, an electrical thermometer sensitive to a millionth of a degree. The dark Fraunhofer lines cause the nicks and deep depressions in the curve. The rays are cut off at the starred places to indicate the zero of radiation, and the scale of intensity is altered at the dagger marks to keep the curves down to moderate height. In the infra-red spectrum (to the right of $A$) great absorption bands are shown due to water vapor in our atmosphere. Nearly all of the nicks to the left of $B$ are due to vapors of metals in the sun. (By permission, from "The Sun," D. Appleton & Co.)

intense, so that the spectrum-energy curve would have its maximum continually shifting towards the violet, as the temperature rose higher.

There is a certain instrument called the "perfect radiator" or "black body" that for any given temperature will give out more radiation of every wave-length than any other source at the same temperature. The laws of spectrum-energy distribution of this instrument are well known. So that if a body radiates nearly like a "perfect radiator" we have only to measure its energy-spectrum with the bolometer, and from the form of distribution-curve resulting, we can tell the temperature of the body without the necessity of testing it with a thermometer.

This is very important. For we can never go with our thermometer to the sun and stars, but it is easy enough to measure their energy-spectrum distribution-curves. In this way we find that the temperature of the sun is far above any that we can command continuously in the laboratory. Its maximum occurs in the blue-green, corresponding to about 6,200° Absolute Centigrade, nearly twice as hot as the electric arc light. Another method of measuring the solar temperature depends on measuring the sun's total heating effect on unit area just outside the earth's atmosphere. This turns out to be on the average 1.94 calories per square centimeter per minute, and indicates the sun's temperature as 5,860°. We strike a mean of the two methods and call the temperature 6,000° in round numbers.

The value 1.94 calories is called "the solar constant of radiation." Its importance is not only theoretical, but it gives a measure of the sun's energy available should we wish to run solar engines for power purposes. But of course we must make allowance for losses in our atmosphere and in the machinery, which indeed are very large. No one yet has succeeded in converting over 3 per cent of the solar radiant energy falling on his apparatus into useful work. The immensity of solar radiation we have already considered. The exact measure just given means that if the total energy of a ray 1 centimeter in cross-section (about 3/8 inch square) should be totally absorbed and used without loss to heat one gram (about 1/450 pound) of water, the water would rise in temperature 1.94° Centi-

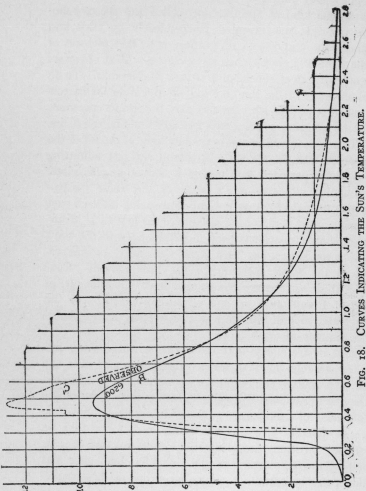

FIG. 18.  CURVES INDICATING THE SUN'S TEMPERATURE.

From laboratory experiments we know that a perfectly radiating body at 6,200° of the absolute Centigrade scale (about 11,000° Fahrenheit Absolute) would give out radiations whose intensity in the spectrum appears in the heavy curve.  From observations of the solar spectrum with the bolometer we find a fairly similar distribution as the dotted curve shows.  A temperature of 6,200° Abs. C. is nearly twice that of the electric arc.  It is but the superficial solar temperature.  Deep down, the sun is doubtless at millions of degrees.  (By permission, from "The Sun," D. Appleton & Co.)

grade (3.49° Fahrenheit) each minute. Expressed in other words, the solar energy outside our atmosphere is equivalent to about 1-1/2 horse power per square yard.

There is a special kind of spectroscope, called the spectroheliograph, whose principle was invented independently by Hale and Deslandres about the year 1890. Its purpose is to take pictures of the sun in the light of a simple chemical element. Most observers use the light of hydrogen or of calcium for these photographs. To do so, they form an image of the sun on a tall slit and allow the narrow strip of the image, which the slit allows to pass, to form its spectrum. Somewhere in the spectrum will be a dark line, say Fraunhofer's $K$ line of calcium. This is really an image in calcium light of the bit of the sun's image which falls on the slit. A second slit just admitting this spectrum line is provided, and behind it a photographic plate. By exact mechanism either the sun's image or the whole spectroscope, it matters not which, is moved uniformly along till each part of the sun's image in succession has passed over the first slit. Meanwhile, the photographic plate has been moved along with the sun's image, if the spectroscope has been kept stationary, or has remained fixed if the whole spectroscope has been moved. Consequently, the whole sun's image has printed itself, bit after bit, in calcium light of Fraunhofer's $K$ line on successive strips of the photographic plate, so that we see a complete solar image photographed with that ray alone.

This ingenious device shows that the elements calcium and hydrogen take remarkable cloudlike forms called "flocculi" over the sun's surface. Of course the flocculi are *not* clouds, for it is far too hot where they lie to condense hydrogen! Rather, these appearances represent differences of temperature as the gases soar high above the solar surface at different levels. Occasionally such forms take on snake-like shapes, twisting their contortions in rare cases over as much as half of the visible disk of the sun. St. John once was operating the spectroheliograph at a time when one of these snake-like wisps of hydrogen flocculus was sucked down into the center of a sun-spot and so disappeared.

This will bring us very naturally to discuss in the next chapter some of the telescopic features of the sun. Before doing so, let us sum up in a few words the remarkable service which the spectro-scope affords to add to our knowledge of our splendid star.

Suppose we knew only the velocity of light, the angular width of the sun's disk, and had applied Kepler's law to map the solar

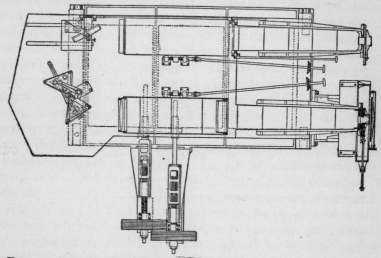

FIG. 19. THE FIVE-FOOT SPECTROHELIOGRAPH OF THE SNOW TELESCOPE (MT. WILSON OBSERVATORY).

An image of the sun falls upon a plate pierced with a long vertical slit (upper right corner). By means of the optical train, comprising lenses mirror and prisms, the light which passes the slit comes to focus upon a second plate pierced with a second long vertical slit (lower right corner). This is slightly curved so as exactly to transmit the rays which fall in a single Fraunhofer line, such, for instance, as the K line of calcium in the violet. By means of the large grooved wheel and screw attached to it, the whole system is moved at a slow speed across the sun's image, so that a photograph may be secured behind the second slit showing the whole sun in K light of calcium.

system, but knew not its scale of miles. With the spectroscope, we could observe the shifting of positions of solar-spectrum lines in the rays reflected from the planets, as they move in their orbits, thereby measuring their relative velocities, and determining our actual solar distance, and the sun's diameter. The accuracy would rival the best measurements by other means. Secondly, we could measure the sun's rotation period by the opposite shifts of lines seen in rays from his east and west limbs. Similar studies would give us the rotation periods of the planets. Thirdly, we could determine, by observing the spectra of a large number of stars, that their spectrum lines showed displacements produced by the motion of the solar system, twelve miles a second, towards the constellation Hercules. Fourthly, we could discover the chemical elements in the sun and the stars. Fifthly, we could determine the minimum possible temperature of the sun's radiating surface by noting the distribution of energy in his spectrum. This would prove to us that the sun's material is wholly gaseous. Sixthly, we could discover that, like the earth, the sun has a magnetic field, and that in sun-spots this is particularly powerful, and has curious peculiarities. Seventhly, we could set a tenth of an atmosphere as the maximum limit to the pressure existing at the radiating surface of the sun. Eighthly, we could photograph the curious cloudlike forms of calcium and hydrogen streaming above the sun's general surface.

Indeed, as we go on to speak of the stars in later chapters, we shall come upon still other wonderful secrets that the spectroscope has told us of all the stars, our sun included. When all these mystery-fruits are heaped so profusely around the entrancing beauty of the solar spectrum itself, we cannot sufficiently admire the powerful instrument which reveals so much to delight both the eye of the body and the eye of reason.

## CHAPTER VII

### THE FEATURES OF THE SUN AND SOLAR ECLIPSES

IT is a disappointment to look at the sun through a telescope for the first time. A bright disk of mottled appearance, with perhaps a dark spot or several of them upon its surface — that seems to be all. Only in the rare brief moments of a total solar eclipse, or when one adds the spectroscope to the telescope to aid his vision, does his physical eye receive an impression of great beauty and grandeur. To the mind's eye, however, the stupendous scale of things on the sun, and the immensity of the forces that work in that great laboratory lend a different aspect to the phenomena. They are insignificant to view only because of the enormous gulf of distance that separates us from them. Could we but come closer, we should see things there that would make us forget Niagara.

*Sun-spots.* — As the sun is about an hundred times as big in diameter as the earth, the apparently little dark spots on his surface are very often of a size to engulf the world. Single spots sometimes exceed 30,000 miles in diameter, and spot groups often cover an area of several million square miles.

Sun-spots show distinctly two parts. The central dark region is called the umbra and the surrounding extension, less dense in shade, the penumbra. As all solar observers know, our atmosphere is much troubled by the heat of the sun's rays. Effects of the same kind as those to be noticed in looking over a hot stove, or a desert, tend to spoil the "seeing." On this account, it is seldom that one has a really satisfactory view of the structure of sun-spots. In the rare moments of fine seeing, solar features appear somewhat like those sketched by Langley, but seldom adequately photographed.

The numbers of sun-spots wax and wane with a somewhat irregular periodicity averaging 11.1 years. This was first shown by Schwabe, in 1843, who had observed the sun-spots regularly for many years.  Wolf of Zurich then collected all available statistics, and assigned a certain scale called "Wolf's sun-spot numbers" to indicate their frequency.  His successor, Wolfer, has carried it out to this day, so that we have accurate records of the sun's spottedness from 1610 until now.  The general results are given in the diagram.

Besides the change in sun-spot numbers, there is a strange shifting in prevailing latitude which must excite our interest.  When the sun's surface is quiescent, the very rare spots that occur lie near the sun's equator.  But as the quiescent period ends, and spots are about to become more prevalent, they appear at latitudes of 30° or so on either side of the sun's equator.  With the aging of the new sun-spot period, which this outspread of position inaugurates, the belt of maximum spottedness slowly drifts back again. By plotting the numbers and latitudes of sun-spots on either side of the equator, Maunder has brought out the very curious figure called the "butterfly diagram" to illustrate this point.

Sun-spots are cooler than their surroundings.  That is the reason why they look dark.  No one should imagine, though, that they are really cool.  If one could screen off all the rest of the sun and take light from the center of a big spot alone, it would be so dazzlingly bright that most electric lamps would look dim compared to it. Only because we see them against a tremendously brilliant background do the spots seem dark.

Sun-spots are whirlpools.  Compare them, if you please, to sandwhirls in a desert, or to waterspouts at sea.  The central dark umbra will be represented by the trunk-like stem of the sand-whirl or waterspout, and the surrounding half-tone of the penumbra by the outspreading of the upper portion like a tree-top.  In the sun-spot, gases from within are rising outward to the sun's surface. This upward motion towards a region of diminished pressure, of course cools the gases by expansion, and makes the darkening. Arrived at the sun's surface, the gases spread abroad, making the penumbra.  Centrifugal force tends to lower the pressure at the center, so that light gases from above are sucked back through the umbral region.

By a brilliant application of Zeeman's discovery of the relations

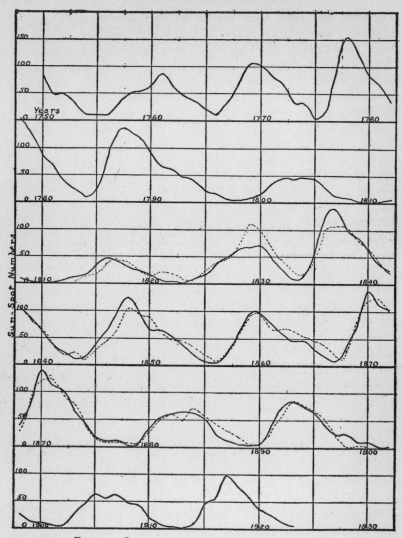

FIG. 20.  SUN-SPOTS AND THE EARTH'S MAGNETISM.

The full curve represents the march of sunspot numbers after Wolf and Wolfer from the year 1750 to 1923. The dotted curve shows the degree of variability of the magnetic declination as compiled from various sources. A tendency to 11-year periodicity, quick rise and slow decline, and greatly varying intensity of cycles are notable.

of magnetism and light, Hale proved the existence of magnetism in sun-spots, and explained the widening and doubling of the spectrum lines therein. He was even able to measure the polarity and strength of the magnetic poles. A most curious result was found. For every north-polar spot, a south-polar spot lies nearby, at least incipiently. If the eastern one of the pair is north-polar in the sun's northern hemisphere, it will be the western one which is north-polar in the southern hemisphere. Strangest of all, these conditions reverse as the sun-spot cycles change. That is, if the eastern spot has been north-polar in the northern hemisphere through one sun-spot cycle, it will be the western spot that is so in that hemisphere in the next.

Not only is there magnetism in the sun-spots, but it exists all over the sun as well, though less intensely. Moreover, when sun-spots are plentiful there are often magnetic disturbances upon our our earth. In Fig. 20 we may see how closely the magnetism of the earth depends on the spottedness of the sun. The electrical phenomenon in the upper air which is called aurora borealis, or northern lights, also shows a close relation to sun-spots. Sometimes when a very great group of them passes the center of the sun, as for example on March 22, 1920, the northern lights become extraordinarily brilliant, and magnetic storms, as they are called, interrupt telegraphic service.

The sun sends out a little more radiation at times when the sun-spots are numerous. Of course there is a contrary tendency on account of the fact that spots are cooler than the sun as a whole. But they occupy so little area, hardly ever so much as 1/500 of the sun's disk, that this tendency doesn't amount to much. On the other hand the increased solar activity at times of many sun-spots may be likened to the stirring of an open fire which brings fresh coals to the front. So it is with the sun. When it is very active the radiating surface is a little hotter, and we may get as much as 3 per cent more solar heat at such times of maximum sun-spots.

Curiously, however, most of our world's land surface is a little cooler at sun-spot maximum. Possibly this may be caused by increased cloudiness at that time. For if it were more cloudy,

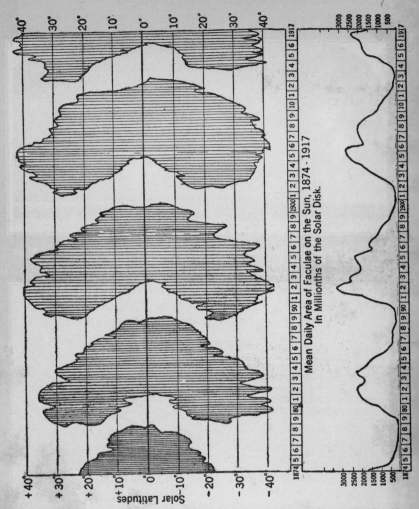

FIG. 21.  THE BUTTERFLY DIAGRAM (from Greenwich Observations).

In the lower curve are plotted the mean daily areas of the solar disk covered by faculæ in the years 1874-1917.  In the upper cross-hatched curves are indicated the latitudes where these solar faculæ prevailed.  Towards the end of a sun-spot cycle of about 11 years average duration, the solar activity is confined near the sun's equator.  When the next cycle begins, the activity starts up at some 30° to north and south of it.

PLATE 15, Fig. 1. WATERSPOUT, COTTAGE CITY, VINEYARD SOUND, MASS., AUGUST 19, 1896. (Photo by J. N. Chamberlain.)

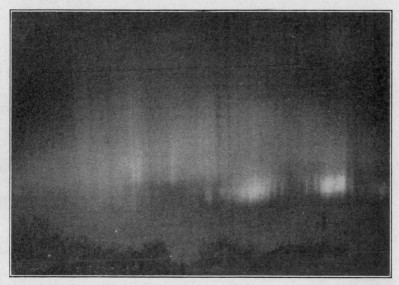

PLATE 15, Fig. 2. AURORA BOREALIS, OR NORTHERN LIGHTS. (Photo by Stormer.)

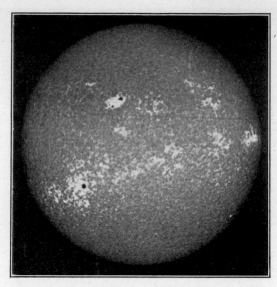

PLATE 16, Fig. 1. THE SUN'S SURFACE PHOTOGRAPHED
WITH THE SPECTROHELIOGRAPH IN CALCIUM LIGHT.
(Mt. Wilson Observatory.)
Note the sun-spot regions strongly marked by
bright calcium flocculi.

PLATE 16, FIG. 2. SUN-SPOT GROUP, AUGUST 30, 1924.
Photographed in red hydrogen light with the 13-foot spectroheliograph and 60-foot
tower telescope by L. H. Humason (Mt. Wilson Observatory). Note the ray structure, so like the lines of magnetic force revealed by sprinkling iron filings on a card
over a magnet pole.

PLATE 17, Fig. 1. SOLAR CORONA OF MAY 28, 1900.

This drawing by P. R. Calvert from Yerkes Observatory photographs represents the form of the sun's corona at the 1900 total solar eclipse. The corona cannot be seen without the eclipse because the bright sky obscures it. The long equatorial arrow-shaped extensions are characteristic of a period of minimum sun-spots.

PLATE 17, Fig. 2. SOLAR CORONA OF AUGUST 30, 1905.

This drawing by Mrs. C. G. Abbot from photographs by the United States Naval Observatory shows the irregular, but everywhere nearly equally extended, corona characteristic of the maximum period of sun-spots.

(These figures by permission from " The Sun," D. Appleton & Co.)

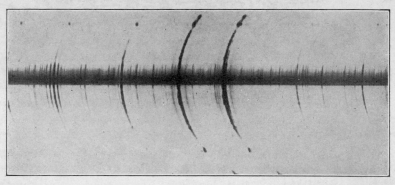

PLATE 18, Fig. 1. A PORTION OF THE " FLASH " SPECTRUM OF THE TOTAL SOLAR
ECLIPSE OF 1905. (Photograph by S. A. Mitchell.)

The spectral region is in the violet from 3800 to 4100 Angstroms in wavelength. The lengths of the lines give an indication of the heights to which the vapors which produce them rise above the solar disk. The two longest and heaviest lines are the H and K lines formed by mixed hydrogen and calcium, and by calcium vapors, respectively.

PLATE 18, Fig. 2. APPARATUS OF SMITHSONIAN OBSERVERS AT THE FLINT
ISLAND TOTAL ECLIPSE OF JANUARY 3, 1908.
A Samoan Marine is studying it out.

more solar rays would be reflected away, and there would be fewer reaching the earth's surface to warm it. Increased temperature at sun-spot maximum is not universal on the earth's surface. After all, the weather is very complicated, and the paradoxical observation of lower temperature when the sun is sending us more radiation, may have an explanation in the change of wind directions, due to the unequal effects of solar heat in clear and hazy regions.

*Faculæ and Granulations.* — Nearly all sun-spots are surrounded by patches of the sun's surface much brighter than the average. These are called faculæ. They usually form just before spots are born, right where the spots are about to appear. Sometimes the spots fail to develop in regions of faculæ, but generally they do come soon after them. All over the sun's surface there is a mottled appearance of difference in brightness, sometimes called granulation. The apparently little patches of bright and darker solar surface are, as a matter of fact, hundreds of miles in extent. Most of these apparently insignificant solar features are really as large as the states of our Union. If one imagines them as New York dark, or Texas bright, they begin to assume more importance.

Sun-spots and all other solar features march across the disk in about two weeks because the sun rotates. Faculæ are more conspicuous when part way in from the edge of the sun's disk than they are either at the edge or the center of it. This is readily understood. At the edge, we are looking very obliquely at the sun's spherical form, so that the objects there are greatly foreshortened. In this way, the faculæ, seen on edge, as it were, seem very small and indistinct. In the center of the sun's disk, though we see them broad-side on, we look straight down into the hotter interior. Against this brighter background the faculæ almost disappear. Faculæ and granulations are not to be regarded like mountains and lakes on the earth. They are not permanently placed objects, but merely regions which for a time are either hotter or cooler than adjacent regions, owing to processes of which we know little, which go on in that wonderful laboratory, the sun.

*Prominences.* — For the remaining features of the sun, we must either use the spectroscope or wait for a total solar eclipse. As these features, the prominences and the corona, are the most beautiful of all, much experimenting has been done to devise ways to observe them at all times, without eclipses. In this effort success has come so far as the prominences are concerned, but not for the corona. It happens that the prominences, which appear like flames

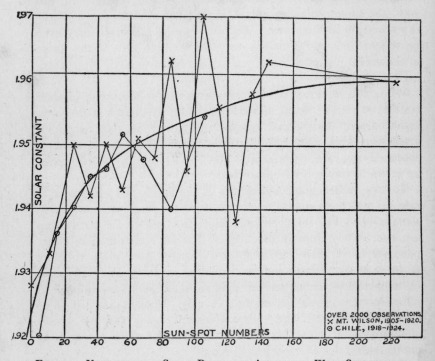

FIG. 22. VARIATIONS OF SOLAR RADIATION ASSOCIATED WITH SUN-SPOTS.

The curve shows that on the whole higher intensities of solar radiation accompany increased solar activity as shown in sun-spots.

leaping out to enormous distances beyond the sun's edge, are composed of but a very few hot gases, mainly hydrogen, helium, and calcium. These gases give out their light in narrow bright spectrum lines.

If the spectroscope is applied to study such lights as these, it does not spread them out into long continuous bands of color, but merely exhibits the few bright lines alone.  Not so with the light of the sky, which obscures the prominences to naked-eye vision.  Skylight is spread out into a long continuous band by the spectroscope, and thus may be dispersed to any desired weakness, while the bright prominence lines remain strong.  In this way, the prominence lines may be made to predominate over the sky spectrum in brightness.  The slit of the spectroscope may even be widened enough to take a very considerable slice of the image of the region just outside the sun's edge, without unduly strengthening the skylight.

When this is done, the crimson prominences stand out in their feathery flowerlike detail, a charming sight.  By means of the spectroheliograph, that special spectroscope which is able to photograph the whole sun and its surroundings with light of a single spectrum ray, the prominences may be beautifully photographed as in the accompanying illustration.

The spectroheliograph also shows us the clouds of hydrogen or of calcium which lie above the sun's surface.  Such pictures are in some respects like cloud pictures taken from above the earth in an airplane.  They show in much more detailed structure than direct photographs do how the brightness changes from place to place in these gases.  These changes are due, no doubt, to differences of temperature accompanying differences of level, as well as to other reactions going on in the sun.  Dr. Hale has named these appearances seen in the spectroheliograph "flocculi," and speaks of hydrogen or of calcium flocculi according to which gas is being photographed by the spectroheliograph.

*Total Solar Eclipses.* — When the moon comes exactly between the earth and sun, she hides the whole sun for a brief time, provided she happens to be near enough to the earth to cover a larger angle than the sun.  Naturally, the chance of that is greater as the earth approaches the greatest solar distance in July, but the length of totality depends very greatly on other circumstances connected with the moon's orbit, and on the latitude of the place where the moon's shadow meets the earth.  Total eclipses of the sun may occur in any month of the year.

If the moon revolved about the earth in exactly the same plane

that the earth revolves about the sun, there would be a solar eclipse
at every new moon. But this is not the case. The plane of the
moon's orbit inclines 5° to the plane of the ecliptic. It is only when
the moon is near the intersections of these two planes, or as astronomers say, near her nodes, that solar eclipses can occur. Whether

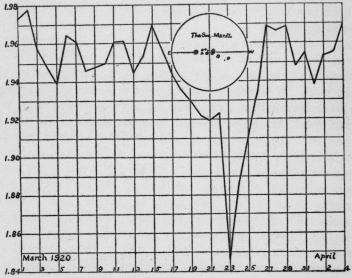

FIG. 23. CENTRAL SUN-SPOTS DIMINISH SOLAR RADIATION.

Note the large variation of solar radiation which attended the great sun-spot
group of March, 1920. The minimum was observed just after the sun-spot group
became central to our view, as it was carried along by the solar rotation. This
sort of phenomenon (though seldom so strongly marked) almost invariably attends
the passage of a sun-spot across the sun's disk.

the eclipse is partial or total depends on the moon's distance at
such times.

Suppose the moon, earth and sun are in such a relation as to
cause a total solar eclipse. If we count forward until the same
situation arises again, we shall have a nearly similar eclipse. It
happens that in the course of 6585.5 days the moon returns to
the same position with respect to distance from the nodes, while
in 6585.3 days she has completed 223 journeys around the world.

These numbers are so nearly equal that a long series or "family" of eclipses takes place separated by intervals of 6585.3 days, or 18 years, 10 days, 7 hours, 43 minutes. This period was known to the ancient Chaldeans. It is called the Saros. There are many of these families, for solar eclipses occur every year.

Not all the solar eclipses of a family will be total, nor will they all be favorable to observe. The moon is so small a body compared to the sun that its shadow tapers rapidly towards a point, and if the radius of the moon's orbit were but a little greater than it is, there would be no total solar eclipses. Very seldom does the diameter of the moon's total shadow on the earth's surface exceed 180 miles. It travels over the ground at a rate of something like 1,000 miles per hour. For while the moon is moving in its revolution round the earth, the earth is revolving about the sun in its orbit and, more than all, the earth makes a complete rotation on its axis in 24 hours. Thus, the total shadow does not linger in any one place ever more than 7 minutes, 58 seconds, and generally not more than 3 minutes. Sometimes the path swept over by totality is as long as 5,000 miles, so that as much as 1,000,000 square miles of the earth's surface may come within totality in one eclipse. However, as the earth's total surface is nearly 200 times as great, and as over 70 per cent of it is on the oceans, and a good deal more is inaccessible, it is clear enough that the chance is small of seeing a total eclipse in any given town.

Figure 24 shows the path of totality and the area of partial eclipse on January 24, 1925. This eclipse was unusual in being total at or near so many great cities and astronomical observatories, and at so populous a region as surrounds New York. Totality occurred about mid-forenoon and lasted a little less than 2 minutes there, so that the duration was hardly of average value. There was much chance of unfavorable weather in Eastern United States at that season of the year, but the event proved unexpectedly favorable. An account of some of the observations will be found in the Appendix, and a photograph of the corona is reproduced in the Frontispiece.

Arago, the noted French astronomer, gives the following very exact and vivid description of the total solar eclipse of July 8, 1842:

"The hour of the commencement of the eclipse drew nigh. More than twenty thousand persons, with smoked glasses in their hands, were examining the radiant globe projected upon an azure sky. Although armed with our powerful telescopes, we had hardly begun to discern the small notch on the western limb of the sun, when an immense exclamation, formed by the blending together of twenty thousand different voices,

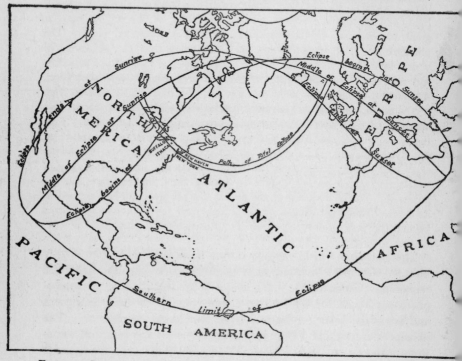

FIG. 24. PATH OF THE TOTAL SOLAR ECLIPSE OF JANUARY 24, 1925 (after the American Ephemeris).

announced to us that we had anticipated by only a few seconds, the observation made with the unaided eye by twenty thousand astronomers equipped for the occasion, whose first essay this was. A lively curiosity, a spirit of emulation, the desire of not being outdone, had the privilege of giving to the natural vision an unusual power of penetration. During the interval that elapsed, between this moment, and the almost total disappearance of the sun, we remarked nothing worthy of relation, in the countenances of so many spectators.  But when the sun, reduced to a very narrow filament, began to throw upon the horizon only a very feeble light, a sort of uneasiness seized upon all; every person felt a desire to communicate his impressions to those around him.  Hence arose a deep murmur, resembling that sent forth by the distant ocean after a tempest.  The hum of voices increased in intensity as the solar crescent grew more slender; at length the crescent disappeared, darkness suddenly succeeded light, and an absolute silence marked this phase of the eclipse, with as great precision as did the pendulum of our astronomical clock.  The phenomenon in its magnificence, had triumphed over the petulance of youth, over the levity which certain persons assume as a sign of superiority, over the noisy indifference of which soldiers usually make profession. A profound stillness also reigned in the air; the birds had ceased to sing.

"After an interval of solemn expectation, which lasted about two minutes, transports of joy, shouts of enthusiastic applause, saluted with the same accord, the same spontaneous feeling, the first reappearance of the rays of the sun.  To a condition of melancholy produced by sentiments of an indefinable nature, there succeeded a lively and intelligent feeling of satisfaction which no one sought to escape from, or moderate the impulses of.  To the majority of the public, the phenomenon had arrived at its term.  The other phases of the eclipse had few attentive spectators beyond the persons devoted especially to astronomical pursuits."

The darkness which prevails during totality is not often highly intense.  On most occasions it is possible to read by the light still remaining.  Some of the light comes from the illuminated atmosphere outside of the shadow path, and some from the prominences and from the solar corona which we are about to describe.  The planets Mercury and Venus are often seen near the sun, and sometimes others.  At the eclipse of January 24, 1925, the planets Mercury and Venus and Jupiter, lying near together to the south and quite a distance west of the sun were easily observed.  Stars may be seen, too, during totality.  During the eclipse just referred to, the stars Arcturus, Antares, Vega, and Altair could possibly be seen.  With photographic telescopes guided by clockwork, stars as faint as the 10.5 magnitude, or about 100 times as faint as the eye can see at night, have been recorded during total eclipses.

As the last thin crescent of the bright sun is about to vanish, it is often noticed that bands of alternately darker and lighter shade seem to dance along the ground. They are best seen by spreading white cloths, such as tablecloths or bed sheets on some favorable spot. Just after the "shadow bands" appear, it is very striking and awe-inspiring to watch the approach of darkness. The observer should take his stand, if possible, on a little eminence where there is an unobstructed view towards the west, whence the the shadow will come. It inspires a sensation very like fear to see the darkness approach with such appalling swiftness, as if it were a thing of evil, about to smite with a plague. The color of all things, too, is very ghastly, for the genial rays of the sun's central parts have long before been cut off, leaving only the dim reddish light of the thin crescent remaining.

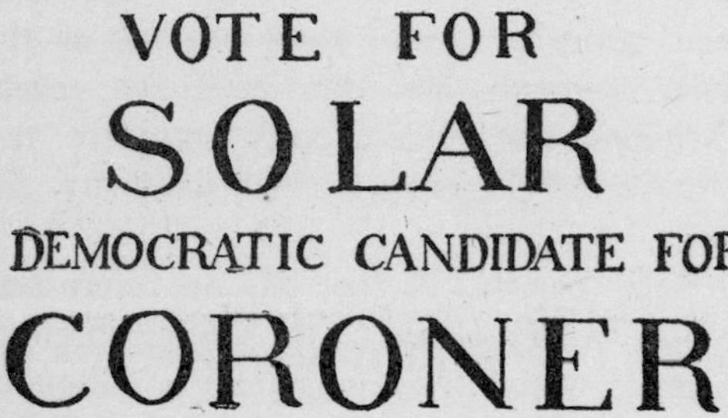

## VOTE FOR
## SOLAR
## DEMOCRATIC CANDIDATE FOR
## CORONER

FIG. 25. AN ASTRONOMICAL INCIDENT OF THE 1924 CHICAGO ELECTION.

Like many another, Mr. Michael Solar was defeated by his Republican opponent, Mr. Wolff, notwithstanding the appropriateness of his name.

The moment the shadow comes, the feeling of oppression and vague fear which I have described gives way to exultation as the beautiful glory of the solar corona bursts upon the eye. Streaming outwards for a long distance of one or more solar diameters, this pearly radiance, with its shapely curves and ray-like structure, forms one of the greatest beauties of the heavens. As with the night-blooming cereus of the tropics, the rareness of one's opportunities to see a total eclipse greatly enhances the enjoyment of its loveliness.

Close up to the dark edge of the moon there lies a ring of crimson, with excrescences here and there, sometimes, as in the eclipse of 1919, extending out nearly the length of the solar radius. This is called the chromosphere, or colored atmosphere of the sun. It is really the same that we see in the spectroscope when the sky-light is weakened as explained above. But at times of total solar eclipse the sight may be enjoyed in all its beauty, for we see it half or even all the way round the sun, depending on the length of totality.  When the moon is but little above the angular diameter of the sun, so that the eclipse is very short, the chromosphere is seen to the best advantage.

The spectrum of the chromosphere shows many of the lines of the ordinary solar spectrum, but reversed.  That is to say dark lines in the ordinary spectrum are seen here as bright ones.  An easy distinction is made between the different chemical elements. Light gases like hydrogen or helium, and, rather strangely, calcium also, extend high up above the general solar surface.  Thus their spectrum lines can be seen quite far above those regions of the chromosphere where heavier elements like iron cease to reveal themselves.  Dr. S. A. Mitchell has made a very complete and satisfactory allotment of the solar elements to their levels by the study of his eclipse spectra.

As for the light of the solar corona, it, too, has an interesting spectrum.  At the eclipse of 1869, Professor C. A. Young observed a strong bright line in the green, which for a long time was thought to be identical in place with one which had been given the number 1474 in Kirchoff's celebrated chart of the solar spectrum.  With the greater accuracy of modern photographic measures, this bright coronal line seems not to be duplicated by any line of the solar spectrum.  It is sometimes assigned to an hypothetical element called "coronium."  This green line is not always easily observed at eclipses, and never without one.  Hence it has proved impossible to map the corona without an eclipse by the device so successfully used for the chromosphere and prominences, as explained above.

The spectrum of the corona is mainly continuous, without well marked lines other than faintly showing dark ones like the ordinary solar spectrum.  Probably the corona is composed to a large degree of fine dusty material on which the electrical forces and the pressure of light from the sun combine to impose the ray-like structure which we see.  Coronal light is probably largely sunlight reflected. There is a well-marked change of form of the corona which goes hand in hand with the march of the sun-spot cycle.  Our two illustrations show the sun-spot minimum type exemplified at the eclipse of May 28, 1900, and the sun-spot maximum type as observed on August 30, 1905.

It is only at times of total solar eclipses that stars close to the sun can be photographed, because the bright sky light overpowers them ordinarily. Hence there are two famous problems which could be attacked only at solar eclipses. First is that of the possible "inter-mercurial planet." While the law of Newton has been found to predict with almost complete accuracy the motions of the solar system, a slight departure from its theory occurs with the planet Mercury. Allowing for all attractions, there should be a slow rotation of the ellipse of Mercury's orbit, but the computed rate of its rotation disagrees by about 40 seconds of arc per century with the observed. Long ago it was suggested that there might be a little planet nearer than Mercury to the sun, whose attraction caused the unexplained discrepancy.

Several observers of the middle part of the nineteenth century thought they saw such a planet, or even several of them. A name, "Vulcan," was even assigned. At the eclipses of 1900, 1901, 1905, and 1908, cameras were employed especially successfully by the Lick Observatory expeditions. Though they photographed all stars to the ninth magnitude, Vulcan did not appear. His existence is now disbelieved.

A totally different explanation of the rotation of Mercury's orbit is a feature of Einstein's theory of relativity. Einstein computed that there should be in fact a departure from Newton's law, just sufficient to make the observed discrepancy. Thus this verification of the requirements of the theory of relativity is regarded as a strong support of it. Einstein predicted another small effect which up to that time was unsuspected. It is that rays from stars, as they pass close to the sun, must appear to be bent through a small angle which varies with the distance from the sun's center.

At the eclipse of May 29, 1919, several English expeditions in Brazil and Africa sought for and found Einstein's predicted star displacement. There were many astronomers not entirely convinced, however. The circumstances of passing from bright warm day into eclipse night are so unusual and sudden that it was feared that some atmospheric or instrumental errors had caused the small star displacements found. Accordingly, at the Australian eclipse of 1921, the Lick Observatory expedition repeated the observation with all the precautions which experience and keen forethought could suggest. The result was even more conclusive. There can be no doubt that Einstein's prediction of star shifting is closely verified by observation.

While we speak of these consequences of the theory of relativity, we may digress from eclipses to say that the third prediction of Einstein, that all solar-spectrum lines ought to be shifted a little towards the red compared to laboratory spectra, does not seem yet to be so well substantiated. The shift is observed, but it does not fall in well with Einstein's prediction, unless certain assumptions of velocities of displacement of solar gases are coupled with the explanation.

Several ancient writers mention eclipses in very interesting ways. Herodotus relates that an eclipse put an end to a battle of the Medes and Lydians. He says "the war between the two nations had continued during five years with alternate advantage to either party. In the sixth there was a nocturnal combat; for after an equal fortune on both sides, and while the two armies were engaged, the day suddenly became night." Thales, the Milesian, had predicted it to the Ionians, and at what time of the year it should happen. The Medes and Lydians, seeing that night had taken the place of day, desisted from their battle, and became inclined on both sides to make peace. It has been supposed that this eclipse occurred on May 28, 585 B.C.

Thucydides, the historian, mentions an eclipse which took place in the first year of the Peloponnesian War. It occurred at noon, and several stars were visible. It is supposed to have taken place on August 3, 431 B.C. Another reference is that of Diodorus Siculus to a total eclipse which occurred when Agathocles, king of Syracuse, was sailing with his fleet towards Africa. Night seemed to fall, and stars appeared in all directions. This eclipse is said to have occurred August 15, 310 B.C.

Total eclipses of the sun, so beautiful and impressive to see, and so connected with astronomical problems that cannot be approached at any other time, have called out many expeditions in the past century. Especially since the spectroscope and photography and the modern facilities of transportation have become available, a rich reward has come from them. Whether the subject has not become somewhat exhausted so that the future additions to eclipse results may be somewhat meager, comparatively, is a fair question. It will be interesting as an example of what astronomers undertake in order to get their results, if we close this chapter with some account of the eclipse of January 3, 1908, when the writer attended as a guest of the Lick Observatory expedition, at the observations on Flint Island in the South Pacific.

The track of totality for that eclipse crossed over a great stretch of the Pacific Ocean, but it happened to avoid almost every bit of land. Hence the party from the United States and a party from the British colonies came together to this tiny island that one could walk all around in a couple of hours. It lies 400 miles from any land, quite out of the tracks of ships, and is visited only twice a year by small sailing boats. They collect the copra which is prepared there as the produce of the coconut palm orchard which graces the island.

Our party embarked from San Francisco for Papeete on the island of Tahiti. Here we remained several days awaiting the gunboat Annapolis, which came from American Samoa to carry us to Flint Island. While waiting, we made an excursion to the Diadem, that beautiful mountain which stands far up a steep valley crowded with tropical verdure. On another day, we visited Chief Tati Salmon. Accustomed to swim as early as to walk, his people were amused to see our clumsy gambols in the little stream that flowed by his house. We had a rare feast of native dishes, with fish speared out of the great ocean while we watched. Our host said: "My people are disappointed with you astronomers. They expected to see wise old bearded men and you are just young fellows, like steamboat clerks." "Ah!" said I, "but tell them that we make spider webs of rock crystal to support our instruments, and live in a land where the Great Dipper never sets, where the rain falls solid from the skies, and where people walk freely on the water." "My people can tell big stories, too," replied Chief Tati Salmon.

It was a neat problem in navigation to make a landfall on little low Flint Island, 400 miles northwest of Tahiti. Director Campbell lent his astronomical experience to reinforce the officers, who were short-handed owing to sickness. We sighted it soon after noon one beautiful day, and were rejoiced that the sea at the landing was almost glassy calm. The island is hedged about with coral reefs, through which a narrow opening has been blasted to permit landing with small boats. It is not every day, however, that a landing is possible, even to the skilful natives. Mr. Hawk, the manager, told us that there had not been as favorable weather for months as on the day we came. Indeed we did not see landing conditions as good again in the month we stayed.

The Annapolis could not anchor, for the island is but a sharp peak rising from immense ocean depths. So she cruised back and forth discharging cargo till evening, and then cast off into the water a lot of lumber, the last of our outfit, and returned to Tahiti. Not until nine o'clock was all secured ashore. We brought the first mail which had come in about five months. The manager learned of the death of his brother in England three months previously, and some of the native families grieved for relatives long passed away in other Pacific Islands.

Dr. and Mrs. Campbell were expert eclipsers, and had provided liberally of every kind of supply from lumber to mosquito netting, and from scientific instruments to condensed soups. A great screened dining hall was erected with bamboo posts and palm-thatched roof, and a half dozen cottages for the staff. It was charming to be awakened at night by the patter of rain on our palm-thatched roofs, and to listen drowsily to the thousands of sea-birds murmuring to each other in the trees.

Besides the provisions brought from home, we had turtle soup, turtle eggs, and turtle steak frequently. For we would go around the beach at nightfall and surprise some great 200-pound sea-turtle laying her eggs, turn her over on her back, and in the morning our native helpers would bring in the game. There were fish of every color, crimson, green, yellow, and pure white, but we had no luck at catching them. Of coconuts in the milk, we could eat our fill.

We never got over being surprised at the weather. Beautiful blue sky, flecked with fleecy clouds, and seeming to promise fair for a whole day, would change in ten minutes into a down-pour of rain. But hardly was the rain begun before it ended in bright sunshine again. Sometimes there were dozens of showers in a day, but nobody thought of minding them, because it was so balmy that dry or wet made no difference.

On some days, real storms came up, and once the island was almost entirely submerged. Our boat floated out to sea, but the natives succeeded in launching theirs, after several attempts, and saved it. Mr. Hawk told us that a few months earlier the waves had gone entirely over the island and flattened the palm-trees like corn-stalks. But they all straightened up again after the storm.

One afternoon, Dr. Campbell measured the distance from our dining hall to the shore, and also the altitude of the highest point of the island above sea-level. At dinner all were asked to write our guesses on both distance and elevation. Someone averaged the guesses. They ranged from 500 to 1200 feet for distance, but their average was within 25 feet of the true measure. On the elevation, the guesses ran all the way from 12 to 33 feet, but the mean value differed only 8 inches from the true one.

We recollected Professor Kapteyn's story of the height of the Emperor of China. In lecturing on the subject of Least Squares, Professor Kapteyn would tell his students that the probable error of a mean is equal to the probable error of a single observation divided by the square root of the number of observations made. "Suppose, now," he would say, "I estimate the height of the Emperor of China. The probable error of my estimate can hardly exceed 10 centimeters (4 inches). Very well. Let a million gentlemen estimate it. Then since the square root of a million is a thousand, we shall have the probable error of their mean result 10/1000 centimeter, or only 1/10 millimeter!" Naturally, the lecturer would go on to point a wholesome moral, but in our case we could not but be surprised at the combined wisdom of our party.

We worked diligently with our preparations. Scores of boxes of instruments had to be unpacked. Piers had to be made to support them. The instruments, being all in pieces for boxing, had to be carefully assembled and adjusted. Nearly every astronomical instrument requires to have some definite relation to the earth's axis. Hence, true north and south lines had to be established. Clockwork driving had to be accurately rated. Dark rooms for photography were prepared. All the instruments had to be sheltered from rain.

At length preparations advanced so far that rehearsals began. All must be ready beyond peradventure at the critical moment. No precious seconds could be spared during totality to make things right, or to do things over. The hand and brain must be so drilled as to be like automatons, and the apparatus must work without a hitch. So we went over the program time after time just as nearly like the actual operation as we could possible contrive. At length, we felt almost competent to observe while sound asleep.

On Christmas day, 1907, our British friends, whose steamer lay nearby, arranged to join us in a great dinner. Their ship's cooks came on shore, and prepared the feast. There was a blazing plum pudding to suit the day, as well as all the other traditional viands for Christmas. We had games and stories, prize poems and all kinds of hilarity. Our British guests gave a hearty lion's roar at parting.

The eclipse day, January 3, 1908, dawned very unpromisingly. The sky was all overcast. A storm seemed brewing. As the forenoon wore on, the clouds fortunately grew thinner. First contact passed, and, as the notch in the sun grew bigger and bigger, we began to hope that during totality the sky, though not clear, would be no worse than very hazy. Then our hopes were dashed by a sudden squall of rain. At eleven o'clock the rain fell in torrents. Same at eleven-ten. The total phase began at eleven-fourteen. My station was about a quarter of a mile from the others, and right out on the beach. I felt that all was hopeless, and hardly cared to keep my instrument dry any longer. Still, aided by a warrant officer from the Annapolis, I held a canvas to keep off the rain.

Then the cloud changed. A sort of indentation of it formed near the sun. The opening spread! Just as the moon extinguished the last solar ray, the cloud shifted clear of the sun! We dropped the canvas, and began to observe just as we had practised an hundred times before.  At the other stations the change came a bit later, but they also observed more than half of totality.  So near was the Flint Island eclipse to being a dismal failure, and yet it was a fine success.

Cheerfully we did the last things, repacked the instruments, developed the plates, and were ready to leave on the very next day.  It was well, for a real storm was at hand.  Far different our embarkation from our calm landing.  Again and again boats were driven ashore and overturned.  Yet the skill of the native boatmen triumphed over the rapidly rising surf, and we got safely on board the Annapolis with all of our outfit just before it would have been quite impossible to launch a boat any longer.

PLATE 19, Fig. 1. THE SHUMAN-BOYS SOLAR ENGINE.

The gigantic mirrors here shown were employed in 1913 at Meadi, in Egypt, to collect solar heat for the purpose of driving a steam engine used for pumping water.

PLATE 19, Fig. 2. ABBOT'S SOLAR COOKER.

The great cylindric mirror focuses 90 square feet of sun rays upon a tube 1¼ inches in diameter filled with engine cylinder oil. Hot oil rises up into the reservoir above, and cooler oil takes its place. In ovens inserted at the back of the reservoir, bread, meat, vegetables, etc., are well cooked. The ovens remain hot day and night.

PLATE 20, FIG. 1.

The Klondike Cosmos is a typical "short-day plant." The specimens on the right, exposed to full length Washington summer days, were unable to flower. The specimen on the left, exposed to an 8-hour day, flowered at a height of a few inches.

PLATE 20, FIG. 2.

The Evening Primrose is a typical "long-day plant." The specimen on the right, exposed to a 10-hour day, is unable to develop flowering stems. That on the left, exposed to the full length of a Washington summer day, is nearly ready to flower.

(Both figures from experiments of Garner, U. S. Department of Agriculture.)

## Chapter VIII

### HEAT, POWER, AND LIFE FROM SUN RAYS

REALIZING, as every sensible person must, that our very lives depend on the sun's gift of heat and light, Sir John Herschel, and independently the French observer Pouillet, devised apparatus, about the year 1830, to enable them to measure the energy of the sun's rays. Pouillet's instrument was a flat box placed broadside toward the sun rays, filled with water and blackened on the sunward side. From the rear projected a thermometer designed to measure the change of temperature of the water-filled box. The device was alternately exposed to the sun and shaded, for equal intervals of time. During the shaded intervals, the influence of the surroundings was measured by the temperature change. These outside effects were added as a correction to the change brought about by exposure to the sun.

In this way the energy of the solar rays received on the whole area of the box was measured by the rise of temperature per minute of the box and the water it contained. The result was expressed in heat units, called "calories per square centimeter per minute." This formidable phrase is universally used to express measures of sun rays, but it needs explanation. Imagine a cube of water 1 centimeter (about 3/8 inch) on edge. It would be about as large as backgammon dice. If the water were well mixed with India ink, it would absorb the sun rays nearly completely. Suppose the absorption was really complete, and that the surroundings neither tended to warm nor cool our instrument. If such a cube of blackened water, contained in a little open dish, were exposed for 1 minute to the sun when vertically overhead, as it would be at noon in the tropics, the water would rise in temperature between 1° and 1.6° C, depending on the clearness of the air. If it rose just 1° C, there would be just 1 calorie per square centimeter per minute of intensity in the sun's rays.

The result, as we have said, would vary with the clearness of the air.   It would also vary with the altitude of the observer above sea-level.   Some readers, recalling how cold it is for those who fly in airplanes to great altitudes, and recalling the snow perpetually covering the peaks of the majestic Andes, even in the tropics, may

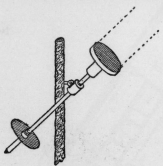

jump to the conclusion that our cube of water would show most heat in the sun rays when at sea-level.   This is not the case.   The higher the station, the less loss of energy the sun rays suffer in the atmosphere, and the hotter they would heat our cube.   If we were outside the atmosphere altogether, the intensity of sun rays would be almost 2 calories per square centimeter per minute, instead of only 1 calorie, as it often is found at sea-level.

FIG. 26.   POUILLET'S PYRHELI-OMETER FOR MEASURING SOLAR HEAT.

The sun shines vertically on the blackened box which is filled with water.   A thermometer inserted in the back of the box records the rate of rise of temperature.   The instrument is kept accurately pointed by observing the shadow upon a disk near the rear end of the thermometer.   Heating or cooling by the surroundings is eliminated by shading the instrument before and after exposure to the sun and noting the rates of cooling.

After Pouillet, other observers took up this kind of measurement.   Forbes, Radau, and Langley deserve special mention.   They showed that since the influence of our atmosphere is different for different solar rays, letting some through almost unimpeded, cutting off some almost completely, and some partially, it is necessary to spread out the rays into the spectrum, and measure the change of intensity in each color separately.   Such measurements must be repeated as the sun rises from the horizon towards the zenith, and the path of its rays in air grows shorter and shorter.   In this way the losses in the atmosphere can be fully estimated, and the intensity of sun rays determined as they would be observed if the astronomer was outside the atmosphere, on the moon, for instance, and had measured them before they suffered loss.

One other factor must be remembered.   It is the alteration of the earth's solar distance. Owing to the ellipticity of her orbit, the earth is about 3,000,000 miles nearer the sun in January than in July. This leads to about 6 per cent greater intensity of solar rays in the depth of winter of the northern hemisphere than in mid-summer. It is only because of the obliquity of the sun's rays, when coming to us from his far southerly winter pathway, that we have colder weather in winter than in summer. If we allow for this distance factor, and reduce to mean solar distance outside the atmosphere, we have what is called "the solar constant of radiation." It is the intensity of solar radiation outside the atmosphere at mean solar distance, expressed in calories per square centimeter per minute.

For twenty years the observers of the Smithsonian Institution have been making measurements of this great constant of nature. They use a modification of Pouillet's blackened box which he called the "pyrheliometer." This Greek expression means literally "heat of the sun measurer." The Smithsonian pyrheliometer has a blackened silver disk enclosed in a metal-and-wood cavity

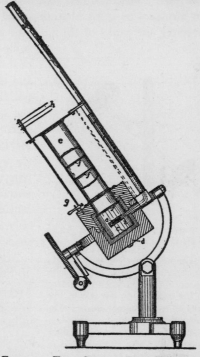

FIG. 27. THE SILVER DISK PYRHELI-OMETER (Abbot's).

For measuring the total heat of solar rays, which enter through the vestibule, $e$, when the triple shutter, $gh$, is opened, and fall upon a blackened radiation-absorbing disk of silver, $a$, in which is inserted the bent-stem thermometer, $b$. The observer notes with his watch the rate of rise of temperature indicated by the thermometer, and corrects it by the average rate of cooling measured before and after the exposure to the sun.

having a vestibule with special contrivances to keep off air currents. The observer, with watch in hand, reads the rise and fall of an ac-

curate thermometer which has a cylindrical bulb immersed in quicksilver in a steel-lined hole drilled radially in the disk of silver.

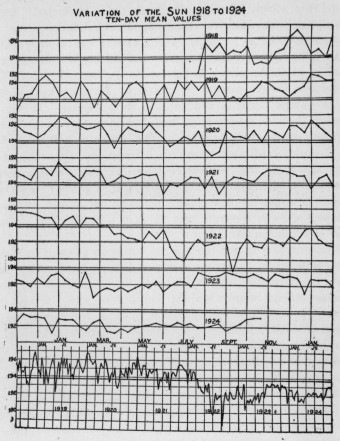

FIG. 28.  VARIATIONS OF SOLAR RADIATION.

The curve shows the march from August, 1918, of ten-day mean values of the
sun's heat as it is at the earth's average solar distance in free space. Note how
deficient the solar radiation was from about March 1922 to March 1924. It would
not seem remarkable if such long-continued changes produced notable modifica-
tions of climates.

But it is not enough to observe in this way the total heat
of the solar beam. The rays must also be spread out into a long

spectrum, and measurements made of the heat of each color, and of rays of no color, invisible to the eye, lying beyond the red and beyond the violet. Langley invented the "bolometer," an excessively delicate electrical thermometer, for this purpose. It measures as little as a millionth of a degree rise of temperature.

The indication is brought about by the heating of a fine flattened thread of platinum, which is blackened to absorb the rays. Thus the metallic thread changes its electrical resistance and causes a flow of electric current in a delicate galvanometer. In this instrument there is a system of tiny hair-like magnets carrying a mirror no larger than a pinhead. The system is supported by a fiber of quartz crystal 1/10,000 inch in diameter. By action of the little magnets the mirror is turned when the minute electric current passes, and as it reflects a beam of sun light, it thereby registers its rotation on a moving photographic plate, as the warmer and cooler parts of the solar spectrum pass in turn over the fine platinum thread of the bolometer.

All this complexity and much more has to be endured in making the measurements of the sun's heat. For our atmosphere treats every ray differently, and we have to study each one by itself. The observations begin when the sun is low, while its rays pass obliquely in long atmospheric paths. They are carried on till the sun is high. From the changes of radiation attending the diminishing atmospheric paths, it can be computed what there would be if the measurements were made outside the air altogether.

The mean value of several thousand measurements of the solar constant is 1.94 calories. However, the sun's output is not constant, but varies over an extreme range of nearly 10 per cent, between 1.82 and 2.02 calories. Variations so wide as this are not common, but values as far apart as 1.96 and 1.89 are not infrequent. The sun's variations are of two types. First, are those attending the march of the sun-spot cycle of 11.1 years average period. Values of the solar constant average 3 per cent higher at sun-spot maximum than at minimum. However, if a large sun-spot, or group of spots, crosses centrally over the sun's disk, a low value of the solar radiation almost invariably occurs on the day after the central passage. Other irregular fluctuations occur from day to day.

Various evidences seem to show that the sun's rays are held back by ray-like solar clouds connected to the sun's outer envelopes. When such a ray points towards the earth, our supply of solar radiation is reduced.   As the sun rotates, these rays sweep by us, and so the changes go on, none of them lasting longer than a few days.

The sun's rays have a genial warmth, but one is apt to be unprepared for the greatness of their possibilities as a source of power.

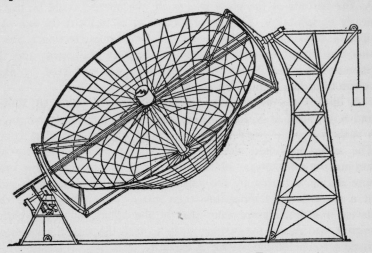

FIG. 29.   THE SOLAR ENGINE OF ENEAS.

The great conical reflector concentrated rays upon a boiler connected by pipes to a steam engine.   The power thus generated was employed to pump water.   (By permission, from "The Sun," D. Appleton & Co.)

It is a fact that if the solar heating that can be gathered on a square yard of surface could be transformed without loss into mechanical work, it would exceed a horsepower.   Many inventors have wrestled with the problem, but thus far none appears to have utilized over 3 per cent of available solar energy for mechanical work.   This poor efficiency in solar engines increases the surface necessary per horsepower to something like a square of 15 to 20 feet on a side, and thus the installation becomes both cumbrous and costly.

Three types of solar engines deserve mention.   First is the type developed by Mr. A. G. Eneas and used for a time to pump water at the South Pasadena ostrich farm. As shown in the illustration, a great conical mirror concentrates the solar rays upon a tubular boiler which propels a steam engine. The instrument is moved by appropriate mechanism to face the sun all day.

A second type is the Shuman-Boys installation of cylindrical mirrors, used in Egypt just before the world war for irrigation work. As the latitude of the place was small, the mirrors could be placed nearly horizontally. They were rotated so as to focus the sun rays upon a horizontal tubular boiler of rectangular section. Steam was thus raised to drive an engine. In both the Eneas and the Shuman-Boys installations the boiler tube was protected by glass covers from loss of heat by air currents.

A third type of radically different design was that of Willsie and Boyle, used at Needles, California, about 1908. They employed a shallow pond of water, with blackened bottom and glass cover. The water grew hot, though by no means near boiling, by absorbing the solar rays. Its heat was employed to run a low pressure engine, actuated by the vapor of sulphur dioxide, which boils at a much lower temperature than water. The efficiency of this device was much lower than that of the others, but by avoiding mirrors and means for turning them to face the sun, the inventors made a compensating saving in expense.

The promoters of both the second and third types of solar engine have claimed to reach the very verge of economical success in competition with coal or oil fuel in these desert localities. Mr. Eneas is inclined to think the methods of Willsie and Boyle most promising of any, but regards solar power as yet an unsolved problem.

In another field, the solar heating has been used with partial success, namely that of cooking. There are two types of solar cooker. The simpler direct type was used with good success by Mr. W. Adams in India in the year 1878. He made an eight-sided conical reflector, within which was fixed, inside a glass jar at the focus, the closed dish containing the food to be prepared. Meat and vegetables could be well cooked in this way within moderate lengths of time. However, cloudiness would stop the process.

The second type was employed in 1920 at the Smithsonian observing station on Mount Wilson, California. The whole cooking operations of a small family, including baking, boiling, stewing, and preserving, were done regularly with the solar cooker. A cylindrical mirror focused the sun's rays upon a blackened tube, parallel to the earth's axis, and containing engine cylinder oil. A simple

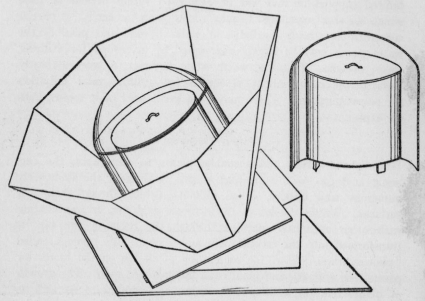

FIG. 30. THE SOLAR COOKER OF ADAMS.

An eight-sided conical wooden structure plated within by mirror glass concentrated the sun's heat upon a cooking utensil enclosed within a glass jar. Thus food was cooked by direct application of sun rays. Clouds, of course, if long continued, stopped the cooking. (By permission, from "The Sun," D. Appleton & Co.)

clockwork kept the mirror facing the sun all day long. The oil, becoming hot, expanded, and thus maintained a gravity circulation through a reservoir above the level of the mirror. Two ovens inserted in this reservoir were bathed by the hot oil, and reached temperatures high enough to bake bread. Being well protected from losses of heat, the ovens kept hot over night, so that cooking could go on at any time, despite occasional clouds. This device was interesting and worked well, but was too expensive for general use without modification.

From time to time, estimates are made of the probable duration of our supplies of coal and oil, which are the products of solar rays of former ages. These estimates differ widely, but agree that these limited supplies of fuel will be exhausted within periods of time which are short compared to man's history on the earth. A partial substitute is already available in water power, and possibly the water power may be largely augmented by inventions for utilizing waves or tides. It is well worth while, however, to work earnestly towards the improvement of means for utilizing solar radiation for power purposes. There may be a great need of it sooner than we expect.

## PLANT GROWTH

Sunlight of certain colors enables plants to seize upon the carbonic acid gas of the air and absorb it through the immensely numerous tiny orifices, called stomata, which throng their leaf surfaces. Within the leaves the carbonic acid gas, in combination with other chemicals supplied through the roots in the sap, is transformed into the complex life-substances. This process, called "photosynthesis" is at the foundation of all life on the earth, for plants feed animals, and plants and animals feed man. The growth of plants requires a certain condition of temperature as well as light. The sun provides both.

Heretofore, these chemical processes which depend on sunlight have not been carried on without the aid of plant-life. It may be possible that laboratory investigation may devise a way to convert radiation into chemical energy without plant aid. If so, it may prove the key to the power sources of the future. At present, the outlook for artificial photosynthesis is not very bright.

While taking in carbonic acid gas, the plants give off oxygen, which is exactly opposite to the life process of animals. These creatures breathe in oxygen, and give out carbonic acid gas as a waste product. Thus, the two great kingdoms of life supplement each other. Some experimenters have utilized the evolution of oxygen to measure the effect of varying conditions on the rate of plant growth. To do this, they employ a water plant called Elodea Canadensis, and allow its little oxygen bubbles to collect in an inverted tube, as they rise through the water.

The chemistry of plant growth is obscure. It seems to depend on the green coloring matter of the leaves which is called "chlorophyll." Yet artificial chlorophyll-bearing cells will not carry on carbon assimilation. Among the principal products of the plant's laboratory is glucose or starch. The rate of plant assimilation of carbon varies with temperature, with intensity of sunlight, and with concentration of carbonic acid gas in the air. The temperatures best fitted to promote growth vary considerably with different plants. This leads to the interesting diversification of plants over the earth's zones. But temperatures below 0° or above 50° Centigrade are highly unfavorable. As this range is but a sixth of the mean absolute temperature of the earth's surface, we easily see how necessary for life it is that the sun's radiation, on which the earth's temperature depends, should not change very widely. Geologists are of the opinion that it is fully a billion years that life has gone on upon the earth. This shows how very long the sun must have maintained nearly its present supply of radiation.

Plants grow more and more luxuriantly under increased concentrations of carbonic acid gas, up to at least ten times the present proportions. Possibly those luxuriant jungles of the geological periods to which we owe our coal may have flourished during enrichment of the carbon contents of the air.

As for solar radiation, much investigation is needed on its relation to plant growth. Neither the actual wave-lengths nor the exact intensities most favorable to plants have been as fully determined as they should be in such fundamental matters. It is known, to be sure, that violet and red lights are useful, and green light useless, to promote carbon assimilation.

With deficient light, plants shoot up very tall. We see this illustrated by potato vines, by thick-growing forest trees, and by the vines which trail from the tree-tops of the dark jungles of the tropics. Curiously enough, red light, though effective to promote growth, acts also like darkness, for it has the tendency to cause excessive increase of stature in plants.

It has been proposed by some to employ plants as solar energy accumulators. For instance, they say, plants may be grown on waste land, their products may be distilled into alcohol and other chemicals, and these will store up the energy indefinitely in a highly concentrated form. While this is so, such quantitative investigations as have been made along this line are not encouraging. The cost is out of proportion to the result, and the available lands inadequate to satisfy large demands.

The efficiency of plants in the conversion of solar radiation into chemical energy has been roughly determined by several investigators. Their results differ widely, but seldom indicate values of the efficiency above 1.5 per cent. These rest on measures of actual leaf area. Inasmuch as plants do not fully occupy their ground, such values show maximum rather than average efficiencies.

There is, perhaps, no field where investigation is more needed, or more apt to produce useful results for mankind than that which is the subject of this chapter. Efficient devices for converting the energy of solar radiation into mechanical work, whether by heat engines or chemical or electrical means, would be a boon indeed. One can imagine a great shifting of population when the deserts, where the sun shines almost continuously, become the power centers of the world. Hardly less fascinating is the possibility of new varieties and increased yields of useful plants, which may come from accurate knowledge of the relations of solar radiation to growth in plants.

## CHAPTER IX

## THE CALENDAR, STAR PLACES, AND NAVIGATION

THE march of time is so important in human affairs that very great attention has always been given to it. By general consent, the unit of time is the day. Yet here trouble begins. If we should define the day as the time elapsing between the successive instants when the sun stands in the central north and south line of the heavens, which we call the "meridian," an accurate clock would soon show that the days so defined are unequal. If, instead of measuring by the sun, we should define the day by some star, or better still by the mean indication of many of them, our clock would have to be a very fine one, superior to any existing in fact, to show the slightest inequalities. Yet our stellar days would be about 4 minutes shorter than our solar days.

Despite the inequality of apparent days, as measured by the sun's place in the sky, we must prefer solar time to stellar time because all of our concerns are controlled by sunlight. It would be highly inconvenient to have to shift the hours of all business steadily throughout the year to make them suit the sun's position. Imagine going to business sometimes at 1 o'clock in the morning, sometimes at 7 o'clock at night! This would happen if we should adopt the stars as our guide in measuring time. Nevertheless, star time is employed for astronomical purposes in order to save much computing. Astronomers use two kinds of clocks, one, agreeing with the stars, furnishes what is called "sidereal" time. The other gives "mean solar" time. They arrange so that the solar time clock shall agree with the apparent place of the sun at certain times of the year, but shall run uniformly. Thus the apparent sun is sometimes ahead, sometimes behind the clock. These differences may reach about 16 minutes each way.

The cause of the inequality of apparent solar days is the ellipticity of the earth's orbit. In our northern summer, for instance, when the sun is furthest away, the earth travels slower. As Kepler's second law tells us, the areas swept over by the radius vector of the earth's orbit in equal times are equal. Hence, if the radius vector is longer in our summer, the distance it moves through in a given time must be shorter to make the area the same.

The discrepancy between sun time and star time arises from the earth's motion around the sun. Each day, as the earth advances towards the east in its orbit, its motion makes the sun come to the meridian about four minutes later than it would if the earth were stationary. In our summer, the change is less than the average, and in winter, more. These deficiencies and excesses accumulate from day to day till, as we have said, the apparent sun gets behind or ahead of the mean-time solar clock by nearly 16 minutes.

Astronomers for many years preferred to start their day at noon, so that the darkness, which is their working time, would all fall in one day. They also count hours up to 24, instead of in two lots of 12 hours each, as most of us do, or in six lots of 4 hours each, as sailors do. For the same sort of reason that astronomers preferred to start the day at noon, people in general have agreed to start theirs at midnight. For their work comes in the daylight, and they prefer to have it during one calendar day. Very recently the astronomers have decided to follow the general public in this matter, and now the astronomical day also starts at midnight.

Some of the ancients used to begin the day with sunset, or with sunrise. This habit is still retained by certain sects in their observance of the Sabbath. The Greeks were accustomed to divide the day into two lots of 12 hours each, extending from sunrise to sunset, and from sunset to sunrise. Their night and day hours were therefore unequal, except at the times of the vernal and autumnal equinoxes. We should find it very difficult to adjust our clocks to this curious system, if it prevailed today.

From time immemorial, the orientals have grouped the days into weeks. Only with the ancient Greeks and in the modern period of the French Revolution was the attempt made to substitute another grouping. The French revolutionists employed ten-day groups, or decades. This arrangement lasted for some years in

France. It is possible that the ancient ideas of the planets may have influenced the seven-day grouping. Regarding the earth as the center of all things, they considered that there were seven planets, namely, Saturn, Jupiter, Mars, Sun, Mercury, Venus, Moon. Our English names of the week-days come partly from the Saxon. Thus: Sun's day, Moon's day, Tiw's day, Woden's day, Thor's day, Frigg's day, Setern's day.

Our months relate to the period of the moon's revolution about the earth. The "synodic" period of the moon's revolution is just a little more than 29-1/2 days. This means the average time elapsing from new moon to new moon, or from full moon to full moon. If we consider the moon's place among the stars, without regard to the sun, we would have a shorter period for her rotation, namely 27 days, 7 hours. The advance of the earth in her own orbit around the sun makes the lunar month longer than it would be if the earth remained fixed.

The earth revolves about the sun in 365 days, 5 hours, 48 minutes, 48 seconds. This time is no even multiple of the lunar month. Neither is it an even multiple of the week nor of the day. Yet it is very desirable that the months, at least, shall fall in the same seasons, year after year. The reconciliation of these odd intervals has cost a deal of study and heartburning, and even now the calendar is not regarded as satisfactory.

Twelve lunar months of 29-1/2 days count 354 days, leaving 11 days and a fraction to finish the year. The old Egyptians used 30-day months, with 5 supplementary days. Their year fell back a day every four years, so that the seasons would shift completely around in 1461 years. In ancient Rome the calendar was extremely confused. Their count of days in the months was especially curious. They fixed three points, the first day, or Calends, the middle day or Ides, and the ninth day before Ides, or Nones. Readers of Shakespeare's play "Julius Cæsar" will "remember the Ides of March." In March, May, July, and October, the Ides came on the 15th and the Nones on the 7th day. In other months these days were the 13th and the 5th. The Romans reckoned backwards instead of forwards from the Calends, Ides, and Nones. Always there were eight days before the Ides, but there might be three or five before Nones. Those before Calends might number as many as nineteen. The Romans began their year with March, so that September, October, November, and December got their names from being then the seventh, eighth, ninth and tenth months.

Julius Cæsar, with the advice of Sosigenes, reformed the Roman calendar. He decreed that common years should have 365 days, but every fourth year 366 days. In order to bring back the vernal equinox to the day of the year it had occupied at the time of Numa Pompilius, second king of Rome, Cæsar introduced two long extra months in the current year, making it 445 days. This is called "the last year of confusion." The first reformed Julian year began with January 1 of the 46th year before Christ. Cæsar adopted the simple plan of making the 1st, 3d, 5th, 7th, 9th, and 11th months of 31 days, the others of 30 days each, excepting February which had usually 29, but 30 in leap years. The Emperor Augustus Cæsar, desiring to make his month August equal to Julius Cæsar's July, changed the lengths of the last five months of the year, and stole one day from February to add to August. However, he corrected one error. Julius Cæsar's decree had not been rightly followed as to the leap years, and every third instead of every fourth year had been given 366 days. This was rectified by Augustus.

Still the Julian year was imperfect, for it was too long by 11 minutes, 14 seconds, on the average. The vernal equinox had occurred on March 25 in Cæsar's time. When the famous Council of Nicæa was held in the year 325, A.D., the equinox had fallen back to March 21, and in the time of Pope Gregory XIII, ten days more to March 11. Hence, in the year 1582, this Pope ordered that 10 days should be suppressed from the calendar, and that thereafter no even century years should be leap years, as they would have been under the Julian system, unless divisible by 400.

The countries of Spain, Portugal, Italy, and France made the change in the same year, and the Catholic states of Germany the year following. In Protestant Germany it was delayed until the year 1700, and in England until 1750. Russia did not make the change from "Old Style" to "New Style" until February 14 of the year 1918, when, of course, she had to drop 13 days.

There naturally was much opposition to the change. Even yet in our own country there are some sections where "Old Christmas," as it is called, is celebrated with quiet reverence on January 6, while "New Christmas," on December 25, calls forth a noisy jollification with firecrackers and guns. It is said that a certain pious couple in England continued for many years to observe Good Friday Old Style. They would go to the church door with all decorum, the old gentleman would rap with his stick, and finding no admittance they would return and read service at home. On the New Style day, they took care to ignore it as conspicuously as their occupations could possibly justify, in order to show their disapproval of such irreligious tricks as changing the calendar.

The Gregorian arrangement is not quite perfect, for it leads to a retrograde departure of one day in 3,323 years in the date of the vernal equinox. It has been suggested to prevent this by causing the year 4,000 and all its multiples to be common years, but neither we nor our readers need be seriously concerned about this modification, which would preserve the present date of the vernal equinox for about 20,000 years. If Pope Gregory had ordained the dropping of the leap year on each year divisible by 128, there would have been no error amounting to a day in 100,000 years.

The Mohammedans do not try to maintain the date of the vernal equinox unchanged. Their calendar dates from the "Hegira," or first day of the month preceding the flight of Mohammed from Mecca to Medina. They reckon time by lunar months, which retrograde through all the seasons in about 32-1/2 years. They prevent much departure of the months from the phases of the moon by suitable extra days in certain months of certain years.

The Hebrew year purports to date from the Creation, said to have occurred 3,760 years, 3 months prior to the Christian Era. Their year has elements weekly, lunar, and solar, for they modify the numbers of days slightly, and insert an extra month occasionally, so as to fit their festivals to chosen week days, and their months to chosen seasons.

The Christian festivals have a curious and highly complicated relation to the calendar. In order to understand the origin of these peculiarities, we must go back to the Council of Nicæa, in the year

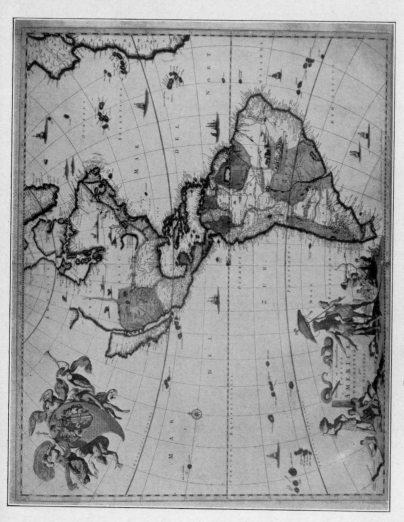

PLATE 21. AN ANCIENT MAP OF THE AMERÍCAS.

Was California an island, or did the early navigators merely assume without proof a water connection from Puget Sound to the Gulf of Lower California? Almost certainly the latter.

PLATE 22. THE YACHT CARNEGIE. (Copyright, Edwin Levick, New York.)
This vessel, built of nonmagnetic materials for the express purpose of making magnetic surveys of the oceans of the world, has sailed over 300,000 miles in all oceans from the tropics to the frigid zones. Charts based on results reached in these cruises carried on by the Department of Terrestrial Magnetism of the Carnegie Institution of Washington, are now used by all sea-going nations.

325 A.D.  Easter was the great moveable feast of the early church, as it is still.  There were some who desired to celebrate Easter on Sunday, while others held to the 14th day of the moon's age as the proper time for its observance, agreeing with the Jewish custom of the Passover.  As the latter believers were in the minority, they were called heretics.

In dealing with this question, the Council of Nicæa laid down the following propositions: Easter should be observed on the Sunday immediately following the full moon that happens upon or next after the vernal equinox.  However, if the 14th day of the moon's age, which is to be regarded as full-moon day, occur on Sunday, the celebration of Easter is to be postponed until the Sunday following, so as to avoid the practises of heretics and Jews.  Probably the fathers who sat in council did not realize how stiff a problem they were proposing, in thus ordering the reconciliation of the solar year, the lunar month, and the Christian week.  They evidently had an eye single to clearing themselves of all taint of heresy.

We shall not go into all the details of the matter, but we ought not to leave the subject without mention of a few of the famous expressions.  Representing the days of the week by A, B, C, D, E, F, G, let A always come on January 1.  Then Sunday, if it were January 4th, for example, would be represented by the letter D in that year.  This contrivance is called the "Dominical Letter" or "Sunday Letter."  In each century the succession of days in the year returns after 28 years.  In another century it may fall differently, because of the Gregorian suppression of the extra day in years divisible by 400.  However, it is possible to make a very compact table giving the "Sunday Letter" forever.

Another expression is the "Metonic Cycle."  This is a period of 19 solar years, which is almost equal to 235 lunar months of 29-1/2 days each.  Thus after a Metonic Cycle the new moons again occur on the same days of the year.  The ancient church calendar was drawn up on the assumption that the length of the year is exactly 365-1/4 days and that 19 years exactly equals 235 lunations.  Both assumptions are a little erroneous, so that it was not many centuries before there came trouble.  In adapting the

Metonic Cycle to their calendar, they assigned 29 and 30 days
alternately to the lunar months, and as this makes in twelve months
only 354 days, they added six extra months of 30 days and one
of 29 to fill out the 19 years. There was some further difficulty
about leap years, but we will not explain it here.

With these arrangements tabulated for a cycle of 19 years, the
same dates of the moon's phases would occur in any subsequent
cycle. It only needed to know the number of the year in the
Metonic Cycle. This is called the "Golden Number." These
artificial arrangements did not ever in actual fact indicate the
moon's phases exactly as they came in astronomically. Differences of as much as two days sometimes occurred. However,
when authorized by the proper officials, these arbitrary provisions
took the place of the actual events of the heavens in regulating
Christian festivals.

After the reformation of the civil calendar by Pope Gregory XIII,
it became necessary to reform the church calendar also. This was
undertaken by Aloysius Lilius, a learned astronomer of Naples.
Rather than merely revise the "Golden Numbers," Lilius introduced
another conception called the "Epact." It signifies the moon's age
at the beginning of the year. Taking into account all the compli-
cations of the problem, it is possible to construct what is called the
"Extended Table of Epacts" by whose aid the "Golden Number"
can be read off corresponding to any desired day. Besides the
table of Epacts, there is another large table giving the arrangement
of Golden Numbers, Epacts, and Dominical Letters in the Gregorian Calendar. Proceeding by certain complicated rules, and with
attention to avoid certain pitfalls, these various tables can be
employed to find the age of the ecclesiastical moon (which is not
the true moon) at any date, or to fix the occurrence of Easter.
It is not a pastime I should recommend to my readers unless they
enjoy puzzles.

After all, the regulations of the Council of Nicæa are not in
fact literally carried out. For the use of the exact instants of the
vernal equinox and of the full moon as it is determined astronomically, would occasionally change the date of Easter by a week from
that which is adopted by the church.

In closing our remarks on the calendar, we may refer to some recent proposals to reconcile the week and month with the year in a more regular fashion. The purpose of these proposals is to avoid the need of new civil calendars for successive years, and to simplify the work of computing pay-rolls and other data in which the month figures. There are two schools of these calendar reformers, one desiring the greatest attainable uniformity, the other moderate improvement with a minimum of change. Both agree however in their reconciliation of the week to the year.

Fifty-two weeks make 364 days. In common years there is one day, and in leap years there are two days in excess. The proposal is to give the extra one or two days different names from ordinary days, so that when they occur there will be a break of one or two days in the consecutive naming of days of the week. Thus, all years may begin on Sunday, if preferred, or on some other day of the week chosen to suit better the general convenience regarding widely observed holidays, such as Christmas and New Year. Many persons who are attracted by the simplicity of this scheme would have a rude shock if it were legally enacted, and they came to fully realize its effect on the Fourth Commandment of the Decalogue.

The other reform, to which no one would see religious objection, is the modification of the months. One proposal is to have thirteen months of 28 days each, with the one or two days additional in common and leap years belonging to no month at all, and celebrated as holidays. A more moderate party, desiring less change, and also desiring a year easily separable into halves, thirds, fourths, and sixths, retains twelve months and suggests four groups of three months, each group containing ninety-one days. These reformers also would have one, or sometimes two, extra holidays belonging to no month at all. Their arrangement of months might be January, April, July, and October of 31 days each, the rest of 30.

Various organizations have passed votes of recommendation of some one or other of these proposed plans, but there is no general agreement as yet about the matter. Such votes are often carried without much consideration or interest, at meetings in which only a small minority of the organizations are in attendance. It may be suspected that, like the metric system, actual legal enactment would find but half-hearted support, and would develop vigorous opposition.

## Star Places, and Latitudes and Longitudes

For convenience in designating stars, astronomers use the terms "right ascension" and "declination." They correspond rather closely to longitude and latitude in geography. Imagine the plane of the earth's equator extended to cut the sky. All stars north of

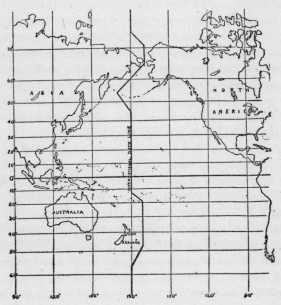

Fig. 31. The International Date Line.

Lying near the 180th meridian from Greenwich, it is somewhat modified so that lands and island groups of similar conditions may use the same date.

it are said to have north or plus declination, and all stars south of it south or minus declination. The declination, like geographical latitude, is reckoned in degrees, minutes, and seconds of arc, so that the celestial poles have 90° declination.

Celestial longitudes, and "right ascensions" have an advantage over geographical longitudes, for they have an undisputed starting point.  Different countries have displayed feelings of patriotism in the matter of terrestrial longitude hitherto, for longitudes have been reckoned from Paris and some other capitals as well as from the astronomical observatory at Greenwich, England, now almost universally used.

It is a curious thought that members of certain sects which regard it as indispensable to salvation to celebrate the Sabbath on a particular day of the week, different from the common practise, are, nevertheless, content to adopt the determination of it which depends on the establishment by international treaties of a date line.  This arbitrary date line lies in the Pacific Ocean at approximately 180° from Greenwich, but yet wanders irregularly so as to avoid separating certain island groups.  Thus, it depends not only on the establishment of an observatory at Greenwich, but on an arbitrary governmental convention, whether two members of such a sect, residing on two nearby islands, shall celebrate the same day, or two adjacent days, as the Sabbath.

Of course, it is too well known to need remark that ships sailing west omit a day, and ships sailing east repeat a day, when they cross the international date line.  The reason is that when Greenwich sees the sun in the meridian at noon it is midnight on the 180th meridian, and either the same day or the preceding day, as we choose.  If we imagine ourselves to be rapidly transported westwards, leaving Greenwich on Sunday noon, we should see the sun sinking back till it rose, and should fly to the 180th meridian supposing we were in earlier and earlier hours of Sunday morning.  When we came to the date line, therefore, we should regard the hour as the midnight which separates Saturday from Sunday.  On the other hand, if our flight had been eastward, we should have seen the sun set and disappear in the west, and arriving at the date line should suppose the midnight to be that which separates Sunday from Monday.

Returning now to the stars, "right ascensions" which correspond to geographical longitudes, are reckoned eastward up to 360° from the vernal equinox.  This is the line which passes from the center of the earth through the center of the sun about March 21, when the sun's declination is zero, or in other words when the sun is in the celestial equator. Instead of reckoning in degrees, astronomers often express right ascensions in hours, minutes, and seconds of star time, or as they say, of "sidereal" time. A sidereal clock records 24 hours, while the stars seem to make exactly one revolution about the axis of the earth. Hence, if a star is in the "meridian," or north and south central line of the sky, when the sidereal clock says zero hours, it will come to the meridian, or will "transit" as we say, at the same hour of the next day and similarly thereafter. It is, therefore, convenient to assign right ascensions in terms of hours, 15° to each hour, so that we have merely to look at the almanac to find the star's place, and then at the sidereal clock to know when it will transit. The sidereal clock-hands of course may be set to point to zero hours, when stars which lie in the vernal equinox are in transit. In that case there is no correction at all. Clock time then gives right ascension directly.

The sun is one of the stars, and like them its right ascension and declination are given in the special almanac called the "Ephemeris." Only because the earth goes round the sun in an orbit inclined about 23-1/2 degrees from the celestial equator, it is clear that in our summer, when the earth is in the southern half of its orbit, the sun will appear to lie among the stars of north declination. In our winter it will be the opposite. Moreover, the line from the earth towards the sun will go through a complete circle in right ascension each year. Hence, the sun's place, unlike the star places, varies every day, and covers in a year all right ascensions, and all declinations between + 23-1/2° and − 23-1/2°.

It is often desired to know approximately at what hour by ordinary civil time a certain star will transit. This involves a number of considerations. We shall not be very exact about them all, but only give the main facts. In the first place, standard time in modern days has been fixed in zones. Thus, in the United States all longitudes east of Pittsburgh use 75th meridian time. Suppose the observer is in longitude 70°. His noon by the "mean sun" (that fictitious object which would appear to travel uniformly like the stars, though making 365 revolutions to their 366) would be at 11 h 40 m, because he is 5° east of the standard meridian. However, the "apparent sun" will be ahead or behind the "mean sun" by an interval stated under "equation of time" in the "Ephemeris." Suppose it is 5 minutes ahead. Then the standard time of apparent noon is 11 h 35 m.

The sun, when it transits at Washington on this date, has, let us say, the right ascension 11 h 32 m 48 s. As we are supposed to be located about 5° east of Washington, the time of apparent noon with us is 5/360 days earlier. A change of 3 seconds in right ascension occurs in this interval of time, hence the sun, as it transits with us, has the right ascension 11 h 32 m 45 s.

The star Arcturus has the right ascension 14 h 12 m 15 s. Hence it lies 2 h 39 m 30 s east of the sun, at the date we are considering, and will arrive in our meridian after that interval of sidereal time shall elapse from apparent noon. In mean solar time, this is 26 seconds less. Therefore, Arcturus will transit at 2 h 39 m 4 s after the sun, 2 h 14 m 4s, P. M., Eastern Standard Time.

Sometimes, particularly in solar work and in navigation, another system of defining places in the sky is used instead of right ascension and declination. Unlike them, it relates only to the instantaneous position of the observer, and has no continuing application. This other system deals with "altitudes," "zenith distances," "azimuths," and "hour angles." The "altitude" of a heavenly body means its angular height above the horizon. "Zenith distance" is the angular depression of the object below the vertical point in the sky called the "zenith." "Azimuth" is the angle measured horizontally from north towards east to a point vertically under the object. Azimuth angles are measured through the full 360°. Altitudes and zenith distances are always less than 90°. The "hour angle" is measured by the number of mean solar hours which will elapse before a heavenly body in the eastern sky will reach the meridian, or which have elapsed since an object in the western sky crossed the meridian. Hour angles may be expressed also in degrees, minutes and seconds, counting 1 unit of time as 15 units of arc, so that 1 hour corresponds to 15°. The formulæ for converting positions expressed in hour angles, altitudes, and azimuths into right ascensions and declinations, are not necessary to our purpose here, though essential to navigators and others.

There are, of course, many details relating to star positions, such as the precession of the equinoxes, nutation, aberration of light, refraction of light, proper motions, wandering of the earth's pole, which are indispensable to exact astronomy. We have explained many of them briefly in Chapters II and IV, and shall describe others as we find occasion further on. In a book like this, intended merely to give the broad outlines of the celestial picture, it is not necessary to treat extensively of them.

## NAVIGATION

We could not safely cross the great oceans without seeing the heavenly bodies. In olden times, when the astronomical knowledge, imperfect as it was, resided altogether with the philosophers, and when there were no maps or charts worthy the name, or instruments of precision which could be used at sea, it was a venture even to cross the Mediterranean. Ships crept along shore from port to port, or from island to island. If driven far out of course, they were lost without means of regaining their desired haven.

The magnetic compass, it is true, helped greatly after its introduction about the year 1400 A.D. Yet even Columbus, when he made his bold famous voyage of discovery, had no means at all of measuring longitude, and but the crudest for measuring latitude. The common instrument of that time for seamen was the cross-staff. With this, one could get roughly the altitude of the sun or stars above the horizon. In the northern hemisphere, where the pole star is available, it would be just possible with these rough means to know latitudes within an hundred miles.

There were no nautical almanacs, as in our own time, to indicate the precise places of the sun and stars, and the fact that they cross over the sky from east to west prevented much use of them even for latitudes. Time keeping was as crude as astronomy. Watches and clocks were unknown. The hours were observed by sand glasses or water clocks at sea, and by sun dials on land.

Such were still the conditions when Magellan's ships sailed round the globe, when the Spanish and Portuguese were sending their argosies to the New World and the Spice Islands, and when Englishmen were seeking the Northeast and Northwest Passages in the frozen polar oceans. In a nautical book of the sixteenth century, about the time of the famous Spanish Armada, the writer says: "Now there be some that are very inquisitive to have a way to get the longitude, but that is too tedious for seamen, since it requireth deep knowledge of astronomy, wherefore I would not have any man think that the longitude is to be found at sea by any instrument, so let no seamen trouble themselves with any such rule."

There are four great inventions which make modern navigation what it is. They are the mariner's compass, the flat representation in maps of the spherical earth, the sextant, and the chronometer. Two others might be added, though of less fundamental importance. They are the patent log and the patent sounding devices. Then there are the great national observatories and their publications which give the exact knowledge of the places of the heavenly bodies indispens-

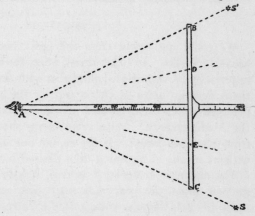

FIG. 32.   THE CROSS STAFF.

An ancient instrument for navigation. The observer sighted from A through B and C upon the celestial objects S, S'. The crossbar BC could be drawn nearer or pushed away till the adjustment was correct. Then the angle SAS' was read upon the scale. Other sights, D, E, were provided for smaller angles. The long bar was 36 inches, the short bar 26 inches.

able to the navigator far out at sea, and the accurate sounding and charting of the coast line of the whole world which keeps him from destruction at the shore. Finally, there is the thorough survey and charting of the magnetic conditions of the entire oceans, without which the compass would lose its value.

Our scope does not permit us to go deeply into this fascinating subject, but at least we must mention the principal uses of astronomy for the navigator. The latitude of a place always equals the altitude of the pole there. The polar star, visible over most of the northern hemisphere, lies within 1-1/2 degrees from the pole. Nautical almanacs indicate where at any time it lies in its small circuit around the true pole. Hence, by measuring with the sextant the altitude of the pole star, and applying the little corrections necessary for its position in its circuit, and possibly for atmospheric refraction, the latitude is found most simply. Yet many more observations of latitude are made on the sun than on the pole star. They require, to be sure, more knowledge and computation to give the result, but this is greatly simplified in books on navigation.

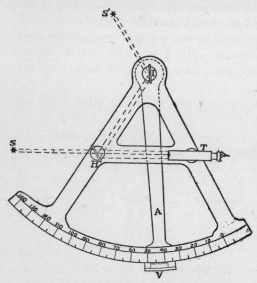

FIG. 33. THE SEXTANT (diagrammatically presented).

The telescope, $T$, observes the star, $S$, directly through the upper (clear) part of the horizon glass, $H$, while it also observes the star, $S'$, by reflection from the lower (silvered) part of $H$ and the mirror, $I$, which turns with the arm, $A$. The vernier, $V$, carried by the arm, $A$, reads off the angle between $S$ and $S'$ on the scale of the instrument.

The problem of longitude at sea was nearly hopeless until the invention of the chronometer by Harrison about the year 1760. It is true that the rapid change of position of the moon among the stars, and the rapid change of configuration of Jupiter's satellites had been suggested and used as means of fixing longitudes. But these methods depended for accuracy on astronomical observations and mathematical theory not yet in existence in Harrison's time. Even now, though these astronomical data are available, they cannot compete with the chronometer for giving longitudes at sea.

In essence, the longitude problem requires the mariner to know the apparent solar time at Greenwich, and the apparent solar time where he is. Their difference gives the longitude. For apparent solar time where he is, the sextant gives him the altitudes of the sun at certain clock hours in morning and afternoon. These observations, corrected for ship's speed and direction, give him the clock time of apparent noon. If, now, he has a chronometer which is so accurate a time-keeper as to furnish him with the time at Greenwich, however long he may have been away from port, then the problem is solved.

It was John Harrison's invention that gave this great boon, for

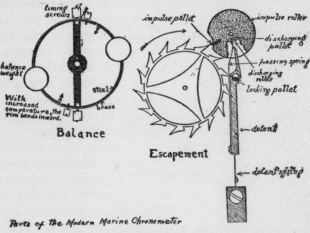

FIG. 34. PARTS OF THE MODERN MARINE CHRONOMETER.

which the British Government granted him a prize of £20,000. An ordinary watch escapement prior to his improvements would change its rate of vibration with temperature. Harrison, by combining metals in the construction, succeeded in eliminating this temperature effect almost exactly. His son, William Harrison, made the testing voyage of the first Harrison chronometer to Barbadoes and return. On the voyage out, the chronometer lost only 5 seconds. On the return it lost 1 m 49 s, for it was placed for dryness in the after part of the ship, where it was subject to much motion, which hindered its going. Even so, it determined the longitude of the home port, after 7 months voyage, within 18 miles.

With later improvements, the chronometer has attained a perfectly marvelous accuracy. It is customary to carry three of these instruments in each very large ship. Voyages are recorded where the mean time by three chronometers, carried far across the equator and return, so that the range of temperature was very great, has varied less than 3 seconds in an hundred days. This error is but one part in three million of the total time elapsed.

An American ship master, Captain Sumner, published in 1847 the celebrated device in navigation for getting both latitude and longitude, now called "Sumner's method." It depends in principle on the fact that the sun or a chosen star is vertically overhead at a given instant at some point on the earth's surface. By means of the tables and the chronometer, this point may be in fact definitely located. Suppose, now, for illustration, that two officers of the same ship observe the altitudes of two stars simultaneously, one being, let us say, 25°, and one 40°. If they should take compasses and draw circles on a globe, with centers on the spots where these two stars are known to be vertically overhead, and with radii equivalent to 90°-25° and 90°-40°, respectively, the ship must be at the instant of observation on the intersection of these circles.

In applying Sumner's method, the sun alone may be used, by allowing for the motion of the ship between two observations several hours apart. In place of a globe, the navigator uses a large-scale map of his region. There is no need of drawing full circles, for he knows within a few miles of where he is. On so large a scale as the map, the little arcs of circles which he requires will not differ sensibly from straight lines. The bearing of the sun is known, and he merely draws his lines on the chart at right angles to its bearing. Such are the simple elements of this masterly device called "Sumner's method." Its actual application in detail may be learned in works on navigation.

Another value of astronomy to navigation resides in the means which it affords to correct the compass. Cloudy weather forces the mariner to depend on "dead reckoning," which is a combination of the compass course steered and the distance run, as indicated by the patent log and the revolutions of the propeller. Almost all modern ships are made of steel, so that the compass has to be compensated for the magnetic material of the ship. But magnetism of steel changes with time and circumstance. Hence, it is necessary to test the compass often by comparing its indications with the true bearings of the heavenly bodies. These comparisons are best made when the objects are known, from their "hour angles" and the nautical almanac, to be nearly east or nearly west.

Naturally, allowance is required for the "variation of the compass," the well-known departure which it has from the north and south, even when far separated from magnetic materials. It is a great boon which the Department of Terrestrial Magnetism of the Carnegie Institution has given to navigation recently, in constructing and equipping the non-magnetic yacht "Carnegie," and measuring magnetic conditions of all the oceans. For the earth's magnetism varies continuously, so that the old magnetic charts, based on observations in wooden ships of the old days, have become obsolete. Chart errors of several degrees in the direction of a freely pointing magnet were disclosed by the "Carnegie" surveys. Thus a ship, sailing by dead reckoning for two days, might easily run from 30 to 50 miles out of her course, merely owing to the errors of the old magnetic charts, now fortunately displaced by modern ones.

## CHAPTER X

### STORIES OF THE CONSTELLATIONS

LONG, long ago, the stars were grouped in constellations. It is hard to see why they are named, or separated by boundaries as they are drawn. A few of them, like Gemini, the Twins, Scorpio, the Scorpion, and Corona Borealis, the Northern Crown, really suggest their names by their configurations. Most of them, however, are like the rose which "by any other name would smell as sweet," or like the child who was called John but might as well have been Samuel.

Nevertheless, some of the names are associated with fine old myths that deserve to be retold. The Queen of Ethiopia, Cassiopeia, and her husband, King Cepheus, had a daughter called Andromeda. Queen Cassiopeia boasted that she was as beautiful as the Nereids, and thereby provoked the vengeance of Poseidon. He sent a flood and a sea-monster who slew both man and beast. In this distress, the oracle of Ammon was consulted, and it gave the intelligence that the calamity could be removed only by exposing the King's daughter to the monster. Accordingly, Andromeda was chained to a rock on the shore.

Perseus, the hero, son of Danae and Zeus, returning from slaying the Gorgon Medusa, whose horrid head he carried in his wallet, found Andromeda, slew the monster, and released her. He married Andromeda in spite of Phineas to whom she had been promised. In a quarrel at their wedding, one glance at the Gorgon's head turned Phineas to stone. The pair returned to the native land of Perseus, where, after other adventures in which the Gorgon's head proved a highly useful weapon, they were the ancestors of the Persides. Many other variations and additions to this famous old story may be found in books of mythology.

The four northern constellations of Cepheus, Cassiopeia, Perseus, and Andromeda, lie adjacently. Nearly everybody knows the Great Dipper in Ursa Major, the Greater Bear. The two Pointers in the bowl of the Dipper show us the pole star in Ursa Minor, the Lesser Bear. If one carries the line of the Pointers just about as far on the other side of the pole, he comes to the two brightest stars of Cassiopeia. The configuration most conspicuously showing is called Cassiopeia's Chair. It also resembles a great capital W, if we omit one of the fainter stars which completes the chair-seat. Cassiopeia sits with her feet towards the bright star Arcturus.

Going on beyond Cassiopeia another length of the line from the Pointers to the pole star, we find Andromeda, whose brightest star forms one corner of the Great Square of Pegasus. From this brightest star we follow eastward in a circle round the pole to the other stars of Andromeda. The four principal ones form a line nearly as long as our measuring space, the polar distance of the Pointers. Still another length of it beyond, towards the east, and we arrive at the constellation Perseus. Its principal stars, seven in number, point roughly towards Cassiopeia, though straggling into several branches. What fixes Perseus more distinctly is that it lies about half-way between the eastern end of Andromeda and the brilliant star Capella in the constellation Auriga, the Charioteer.

The constellation Cepheus is not so conspicuous as the other three whose story we have joined with his. Cepheus lies a little west of a line from Andromeda to the pole, and a little nearer the pole than Cassiopeia. It has six principal stars.

Right across the pole from Capella, and about equally distant from it, we pass to Vega, that beautiful white star nearly overhead in the early evening in Autumn. Just west of Vega is a straggling collection of stars, of which eight are fairly bright. This is the constellation Hercules, named after the Latin form of Heracles, the great national hero of the Greeks. He led a very active life on account of the persecutions of Hera, Queen of the Olympian gods, the sister and wife of Zeus.

Hercules was related to Perseus both through his mother Alcmena, a Perseid, and his father Zeus, who appears to have been father to almost every hero in Greek mythology. Hera began her tricks even before his birth by causing Eurystheus to be born before him, so that Hercules should not rule the realm of Perseus. After killing his teacher of music, he had various adventures in exile. After his marriage and his killing of his own children in a frenzy induced by Hera, he was forced in expiation to serve Eurystheus, and began the celebrated twelve labors of Hercules. These were: (1) Wrestling

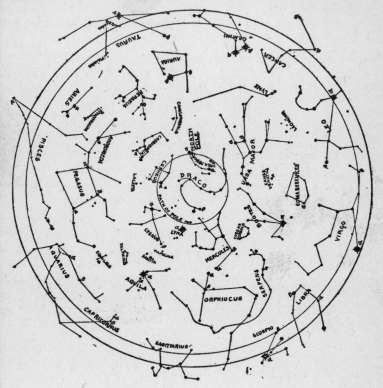

FIG. 35. THE CONSTELLATIONS. NORTHERN HEMISPHERE.

with the Nemean lion. (2) Killing of the Lernean hydra. (3) Capture of the Arcadian hind. (4) Capture of the boar of Erymanthus. (5) Cleansing the Augean stables. (6) Shooting the Stymphalian birds. (7) Capture of the Cretan bull. (8) Capture of the man-eating mares. (9) Seizure of the girdle of Hippolyte, Queen of the Amazons. (10) Bringing off the oxen of Geryones,

PLATE 23. THE GREAT STAR CLUSTER IN HERCULES. (Mt. Wilson Observatory.)
Over 50,000 stars have been counted in this cluster, but its distance is so great that doubtless many times this number exist there invisibly.

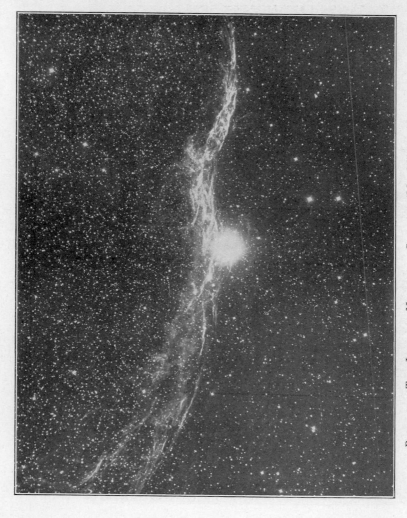

PLATE 24. THE LACELIKE NEBULA IN CYGNUS. (Mt. Wilson Observatory.)

Notice how few of the stars are on one side of the nebula compared to the other. Probably there is obscuring gaseous matter lying between us and the stars on the leaner side.

PLATE 25, Fig. 1. THE PLEIADES AND ASSOCIATED NEBULOSITY.
(Lick Observatory.)

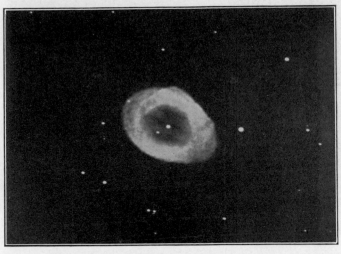

PLATE 25, Fig. 2. THE RING NEBULA IN LYRA.
(Mt. Wilson Observatory.)

PLATE 26. THE GREAT NEBULA IN ORION. (Mt. Wilson Observatory.)

A mass of gas probably illuminated by the influence of a neighboring star. To the eye the whole nebula appears starlike and lies in Orion's sword.

during which adventure he set up the "Pillars of Hercules" at the Strait of Gibraltar. (11) Bringing the golden apples from the garden of the Hesperides. (12) Conveying Cerberus from Hades to the upper world.

After accomplishing these feats, all of which led him into extra adventures, Hercules engaged in a variety of extraordinary affairs, helped the gods in war, destroyed sea-monsters, set bound Prometheus free, wrestled with Antaeus, son of Poseidon and Ge (Earth), who had to be uplifted into the air to overcome him, because every time he touched mother earth he became stronger. We cannot even mention all of the encounters of Hercules, and must refer our readers to Greek mythology. Evidently he well deserves a constellation.

West of the constellation Hercules is the lovely Corona Borealis, or Northern Crown, and beyond that Boötes, the Ploughman, with its splendid reddish star Arcturus. Immediately south of Hercules are the two constellations Serpens, the serpent, and Serpentarius or Ophiuchus, the serpent-holder. To the east of Ophiuchus is Aquila, the Eagle, with its brilliant white star Altair, and north of Aquila and west of Hercules lies Cygnus, the Swan.

The remaining big northern constellation is Pegasus, the Winged Horse, which adjoins Andromeda lying east of Aquila. It is easily marked by what is called the Great Square of Pegasus, four fairly bright stars, not exactly forming a square, the northeastern one of which is Alpha Andromedæ. Pegasus, in mythology, was a very remarkable horse. He sprang from the trunk of the Gorgon Medusa after Perseus cut off her head. Bellerophon caught him as he drank of the spring Peirene, and mounted on Pegasus killed the Chimæra, and overcame the Solymi and the Amazons. Overconfident, Bellerophon tried to fly to heaven, but Pegasus threw him off and continued on riderless. In heaven, Pegasus served Zeus, fetching him his lightning and his thunder. When Mount Helicon, under enchantment by the song of the Muses, began to float towards heaven, Pegasus prevented it by stamping on the ground. The fountain of the Muses, Hippochrene, gushed out where his hoof fell. On account of his connection in this way with the Muses, Pegasus is referred to frequently in literature by authors who speak in a flowery way of "my Pegasus," meaning the inspiration of their writings.

Omitting mention of several minor northern constellations, and passing over the twelve signs of the Zodiac for the moment, let us now see about some of the mythological characters celebrated in the

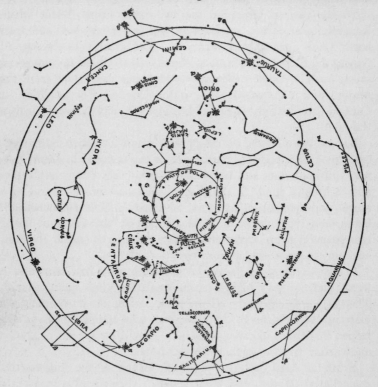

FIG. 36. THE CONSTELLATIONS. SOUTHERN HEMISPHERE.

southern heavens. Foremost from every point of view is Orion. He was a mighty hunter of surpassing beauty and enormous strength, son of Hyrieus or of Poseidon. Eos, the dawn-goddess loved him, and carried him away to Delos. The gods were angry, and Artemis killed him with her arrows. In the lower world, Odysseus saw his shade driving the wild beasts in the hunt as he had done on earth.

After death he was changed into the famous constellation, the grandest of the entire heavens. At its northern end is Betelgeuse, the red giant star, and at its southern end Rigel, the splendid blue one. Midway lie the belt and sword stars, themselves glorious in almost any company except that of Betelgeuse and Rigel.

To the east of Orion lie the two dogs, Canis Major with its wonderful star Sirius, brightest of the entire heavens, and further north Canis Minor, with Procyon. The great constellation Argo Navis, the Ship of the famous Argonauts of Greek mythology who sailed for The Golden Fleece, stretches east and south from Canis Major, well on towards the southern pole. Its brightest star, Canopus, second only to Sirius, lies just half way between Sirius and the south pole.

Beyond Argo Navis, the Ship, lies the famous constellation Southern Cross, disappointing perhaps from the unequal brightness of its four principal stars and the lack of one at the center, but yet very apt to bring a lump to the throat when one sees it after long absence, and remembers for what it stands. Half surrounding the Cross, and lying north of it, is Centaurus, the Centaur, with its two splendid stars Alpha and Beta Centauri, of which the first is our sun's nearest stellar neighbor.

In the Greek mythology, the Centaurs were half man and half horse, and not very highly recommended for their moral character. They attempted to carry off the bride Deidameia on the day of her marriage to Peirithous; but Theseus, who happened to be there, helped Peirithous to drive them off. They drew the car of Dionysus and carried Eros in some of his escapades.

North of Argo and east of Canis Minor is the long-stretching constellation Hydra, the Watersnake. This gigantic monster was the offspring of Typhon and Echidna, and possessed nine heads, of which the central one was immortal. Hercules slew the Hydra with the help of Iolus, as one of his twelve famous labors. As they cut off one head two grew in its place, but at length they burned out the roots with firebrands, and having cut off the immortal head, buried it under a monstrous rock. Arrows dipped in the blood of the Hydra served Hercules for fatal weapons.

West and south of Orion is another very extended constellation called Eridanus, or the River. It ends not very far from the south pole in the bright star Achernar, or Alpha Eridani. North of Eridanus is Cetus, the Whale, which contains Mira, a noted variable star. There are quite a number of other smaller southern constellations, which we need not speak of individually here.

There remain the twelve well-known constellations called like Signs of the Zodiac: Aries, the Ram; Taurus, the Bull; Gemini, the Twins; Cancer, the Crab; Leo, the Lion; Virgo, the Virgin; Libra, the Balance; Scorpio, the Scorpion; Sagittarius, the Archer; Capricornus, the Goat; Aquarius, the Water-bearer; Pisces, the Fishes. In the Appendix will be found a list of all the constellations.

The borders of the constellations are defined arbitrarily in accordance with ancient custom. Within them the stars have received letters of the Greek alphabet, which generally run in the order of brightness, although there are a good many exceptions. Many of the stars named Alpha or Beta, and some fainter ones also, have special names, as, for instance, Alpha Lyræ is Vega, Beta Orionis is Rigel, Omicron Ceti is Mira. Modern telescopes have revealed so many stars that Greek letters fail to suffice, and so the Arabic numerals have been added in many cases. Besides this expedient, one still more generally used is to give a star the number which it has in a certain star catalogue, as "Boss 3972" and the like. In star catalogues it is almost universal to arrange the stars in the order of increasing right ascension.

We must now give some mention of a few of the more interesting objects which occur in the various constellations. We shall begin with the northern heavens, continue with the Zodiac, and end with the southern constellations in this enumeration. Readers will find much more detailed information of this kind in Webb's "Celestial Objects for the Common Telescope."

Polaris, little more than a degree from the pole, is Alpha Ursæ Minoris. A small telescope shows it double, and the brighter of its pair of stars is known by aid of the spectroscope to be triple. The telescope cannot show this. The brightest of the spectroscopically triple stars is a variable star of four days period. It is of the so-called Cepheid type which we shall explain in a later chapter.

In Ursa Major is the Great Dipper. The two stars at the end

of the bowl are the Pointers which find for us Polaris. The star at the bend of the Dipper handle is Mizar, easily seen to have a smaller star, Alcor, close by. But Mizar itself is triple.

East of Ursa Major are two little constellations, Canes Venatici and Coma Berenices. In Canes Venatici is a wonderful spiral nebula. Coma Berenices, "The Hair of Berenice," is named for the great cluster of faint naked eye stars, which fancifully represent beautiful tresses.

In Boötes, east of these, the finest object is Arcturus, or Alpha Boötis. North of it lies a kite-shaped figure of five stars, the southern of which is the fine double, Epsilon Boötis.

Passing by the beautiful Corona Borealis, we come to Hercules. Its brightest star, Alpha Herculis, is a very red double of irregular variability. Though not very bright, Alpha Herculis gives us a great deal more heat than white stars much brighter. The constellation has several other double stars, but its greatest feature is the "Great Cluster in Hercules." This is a swarm of stars which are very faint on account of their immense distance, though really very bright. There are perhaps millions of stars in this one cluster.

East of Hercules is Lyra, whose bright gem is Vega, or Alpha Lyræ. Our sun is travelling at 12 miles a second nearly towards Vega. Just east of Vega lie two little stars, Epsilon and Zeta Lyræ, which form with Vega a shapely little triangle. If one has sharp eyes, he can see Epsilon, the more northern of them, double. To a large telescope, each of the two visible stars in Epsilon Lyrae is also double. Zeta Lyræ is also a double star. A short distance south of them is Beta Lyræ, a double star whose components, revolving, partially hide each other alternately. Thus it is an eclipsing variable of about 13 days period. Southeast of Beta lies the famous "Ring Nebula in Lyra."

The principal stars of the constellation Cygnus, next east of Lyra, form what is sometimes called the Northern Cross. Its stars are not as bright as the finest ones of the Southern Cross, though in form the Northern Cross is perhaps superior. Yet Deneb at the head of the Cross, is very conspicuous. Albireo, at the foot, is a very fine double star for small telescopes. Southeast of Deneb is 61 Cygni, the first star whose distance was measured by Bessel, and one of the nearest stars to us. It is the western one of three little stars near together which form a nearly equal-sided triangle. The Milky Way is divided in Cygnus. It has some very interesting dark holes and rifts. There is also a very extensive nebula, which in photographs appears much like a streaky, fine-spun, cirrus cloud.

East of Cygnus, in Cepheus, are some remarkable variable stars. Delta Cephei is the typical one. These stars are very massive, very blue, and vary regularly in periods of a few days. It is supposed that, like the heart, they are pulsating, and that this is the cause of their variation. Beyond Cepheus is Cassiopeia, in which constellation appeared, in 1582, Tycho Brahe's wonderful New Star, which for a time was brighter even than the planets.

Southeast of Cassiopeia lies brilliant Capella or Alpha Aurigae, a star called sometimes "the Goat." A little southwest of it lie three small stars called "The Kids." Capella is a spectroscopic double.

West of Auriga lies Perseus, from which direction come the August meteors. In February, 1901, the brilliant new star, Nova Persei, for a few days rivalled the brightest stars of the heavens. A still more famous star is Beta Persei, or Algol, a three-days period eclipsing variable.

West of Perseus, we find Andromeda, from whose direction come some of the November meteors. The Spiral Nebula of Andromeda is its greatest feature. Gamma Andromeda is a fine double. Next to the west comes Pegasus, notable for the Great Square, of which the northeast star is Alpha Andromeda. The northwest one of the square, Beta Pegasi, is very red, and, like Alpha Herculis, sends more heat to us than many brighter stars.

Much further west is brilliant Altair, or Alpha Aquilæ, lying in the Milky Way. A few degrees west of Altair is Nova Aquilæ of June, 1918, which for a time outshone all the stars except Sirius.

We now turn to the Zodiacal constellations, beginning with Taurus, which contains the Pleiades and Hyades, and the fine bright-red star Aldebaran. It is very easy to find in the autumn and winter months, lying much south and a little east of Capella. The Pleiades, or "Seven Sisters," for most eyes are but six, forming a configuration like a little dipper. Carefully looking, we may see the seventh, Pleione, near the star at the end of the handle.   Photographs show the stars of the Pleiades wrapped in nebulosity.   The Hyades is the great V-shaped figure lying east of the Pleiades, and with Aldebaran near its point.   The Hyades and the Pleiades are each really open clusters of stars having common motions in space.

Next east is Gemini, whose bright stars, Alpha and Beta, are named Castor and Pollux after the twin brothers of Helen of Troy. They went with the Argonauts for the Golden Fleece.   On the return voyage there was a great storm, which immediately became calm when Orpheus, aided by Apollo, caused the two stars to shine above the heads of the twins.    So Castor and Pollux became sailors' deities.   As Castor is now fainter than Pollux, it seems likely that there has been a change of their relative brightness since the days of the ancients, who made Castor Alpha Geminorum.   It is a double star, and each of its companions is also double.

The faint constellation of Cancer, the Crab, has within it the open cluster of Praesepe.   Beyond Cancer is Leo, the Lion, whose gem is the fine star Regulus at the end of the handle of the "Sickle." From the direction of Leo come November meteors.   East of Leo comes Virgo, the Virgin, with the splendid star Spica.   In Virgo are many spiral nebulæ, not visible except with great telescopes.   At present, the autumnal equinox lies in Virgo.   Libra, the Balance, contains no very remarkable objects.

Next comes Scorpio with the great red star Antares.   There is a little companion to Antares which may be seen with a moderate sized telescope.   The Milky Way is very bright in Scorpio, and there have been several "new stars" in this region.   Sagittarius, the Archer, also lies in the Milky Way, which has its most splendid and interesting region here.   There are in its brightest parts great dark lanes and patches devoid even of little stars.   They probably indicate dark nebulous matter nearer to us than the stars behind.

The constellation Capricornus is not very remarkable, though its brightest star Alpha is a naked-eye double.   Aquarius, too, offers little of interest, and Pisces, also, is inconspicuous, but includes the present location of the vernal equinox.   Finally, we come to Aries which was once the constellation of the vernal equinox, but now contains little remarkable.

Of the southern constellations, Orion is easily the most wonderful. The giant red variable star Betelgeuse, over 250,000,000 miles in diameter, is Alpha Orionis, but Rigel, Beta Orionis, is probably six times as hot, and so are the fine stars in Orion's belt. The central star of the sword, Theta Orionis, lies in the midst of the Great Nebula of Orion, and is really a multiple star of six companions. The whole constellation is enwrapped by nebulosity.

In Cetus, the Whale, is the star Omicron Ceti, or Mira, "the wonderful," which varies through a great range suddenly every eleven months. The cause of its variation is unknown. Each of the three little constellations, Dorado, Hydrus, and Tucana, which lie near the south pole, offers something interesting. In Dorado is the Greater Magellanic cloud, and in Hydrus, the Lesser. These luminous clouds of distant stars are like strayed bits of the Milky Way, but are in no sense a part of it. Tucana presents to us the fine globular star-cluster "47 Tucanæ."

Canis Major, with Sirius our brightest star, and Canis Minor with Procyon, are both sufficiently striking. Each of these two surpassing brilliants is a double star to the largest telescopes. The great constellation Argo Navis presents our second brightest star, Canopus, and also the extraordinary red variable, Eta Argus. Within the past century, this star has sometimes been almost as bright as Sirius for years, though now it is beyond the range of the unaided eye. Adjacent to this star is the curious Keyhole Nebula. Near Eta Argus is the Southern Cross, whose brightest star, Alpha Crucis, is double. Surrounding the Cross is Centaurus with its splendid pair, Alpha and Beta Centauri. Alpha is the sun's nearest stellar neighbor.

The reader may locate the various interesting objects we have mentioned by consulting the accompanying little charts. In the Appendix is given a list of the constellations. It includes many smaller ones which we have not thought necessary to speak of because they lack interesting features.

# CHAPTER XI

## *THE SYSTEM OF OUR STARS*

LET us now launch far out into the great universe. To the naked eye it is just an unorganized assemblage of big stars and little ones lying in all directions from the sun. City dwellers, among their gleaming lights, hardly even see the stars. Probably few of them realize that they rise and set like the sun. The Milky Way, which is the most outstanding feature of the whole celestial system, is unknown to a majority, perhaps, of our people.

All is changed as one seeks some open country-place with wide horizon on a crisp, clear, moonless night. The stars stand out like jewels, and among them stretches, like the rim of a gigantic wheel, the Milky Way, or "Galaxy," encircling the whole earth. One wonders what kind of a faintly glowing cloudy creation it may be, until he looks again with a small telescope, and lo! the gauzy cloud becomes a perfect host of stars, compared to which all other parts of the heavens look bare and deserted. It dominates the field of stars so masterfully, that astronomers often speak of the whole system of them, centering about the Milky Way, as the Galaxy.

This gives a natural reference plane for our starry universe. With a little care, we find that the crowded Galaxy is like a flat ring, symmetrically placed among the stars, whose poles are in the northern constellation Coma Berenices [1] and the southern constellation Cetus. It stretches with varying brightness through the constellations Aquila, Vulpecula, Cygnus, Cepheus, Cassiopeia, Perseus, Auriga, Taurus, Orion, Monoceros, Argo, Crux, Circinus Norma, Scorpius, Sagittarius, Serpens, Orphiucus, Scutum Sobieski, Taurus Poniatowski.

Astronomers, in dealing in the large with the structure of our starry universe, very naturally reckon positions from the Milky Way or Galaxy, and speak of Galactic latitudes and longitudes, as we

[1] Right Ascension 12 h 50 m, Declination N 27° 12′.

locate places on the earth by terrestrial latitudes and longitudes. Let us follow them in the census of the heavens, inquiring how many stars there are and how located.

We are confronted at once by an embarrassment, because the numbers of stars seen depend on the power of the telescope used, and on the clearness of the sky, and other factors. Evidently some standard conditions must be chosen. Astronomers have classified the stars by their apparent brightness. They use the term "magnitude," which is a very old one. The ancients used this classification, calling the brightest stars first magnitude, those about as bright as the pole star, second, and so on. In the nineteenth century, when greater accuracy was desired, the actual apparent brightness for average stars of the several magnitudes, already assigned roughly by common consent, was carefully measured. It proved that these conventional assignments could be nearly reproduced by making the exact rule that a difference of 5 magnitudes corresponds to exactly 100-fold in difference of apparent brightness, and that each magnitude differs in brightness from the next by the fifth root of one hundred ( $\sqrt[5]{100}$ ) fold in brightness.[1]

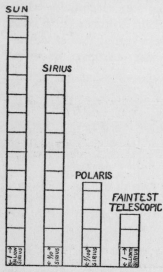

FIG. 37. The range of brightness of the heavenly bodies. In order to bring the diagrams within a page the scales are altered as shown by the arrows from units of 1 billion times to units of 1 billionth times the brightness of Sirius.

[1] This rule expresses itself very simply in logarithms. For the logarithm of 100 is 2, and the logarithm of $\sqrt[5]{100}$ is 2/5 = 0.4. Hence, to find the actual difference in brightness between two stars, multiply the difference in magnitudes by 0.4 and look up in a logarithm table the number corresponding. For example, the magnitudes of Vega and of Alcyone (in the Pleiades) are 0.1 and 3.0. The difference is 2.9. Multiplying by 0.4 we have 1.16, which is the logarithm of 14.5. Hence, Vega is 14.5 times as bright as Alcyone.

Conversely, we may express in magnitudes a known difference in brightness. For example, the sun gives 57,600,000,000 times as much light as Capella at the

Stars may be viewed visually, or photographed and studied at leisure. The naked eye cannot see them fainter than the sixth magnitude, but by using the telescope the visual scale can be carried on to fainter stars. As the eye is most sensitive to greenish yellow rays, whereas the ordinary photographic plate responds quickest to blue-violet ones, it makes a difference in the star magnitudes which means of observing is used. We shall return to this a little later, and show how this embarrassment has been turned into an advantage to supplement the spectroscope in star observing. Now we

NUMBER OF STARS BRIGHTER THAN SUCCESSIVE MAGNITUDES
Harvard visual scale

| Magnitude | No. of Stars | Ratio | Magnitude | No. of Stars | Ratio |
|---|---|---|---|---|---|
| 0 | 3 | | 8 | 46,200 | |
| | | 3.7 | | | 3.0 |
| 1 | 11 | | 9 | 139,300 | |
| | | 3.5 | | | 2.7 |
| 2 | 39 | | 10 | 380,000 | |
| | | 3.4 | | | 2.7 |
| 3 | 133 | | 11 | 1,026,000 | |
| | | 3.4 | | | 2.5 |
| 4 | 446 | | 12 | 2,590,000 | |
| | | 3.3 | | | 2.3 |
| 5 | 1,466 | | 13 | 5,890,000 | |
| | | 3.2 | | | 2.2 |
| 6 | 4,730 | | 14 | 13,120,000 | |
| | | 3.2 | | | 2.1 |
| 7 | 15,000 | | 15 | 27,500,000 | |
| | | 3.1 | | | 2.1 |
| 8 | 46,200 | | 16 | 57,100,000 | |

earth's distance. The logarithm is 10.76. Dividing this logarithm by 0.4, we find − 26.9 as the difference in magnitudes between Capella and the sun. But since the magnitude of Capella is + 0.2, we can express that of the sun only by the *negative* quantity − 26.7. There are only two other stars, Sirius and Canopus, so bright that their assigned magnitudes are negative. They are − 1.6 and − 0.9, respectively. The moon, Venus, Jupiter, and Mercury, which all shine by reflected sunlight, also have negative magnitudes, changing in value from night to night, according to the positions of these bodies relative to the sun. We should always remember that the brighter a star, the less, speaking algebraically, is its magnitude.

will go on to the census of the stars by magnitudes, and what it shows about the shape of the space the stars occupy. Only the first eight or nine magnitudes have really been counted completely, but the higher ones are closely estimated from sample counts of many regions of sky. (We give data collected by Seares.)

For the first eight magnitudes, there is a slowly declining ratio of gain, but beyond this the decline of the ratio is faster. Taking into account the slower rate of gain, it is estimated that to the twentieth visual magnitude, which, indeed, is slightly beyond the limit the eye can see with the 100-inch reflector on Mount Wilson, the stars number 500,000,000. If the slowing up of the rate of gain continues as indicated, there cannot be many stars fainter than the thirtieth magnitude. Their total number is therefore limited — something like thirty or forty billions. To state it comparatively, there are in our system about twenty stars for every human being now alive.

This conclusion does not allow for the bodies of starlike size, perhaps very many in number, which are dark, or which shine feebly by reflection, as the earth and moon do. Neither does it allow for the possibility that the decline of the ratio of gain in numbers, from magnitude to magnitude, may imply an obstruction of light in space.

It is easy to see that probably the faintness of the stars of high magnitude is largely due to their immense distance quite as much as to their intrinsic faintness. But it may be that a part of it depends on loss of light on the way to us. We have seen, in considering the solar system, that millions of meteors strike the earth's atmosphere daily. If space, generally, is tenanted by such objects in equal profusion, even though they are individually very small, they must, by their immense number, cut off and absorb some light in the course of such enormously long journeys as light makes in coming from the faintest stars to us.

Furthermore, the escape of atoms and molecules of gas from the atmospheres of stars and planets (and doubtless other stars besides the sun have planets) must also provide some obstruction to light. These atoms and molecules, however, being small compared to the wave-length of light, would tend to scatter the violet rays more than the red. So we should expect the faintest stars to be redder than the brighter ones, on the average. Apart from a special exception, which we shall mention later, this does not appear to be confirmed, so that astronomers tend to think light-scattering by molecules and atoms in the depths of space is not important.

The argument does not apply as regards bodies similar to meteors, for they would weaken rays without altering their color. Accordingly, we are not in a position to say with confidence that there is no light absorption. Hence, we cannot say that the number of the stars does not exceed thirty or forty billions, but we certainly can say it is not much less.

*The Milky Way a Crowded Retreat.* — Turning from number to arrangement, we can learn something very interesting about the probable shape of our starry system. Let us arrange our star counts in zones parallel to the Milky Way, or Galaxy, and use the term "Galactic Latitude" to designate the angular distance on either side of the central line of the Galaxy. Rather than give entire numbers for the whole zones, let us give average numbers per square degree. The result is somewhat as follows:

AVERAGE NUMBERS PER SQUARE DEGREE OF ALL STARS
BRIGHTER THAN CERTAIN DESIGNATED MAGNITUDES

| Magnitude | At Galactic Latitudes: | | | | | | | |
|---|---|---|---|---|---|---|---|---|
| | 5° | 15° | 25° | 35° | 45° | 55° | 65° | 80° |
| 9.5 | 10 | 7.3 | 5.5 | 4.4 | 3.9 | 3.7 | 3.5 | 3.4 |
| 10.5 | 29 | 20 | 14 | 11 | 10 | 9 | 8 | 8 |
| 11.5 | 81 | 53 | 36 | 28 | 23 | 21 | 19 | 17 |
| 12.5 | 210 | 130 | 86 | 63 | 51 | 44 | 39 | 35 |
| 13.5 | 510 | 300 | 192 | 135 | 105 | 88 | 75 | 64 |
| 14.5 | 1,140 | 680 | 400 | 267 | 200 | 160 | 132 | 112 |
| 15.5 | 2,480 | 1,480 | 800 | 514 | 370 | 282 | 230 | 195 |
| 16.5 | 5,500 | 3,160 | 1,590 | 933 | 660 | 500 | 400 | 330 |

It is plain that stars of all degrees of brightness are much more numerous in the Milky Way than near its poles. But this effect is greatly augmented for fainter stars.   Thus comparing the star density at 5° with that at 80° of Galactic Latitude, we find:

| Magnitude | Density Ratio |
|-----------|---------------|
| 9.5 | 3.1 |
| 12.5 | 6.1 |
| 16.5 | 16.6 |

What does this mean?  Evidently that, since the faint stars do not exist proportionately plentifully towards the poles of the Galaxy, either we look right through the star system to vacant space within a comparatively moderate distance in that direction, or else some very regularly distributed and gradually augmented absorbing me-

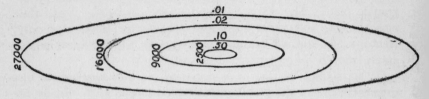

FIG. 38.  OUR STAR SYSTEM.  (After Kapteyn).

The ellipses represent boundaries of regions, at right angles to the plane of the Milky Way, where the star density [number of stars per unit of volume] is 0.01, 0.02, 0.10, and 0.50 compared to the star density near the sun. These boundaries lie at distances 27,000, 16,000, 9,000 and 2,500 light years distant in the plane of the Milky Way, but only 1/5 as far distant towards its poles. Thus our Galaxy is watch-shaped.

dium cuts off more of the light rays that come to us from thence. It is so much simpler to conceive the former alternative, that all astronomers are agreed that we should regard the stars as situated in a space shaped like a lens, a watch, or an oyster-shell, extending immensely farther in the plane of the Milky Way than it does at right angles thereto.  But the thinning out of stars of fainter magnitudes seems most probably to indicate that even in the Galaxy itself we see through the entire star system.

In other words, the stars do not appear to extend out to infinite distance in any direction, and much less far toward the constellations Coma Berenices and Cetus than towards constellations like Sagittarius, Perseus, and Aquila which lie in the Milky Way.  This conclusion is supported by another fact long ago pointed out. If the stars existed without bounds in all directions, their number would be infinite, and they would totally close in the view in every direction, even though each individual was almost a mere point. So that, unless their light was absorbed in coming to us, the whole heavens would blaze like the sun. This is not so, and the limited extent of the starry system readily explains it.

*The Star Classes.* — As we stated above, in rating the brightness of stars, their rank depends on the means used to observe them. For if we compare photographically two stars which appear equally bright to the eye, we shall very likely find them as much as one or two magnitudes apart, according to the impressions of the photographic plate. The eye sees best by greenish yellow light, while blue, indigo, and violet rays are more active photographically. Hence, a blue star will outrank a red one upon the ordinary photograph, though the eye pronounces them equal.

On account of this fact it is necessary, as we have said, to distinguish between visual and photographic magnitudes. As by far the majority of the present-day star-observing which deals with faint stars is photographic, most catalogues of such stars give photographic magnitudes. Sometimes, however, the so-called "isochromatic" plates are used in star photography, together with yellow ray-filters which sort out and transmit nearly the same colors which are most effective to the eye. On such photographs the stars stand out in about the same rank of brightness that they would if measured by the eye itself. Such observations are called "photo-visual" and the magnitude values they furnish are called "photo-visual magnitudes." Photographic plates cover so much sky, and furnish so permanent a record, that this special kind of photographic observing is for some purposes quite preferable to eye work.

We have, in this way, two kinds of scales of star magnitudes — the photographic and the photo-visual, equivalent to the visual. Thus arises an important quantity only recently come into use, called the "color index." It is found by subtracting the photovisual from the photographic magnitude. For a blue star, the photographic magnitude will be relatively smaller, and for a red star relatively larger than the photo-visual. (One is always apt to trip here, forgetting that the brighter the star, the smaller its magnitude.) We found in Chapter II that it is convenient to classify the stars by the appearance of their spectrum. Parallel to this spectrum classification, there runs the color index scale. The whole story, illustrated by typical stars, is as follows. The color indices and temperatures given here relate to the type and are not exact, perhaps, for the individual star named.

| Star | Rigel | Sirius | Procyon | Sun | Arcturus | Betelgeuse |
|---|---|---|---|---|---|---|
| Constellation | Orion | Canis Maj. | Canis Min. | — | Boötes | Orion |
| Color | Blue | White | Pale yellow | Yellow | Reddish | Red |
| Spectral Class | B | A | F | G | K | M |
| Color index | −0.4 | 0.0 | +0.4 | +0.8 | +1.2 | +1.6 |
| Color class | b | a | f | g | k | m |
| Surface temperature | 16,000° | 11,000° | 8,000° | 6,000° | 3,500° | 2,700° |

The roughly estimated surface temperatures given are centigrade degrees, reckoned from absolute zero, − 273° C. In Plate 28, the reader may see the differences of spectrum for these types of stars. Expressed in words, the typical features are as follows. The descriptive terms "spark," "arc," "flame," refer to the several common ways of exciting spectra in the laboratory by the electric spark, electric arc, and the flaming arc. The spark is much hotter than the arc, and this much hotter than the flame of the outer part of the flaming arc.

### CHARACTERISTICS OF TYPICAL STELLAR SPECTRA

Spectral Class

| B | A | F |
|---|---|---|
| The few Fraunhofer lines are mainly of hydrogen and helium. Oxygen, nitrogen show less conspicuously. | Hydrogen lines predominate. Helium lines disappear. Lines of metals come in faintly, especially spark lines. | Metallic lines conspicuous. Arc lines of metals appear. |

PLATE 27. STAR CLOUD IN SAGITTARIUS. (Barnard.)

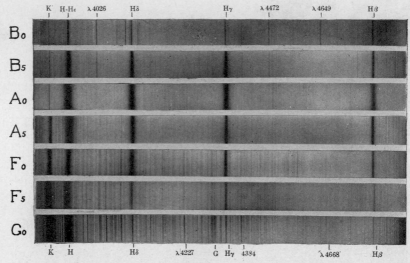

PLATE 28, FIG. 1. TYPICAL STELLAR SPECTRA, B₀ TO G₀

Spectra of stars ε Orionis, q Tauri, α Canis Majoris, β Trianguli, δ Geminorum, α Canis Minoris, α Aurigæ. (A spurious line occurs to left of Hβ in the spectrum B₅.)

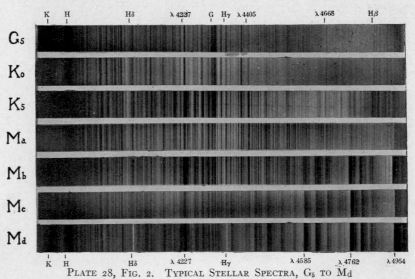

PLATE 28, FIG. 2. TYPICAL STELLAR SPECTRA, G₅ TO M_d

Spectra of Stars κ Geminorum, α Bootis, α Tauri, α Orionis, ρ Persei, W Cygni, o Ceti. (Both figures from observations of Detroit Observatory, University of Michigan.)

## Spectral Class

| G | K | M |
|---|---|---|
| Solar type. Metallic arc lines predominate. Flaming arc lines also conspicuous. | Sun-spot type. Arc lines strong. Flame lines also conspicuous. Bands of compounds appear. | Flame lines prominent. Heavy absorption bands appear and are the conspicuous feature, indicating spectra of molecules, notably titanium oxide. |

Accompanying the fall of surface temperature from B type to M type, the region of greatest intensity in the spectrum shifts steadily from violet to red, and when indicated on a wave-length scale is found beyond the visible end of the violet for B type, and beyond the visible end of the red for M type stars.

*More Homes in the Milky Way.* — Now that we have divided our stars into tribes, as it were, we shall find that some of them, like human tribes, have homes. This comes out as follows. The table gives numbers of stars within equal areas situated at certain average Galactic latitudes.

NUMBERS OF STARS ABOVE 6¼ MAGNITUDE OF SPECTRUM TYPES
AT DIFFERENT GALACTIC LATITUDES

| Galactic Latitude | B | A | F | G | K | M | All |
|---|---|---|---|---|---|---|---|
| 60° | 37 | 296 | 156 | 128 | 378 | 101 | 1,096 |
| 40 | 85 | 345 | 152 | 128 | 377 | 108 | 1,195 |
| 20 | 227 | 539 | 200 | 170 | 459 | 126 | 1,721 |
| 8 | 367 | 705 | 212 | 183 | 505 | 122 | 2,094 |
| All | 716 | 1,885 | 720 | 609 | 1,719 | 457 | 6,106 |

Looking down each column of this grouping of bright stars, we see that the red M stars are quite cosmopolitan, showing little preference for one part of the sky over another. The F, G, and K stars concentrate very slightly toward the Milky Way region. But of the blue B stars, there are ten times as many in the Milky Way

neighborhood as at 60° from it, and the A types show a similar
but less decided preference. The total numbers of bright stars of
the several clans are also interesting. The M types are very few,
B, F, and G somewhat more numerous, but A and K types include
six-tenths of the whole number of these bright stars. It is quite
changed for faint stars.

This immediately leads us to inquire whether the blue stars are
concentrated towards the center of the star system, or are scattered
all the way out to the bounds of the Milky Way. The answer is
very decisive. We must first of all remark that though our solar
system is not in the exact center of things, as was suggested by some
astronomers many years ago, it lies comparatively near the center
and not near the confines of the immense extension of the Milky
Way. In the second place, we may assume, as indeed we shall show
later, that the B stars are nearly equal to each other in real absolute brightness. The reason that they apparently differ is mainly
because some are further away than others.

With these two ideas in mind, consider this little table which,
like an earlier table shows the change of ratio of numbers of stars
brighter than a given magnitude.

| Visual Magnitude | Ratios: | | | |
|---|---|---|---|---|
| | B | A, F | G, K, M | All |
| 2.5 | | | | |
| | 3.1 | 2.9 | 4.0 | 3.4 |
| 3.5 | | | | |
| | 2.7 | 3.2 | 3.5 | 3.2 |
| 4.5 | | | | |
| | 2.6 | 4.4 | 3.2 | 3.4 |
| 5.5 | | | | |
| | 1.7 | 4.1 | 3.2 | 3.3 |
| 6.5 | | | | |

We see from the second column that the blue B stars are increasing more and more slowly as they grow fainter, and with a few

more magnitudes the gain will probably cease altogether. This seems to mean that beyond a certain distance, corresponding to which average stars become apparently of eighth or ninth magnitude, there are no more of them. Quite the contrary with A and F, and as for the G, K, and M types, they practically hold their own in rate of increasing numbers.

Hence, it appears that the blue B type stars are few in numbers and are concentrated in the middle of our starry system. Thus, if we could take our stand outside of it, at an immense distance, so that the whole of our stars would run together into a hazy cloud, as the Milky Way does to the naked eye, it would probably be a yellowish cloud. The blue part of its make-up would be insignificant. This conclusion is supported by color indices of stars too faint for the spectroscope to observe. At the sixteenth magnitude, there are no stars in some regions of the sky bluer than color-class f. Much more observing is needed to fully prove the matter, but apparently the blue stars are really few, and are central in our starry system.

While we talk of the tribal homes of the stars, we may naturally turn a little aside to see the same sort of thing among the nebulæ — those celestial cousins of the stars of whose exact kinship we know so little. We are sure that these cloudlike objects are neither terrestrial clouds nor any part of our solar system, because they keep their places among the stars. They fall into four classes: (1) Those which are diffuse, resembling our earthly clouds. Of such are the nebulæ in the Pleiades, in Orion, in Sagittarius, and in Cygnus. (2) The planetary nebulæ, small clear-cut forms with a central star. (3) The spiral nebulæ, somewhat like the forms of spiral sea-shells. (4) The elongated and globular nebulæ, neither exactly planetary nor exactly spiral but, like them, definitely formed not vaguely diffuse.

Now it is a very interesting thing that no spiral nebulæ fall in the Milky Way, although there are perhaps hundreds of thousands of them in the sky, and that nearly all of the diffuse nebulæ and planetary nebulæ do fall in the Milky Way, and hardly any of them much outside of it.

"New stars" also have a very curious preferential distribution. We sometimes think of our universe as a grand system which began in some unknown way almost an eternity ago; which, in our time, pursues its majestic course without a ripple to mark the even current of its flow; and which imperceptibly moves towards some far-off end lying almost an eternity in the dim future. But there are, nevertheless, evidences of tremendous catastrophes occurring. Thus, in February, 1901, there suddenly blazed a star in the constellation Perseus that for a few days rivalled the brightness of Sirius, and then faded away, with fitful little recoveries, until now it is thousands of times too faint for the eye to see. Quite as bright for a time was the new star in Aquila, in June, 1918. There have been 78 of these new stars, bright enough to attract attention, since the time of Tycho Brahe, who observed one on November 11, 1572, which for several days exceeded Jupiter and rivalled Venus in its luster, being visible even in daytime. No doubt there are very many new stars, fainter at maximum than fourth magnitude, which are never noticed among the starry host.

The causes of such outbursts, we must reserve for a later chapter. What interests us just now is the curious distribution of the 78 new stars of record. No less than 22 of them came within the boundaries of the Great Spiral Nebula of Andromeda, 6 in other spiral nebulæ, 2 in nebulæ not plainly spiral, 39 within the borders of the Milky Way, and only 9 in all the remainder of the sky. Not even the blue B stars show so remarkable a distribution as this.

To complete this curious business of tribal homes of the celestial objects, let us turn to the star clusters, of which there are a good many, reminding one of swarms of bees. They are closely crowded little groups containing oftentimes as many as 50,000 stars in a group no bigger, apparently, than a great sun-spot, though of course actually enormously bigger. These clusters, too, are nearly all found in the region of the Milky Way.

What do these queer things mean? It is just as strange for the spiral nebulæ to avoid the Galaxy as for the blue stars, the diffuse nebulæ, the new stars, and the clusters to frequent it. We shall have to lay these facts up in our minds until we have gone on to see something about the motions and distances and masses involved before seeking a reason for them.

*Multiple Stars.* — Among the immense multitude of the stars, we do not positively know that there are any besides our sun attended like him by a large train of planets, their satellites, comets, and meteors. There is nothing strange about this, for if we stood on a world circling the nearest star, Alpha Centauri, we should need a telescope 25 feet in diameter barely to see the great planet Jupiter, even if it could be seen lying immersed in the powerful glare of the sun. This illustrates how impossible it is for telescopic vision or photography to descry worlds among the stars. They may very well be there in multitudes without our seeing them.

Gravitation is no more useful than direct vision. Even the gigantic Jupiter hardly pulls the sun over an orbit of the sun's own diameter. As all the stars are so far away that their diameters are immeasurably small to the largest telescopes, and only discoverable by special means to be described later, it is clear that we cannot expect worlds like ours, hundreds of thousands times smaller than the sun, to indicate their unseen presence by gravitational pull on their governing stars.

Therefore, we are now, and probably always shall be, at the mercy of imagination when we think of the question of possible worlds like ours among the starry host. But among so many, it would certainly be extraordinary if there are actually no stars like our sun in this respect. We may, therefore, believe there is great probability that there are indeed many worlds like ours, and that there is no reason either to affirm or to doubt that they contain as intelligent beings as ourselves.

We know very well that the great stars often go in pairs, or even in larger families of three or four, circulating about one another. Many such binary or multiple stars are so widely separated as to be easily seen individually with the telescope. A pretty example is Epsilon Lyræ, the northern star of the two which form a small triangle with Vega. A keen eye can detect that Epsilon Lyræ is a little elongated, or perhaps even that it seems separated. An opera glass shows its doubling easily. But with a moderate-sized telescope, each of the pair of stars is seen itself to be a pair. The four together make a charming sight.

Several thousand telescopic binaries are known, and many of them have been under exact observation for so long that they already show motion in orbits, or even in many cases complete revolution, or numerous revolutions, about each other. In some cases, the orbits are completed within five years, while in some, the periods are thousands of years.

It is specially interesting that a few stars have been recognized

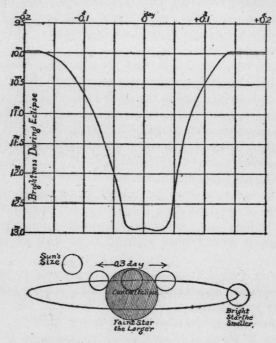

FIG. 39. THE LIGHT VARIATION OF THE STAR R R DRACONIS AND WHAT IT MEANS. (After Shapley.)

The period of revolution of the two bodies is 2.831 days. The larger star gives but 1/16 as much light as the smaller, which is of about the same diameter as the sun.

as double by the telescope, before the companion has been discovered. Such was the case with both Sirius and Procyon. The paradox is explained by the fact that the positions of these two stars were found to fluctuate in the same way as they would if each had a companion. In the case of Sirius, the astronomer Auwers computed the orbit of the otherwise unknown satellite, which was later on discovered, in the year 1862, by Alvan G. Clark while he was testing a large telescope which he had just completed. The companion of Procyon was also predicted by Auwers, who found that Procyon revolved in a circular orbit about a second of arc in radius. Though carefully searched for under very favorable conditions, no one saw the companion until 1895, when it was discovered by Schaeberle with the 36-inch telescope of the Lick Observatory. Auwers' orbit was substantially verified.

Besides the telescopic double stars, there are many others so close together that the telescope is unable to separate them. Their binary character reveals itself in one of two ways. If two stars are in mutual revolution, in orbits in a plane so nearly containing the earth that one of the stars occasionally eclipses the other to our view, either partially or totally, the effect is to alter in perfectly regular periods the brightness of the apparently single star. It matters not, as far as producing some alteration of brightness is concerned, whether the stars are equal or unequal in size and brightness, or even if one of them be dark altogether. But from the curve of variation of light, an astonishing amount of information can be gathered about such eclipsing systems, as we shall see in the next chapter.

Such a star is Algol (Beta Persei). A light curve is given in Figure 39 of an eclipsing variable differing from Algol in some particulars of the system it represents. Dr. Roberts, and after him Dr. H. N. Russell, investigated the theory of eclipsing variables very thoroughly. In the hands of Russell's pupil and colleague, Dr. Shapley, now Director of Harvard College Observatory, there was gotten out by Princeton University Observatory, in 1915, a fine volume giving results of application of the theory to ninety stars.

The other way of discovering double stars, too close together for telescopic separation, is by the spectroscope. We have seen how the spectroscope revealed the rotation of Uranus. The spectrum lines were displaced due to the motion of the planet's opposite edges to and from the earth. It is the same principle with a double star. In one part of the orbit the motion of revolution augments, and in another part diminishes whatever velocity of approach or re-

cession the star as a whole may have along the line of sight from
the earth. So the regular periodic variation of velocity in the line
of sight observed with the spectroscope, is evidence of a double or
multiple star. There may be no telescopic evidence of it, because
of too great closeness, and no eclipsing because the plane of the
orbit is too much inclined.

It is not at all necessary that the two components shall both give
light. Sometimes they are both so luminous as to give doubling of
the spectrum lines at cetain parts of their orbit, when one star is
approaching and the other receding. But very often one component
is dark, or too feebly luminous to give any evidence of its spectrum.
We shall see in the next chapter how much wonderful information
comes from this sort of thing.

No sooner had this kind of observing been regularly entered upon,
than the surprising fact came to light that double stars are exceedingly common. Of the 21 brightest stars with names mentioned in
Chapter I; no less than eleven are certainly attended by revolving
companions, as shown either by the telescope or spectroscope, or
both. Several others of them may be double systems, but the evidence is not sure. In general, of the thousands of stars whose
motions have been observed several times by means of the spectroscope, nearly one-third are double or multiple. If this state of
things is not exceptional with the stars bright enough to observe
in this way, we may estimate the number of binary stars at something like ten billion. This includes merely those whose secondary
fainter components are massive enough to be on something like
equality with their primaries in gravitational power. There may be
many more which, like the sun, have little planets.

*Dark Sky and Bright.* — In speaking thus far of the system of
the stars, and of the remarkable way in which the Galaxy dominates
its structure, we have failed to note some curiosities of texture in
the Galaxy itself, or to speak of two other objects something like
it which are called the Magellanic Clouds. Most telescopic photography deals with extremely small regions of sky, no bigger than the
moon and often very much smaller. But the late Professor E. E.
Barnard added very much to our appreciation of the heavens as
a whole by photographing large regions at a time, with what is

called a portrait lens. A special outfit of this kind, named the Bruce telescope after the donor, was used by Barnard at the Mount Wilson and Yerkes Observatories, and yielded some of the loveliest and most interesting of astronomical photographs. Among them are a great many taken in the Milky Way. These frequently show, in the very brightest of regions, dark spaces with scarcely a single star. Often these regions are like lanes or paths branching about among the densest clouds of stars.

Far to the south, beyond the view of persons in the United States or Europe, lie the two Magellanic Clouds, named after the great Portuguese navigator, Magellan. Like the Milky Way in appearance, but much smaller, and forming merely patches of sky instead of a dominating encircling belt, they nevertheless contain some highly interesting features, especially large numbers of a remarkable class of stars of variable brightness, called the "Cepheid variables."

And now, having glanced over the numbers and curious arrangement of the stars, their classes of different brightness and color, the nebulæ, star clusters, double stars, bright and dark star-clouds that lie among them, we have opened up so many questions that we must reserve several following chapters to the discussion of them. First of all we shall turn to the distances, sizes, and motions of the stars, which will occupy the next chapter.

## Chapter XII

### *THE DISTANCES, SIZES, AND MOTIONS OF THE STARS*

When Copernicus assigned to the earth the humbler part of revolving about the sun instead of being center of all things, as Ptolemy had regarded it, he required of his followers a great faith. For nearly 300 years, they had to believe that the stars are so far away that the earth's yearly cycle of 500,000,000 miles around the sun neither brings any of them apparently nearer, nor makes the nearer ones seem to cross over those more distant. In other words, the stars must be so very far away that the radius of the earth's orbit, 93,000,000 miles, is as nothing in comparison. It was not until Bessel, Henderson and Struve measured star distances, about the year 1840, that this faith began to be replaced by certainty. At the beginning of our present century, hardly over an hundred star distances had been measured, and a third of these depended on angular measurements too small to be trusted as real.[1]

Shortly after the year 1900, the present photographic parallax method began to be actively used. It requires a series of exposures of a star field at six-month intervals. In this way, the parallactic displacement of the star to be measured, which lies in the center of the plate, is observed against the background of supposedly more distant stars, its chance companions. Unless the parallax amounts to more than 0.01 seconds of arc, very few observers can detect it, and 0.005 seconds may be set as a lower limit to the trustworthy parallaxes of separate stars attainable by this method. This corresponds to a distance of about four quadrillion miles,

[1] Astronomers are more apt to speak of the "parallax" of a star than of its distance. The parallax is the angle which the radius of the earth's orbit, 93,000,000 miles, presents when viewed from the star. Few parallaxes exceed 0.2 seconds of arc. This is about the same angle that the width of a telegraph wire presents at 4 miles distance. A star whose parallax is 0.2 seconds is distant about 96,000,-000,000,000 miles. To know the distance in miles of a star whose parallax is given in seconds, divide 19,200,000,000,000 by the parallax. To express the result in light-years, divide the number of miles by 5,900,000,000,000, or the number 3.26 by the parallax in seconds of arc.

which requires light nearly 650 years to travel, and seems far enough, goodness knows! But we shall soon see that it is but little past the threshold of the starry sky. Half a dozen well-equipped observatories have worked diligently on these photographic parallax measurements for the past twenty years. The most prolific have been the Allegheny, McCormick, Mount Wilson and Yerkes observatories. Altogether they have determined nearly 2,000 parallaxes, but a great number of the results are too small to mean anything except that the stars in question are over 300 light-years distant. These so-called "trigonometrical parallaxes" are of very high value in astronomy, and form the basis of much of the surprising progress of the past ten years.

If we content ourselves with average distances of large groups of stars, we can go much further by studies of so-called "proper motions." It has been found by comparing the observed places of the stars, carefully obtained by such men as Bradley and the distinguished astronomers of the last 170 years, that though the heavens change very slowly in configuration of stars, yet they do change. One star goes hither, another yonder by very slight angular amounts. These little wanderings are called "proper motions." They are always expressed in angular measure, sometimes as the angle covered in a year, but often stated as so many seconds of arc per century. Very few proper motions exceed 100 seconds per century, and from this they go on down to zero.

The late Professor Lewis Boss, of Albany, New York, published, in 1910, his "Preliminary General Catalogue" under the auspices of the Carnegie Institution. In it, he gives the most careful determinations of the places and proper motions of some 6,000 of the brighter stars. About twice as many, not quite so accurate, are given in the Greenwich Observatory catalogue of 1910. Also the late Professor J. C. Kapteyn of Groningen, Holland, and his colleagues have done a great work, for many years, in collecting and extending knowledge of proper motions for fainter stars.

Boss, Kapteyn, and others examined the relations between brightness and proper motion. It is perfectly clear, of course, that if a star moves at a certain rate in a certain direction, the angle apparently moved over in a century will depend first on how far away the star is, and second on how the direction of the star's motion lies compared to our line of sight. The greatest effect will be produced if the motion is exactly at right angles to the line of sight, and if the star is near. If it is assumed that there is no reason why the stars should go in one direction rather than another, or in other words that their real motion is at random, we may say that the average apparent proper motion of a large number of stars is just about eight-tenths of the real average value. For we see some of the motions fully extended and some foreshortened to nothing, and on the average they are foreshortened to about eight-tenths their value.

Actually there are many other factors to consider. The star motions are not altogether at random directions in space, but have certain preferential motions. Stars of different spectrum types differ in speed, and differ in real brightness. Hence the proper motions offer no royal road to relative distances, even when averages from very large groups of stars are considered. But the late Professor Kapteyn, after long and profound investigation, determined certain formulæ for average parallaxes corresponding to average proper motions for the various magnitudes and types of spectrum. These have lately been revised by his successor Van Rhijn, using newer data.

The immense distances of stars may be seen if we translate his parallax value o.″0014, given for proper motion 0.000 and magnitude 10, into light-years and into miles. The numbers are over 2,300 light-years and 14,000,000,000,000,000 miles.

So we can estimate star distances from proper motions taken wholesale. There are some other interesting by-products of proper motions which give us the relative distances of certain families of stars. Looking back from the observation-car platform along a railroad track, while riding smoothly on a long continental journey, we sometimes see miles at a stretch where the track is straight, and the two rails seem to approach till they meet in the dim distance. Though they seem thus to approach and meet, we know that they are parallel. Similarly, if a lot of stars were moving along together in parallel paths, these paths would seem to us to meet in one point. Or to turn the proposition round-about, if the directions of motion of a lot of neighboring stars seem to meet in a point, these stars probably form a physically connected system or cluster, whose individual members are moving in parallel paths at equal rates. If the rates were very unequal, though the paths were parallel, the stars would not be neighboring ones, for they would have become widely separated during the immense time which star processes consume.

If the cluster is quite a deep one, so that some of the stars composing it are a good deal further from us than others, their proper motions will seem correspondingly smaller, though we know that actually the motions are closely equal. In such a case, the parallaxes are directly proportional to the apparent proper motions. If by any means one parallax can be measured, all become known immediately.

Professor L. Boss discovered such a moving cluster in Taurus. It includes, besides many fainter stars, several whose distances are known by trustworthy measurements. Accordingly, all the other distances in this group are as well determined as their proper motions, and these will be more and more accurately known as time goes on. There are several other well known moving clusters, for instance, one including the bright stars of the Great Dipper, another, the Pleiades.

### Spectroscopic Studies of Motion and Distance

We have considered already how much the spectroscope has told about motions of the sun and planets. Its offerings in this line for the stars are even more remarkable. Beginning just before the opening of the twentieth century, photographic spectroscopic work became standardized. Dr. W. W. Campbell of Lick Observatory, who soon became its Director, developed the photographic stellar spectroscope to high perfection, and also installed this line of observing at a branch station in Chile. So these two Lick Observatory spectroscopic investigations went on for many years, till they covered all the bright stars of both hemispheres to the fifth magnitude. The work was published by Dr. Campbell in 1910, and is a classic.

Every star spectrum photographed was accompanied above and below by a comparison spectrum of the light of the electric arc, showing the bright lines of iron or titanium. From these comparison spectra, the precise positions of the star spectrum lines were measured. The departures from standard places indicated just how rapidly the individual stars were each approaching or receding in the line of sight from the earth. By allowance for the earth's own motion, all could be referred to the sun, so that Dr. Campbell determined how rapidly each one of his 1300 stars was moving in the direction to or from the sun.

The general features of the spectra of all of these stars, and many more, had already been photographed by Harvard College Observatory, either in Cambridge or from its branch station at Arequipa, Peru. The stars were already classified on the Harvard scale, B, A, F, G, K, M, with finer gradations, such as B5, *et cetera*. But before tabulating his results by spectrum classes, Dr. Campbell had to apply to them certain corrections.

In the first place, many of the stars proved to exhibit variable velocities in the line of sight. This necessitated several sets of measurements, and usually revealed that the bright star was accompanied by another faint or obscure one, forming with it a revolving system. It was necessary, in such cases, to free the line of sight motion of the pair from the temporary fluctuations due to mutual revolution. Dr. Campbell found that nearly one-third of all the stars observed were of this binary character.

In the second place, the sun itself, like other individual stars, is in motion, and the solar motion, of course, modifies the results on all the stars. This had been known indeed for many years. Sir William Herschel had suspected it by the run of the few proper motions known in his day. He had even made a very close guess as to the actual direction of motion, but of course, could not know the speed. It was only after trustworthy parallaxes became fairly numerous that the best proper-motion data could give, not only the direction, but the speed of the sun, with some accuracy. For though it could be determined that the stars toward which the sun approaches are apparently separating, and those in the opposite direction from which the sun is receding are closing in (as trees behave when one approaches or recedes from the edge of a forest) the angular distances involved must be reduced to actual or linear ones before the sun's speed becomes known.  Enough parallaxes were available to Prof. L. Boss so that in discussing his "Preliminary General Catalogue," published just before Campbell's spectroscopic work, he gives both direction and speed of the solar motion.

Campbell, however, was able to determine the solar motion in both direction and speed from the Lick Observatory spectroscopic results alone.  In spectroscopic line-of-sight work, averages of large numbers of apparent motions give only half of the true average motion, if the directions of motion are at random in space.  But the solar motion shows itself in full to increase the apparent rate of approach of stars in the direction we are going, and to produce an apparent rate of recession of stars in the direction we are leaving behind.

Campbell and his colleagues worked out the solar motion in both direction and speed compared to all the stars he observed, and also compared to each spectrum class separately.  Suppose a lot of the stars, the blue ones of class B, for instance, formed a cluster with a common motion of their own.  When referred to these, the solar motion must be different from its values referred to other stars not of that cluster.  It is hardly possible to avoid systematic effects like this, either in spectroscopic or proper-motion work. The limited amount of observations available relate mainly to bright stars, presumably near us on the whole.  Very possibly they may all belong to one family affected with some common motion.

Here are some of the results on the motion of the solar system and the place it is approaching in the sky.

THE MOTION OF THE SOLAR SYSTEM

| Author | Date | Method | Number of stars used | Apex of Solar Motion | | Speed Kilometers per second |
|---|---|---|---|---|---|---|
| | | | | Right ascension | Declination | |
| W. Herschel | 1783 | Proper motion | 13 | 262° | + 26° | — |
| Boss........ | 1910 | Proper motion | 5,413 | 270.5 | + 34.3 | 24 |
| Campbell... | 1911 | Radial motion | 1,193 | 268.5 | + 25.1 | 19.5 |
| Adams and Strömberg | 1918 | Radial motion | 1,405 | 270 | + 29.2 | 21.4 |

So the sun travels in the direction of the constellation Hercules, not far from the bright star Vega, at a speed of about 20 kilometers, or 12 miles, per second, compared to the brighter stars of our system. Knowing the motion of the sun, its effect can be removed from the apparent motions of the stars. This leaves to each of them the real velocity of approach or recession, measured along our line of sight, which it would have respecting the sun if the sun stood still at one place in our starry system.

In the year 1910, when Boss and Campbell published their classic papers, it was still too early to combine proper motions and radial motions so as to know the total motion of the stars in space, except in a few cases. For the "proper motions" of Boss were merely angles as yet. Only a few of them could be turned into linear velocities like the spectroscopic values, because the star distances were mostly unknown. When once the motion in the line of sight is measured for a star whose distance and proper motion are both accurately known, then, when the solar motion is eliminated, the actual speed and direction of the star in space is easily found by combining the three results.

This could not be done for many stars in 1910, so Campbell contented himself with working out average velocities for the different spectral classes. He found the following curious results among others:

| Spectral Class | Number of stars | Average radial velocity Kilometers per second |
|---|---|---|
| O and B | 141 | 8.99 |
| A | 133 | 9.94 |
| F | 159 | 13.90 |
| G and K | 529 | 15.15 |
| M | 72 | 16.55 |
| Nebulæ | 13 | 23.4 |

About the time Campbell's results came out, "line of sight" spectroscopic work was begun by Dr. W. S. Adams on Mount Wilson, with the 5-foot reflector, which was then new. As this instrument collects nearly 2-1/2 times as much light from a star as the 36-inch Lick refractor, it permitted Adams to observe stars a full magnitude fainter than Campbell. When, some nine years later, the 100-inch reflector became available on Mount Wilson,

PLATE 29. A GROUP OF NEBULOUS FORMS. (Mt. Wilson Observatory.)
Showing the gradations from circular through elliptical to cusp- or spindle-
shaped and finally to the spirals seen broadside and on edge.

PLATE 30, FIG. 2. STELLAR INTERFEROMETER. (Mt. Wilson Observatory.)

The steel beam, 20 feet long, is fixed to the top of the tube of the 100-inch refractor. The four triangular projections act as mirrors to bring two separated beams of light from a star and cast them downwards to be observed for interference. When the distance of the two outer mirrors is just sufficient, the interference disappears, and the diameter of the observed star is calculated.

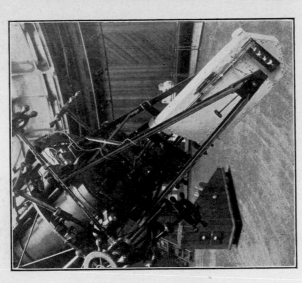

PLATE 30, FIG. 1. SPECTROSCOPE ATTACHED TO THE LICK REFRACTOR.

With this spectroscope, Dr. W. W. Campbell made the classic investigations of the motions of stars in the line of sight published in 1910. The instrument is built after his designs and is a masterpiece in its rigidity, its temperature control, and its adaptation to the purposes of the research.

still another magnitude could be added.  So, Dr. Adams and his colleagues have been able to observe a very large number of radial velocities for fainter stars.

In the year 1914, Adams and Kohlschütter discovered a fact about star spectra which has already had a tremendous effect in pushing forward our knowledge about the heavens, and holds even greater promise for the future.  They noticed that though the Harvard scale B, A, F, G, K, M, with its subdivisions, represents very closely the characters of the star spectra, there are some Fraunhofer lines which differ decidedly in stars of identical class. Comparing these differences with the real brightness, which could be readily computed from the parallaxes available, then well up in the hundreds, they found that the appearance of these spectral lines is a real guide to the actual brightness, or "absolute magnitude," [1] of the stars.

Adams worked out the relation with great skill, and soon was able to assign to any good spectrum of types F, G, K, or M, the "absolute magnitude" of the star.  Knowing this, and the apparent magnitude, the distance follows at once.  Quite recently, Adams and his colleagues have extended the method to cover stars of types B and A also, though perhaps not quite so satisfactorily.  Hence, it is now possible to determine approximately the distance of any star whose apparent "magnitude" is known, if its spectrum can be well photographed.

The proof of any discovery is successful predicting.  This test, the spectroscopic parallax methods meet brilliantly.  New photographic "trigonometric" parallaxes [2] of high class almost always agree very nicely with the previously determined spectroscopic value. Much confidence is now felt in this new method.  No one will prefer it for very near stars, but it is applicable to stars thousands of light-years distant, where the trigonometric method cannot give any estimate, but merely indicates great but unmeasurable distance.

We shall mention a little further on, perhaps, one or two other

[1] "Absolute magnitudes" express the brightness which stars would have if they were all at equal distance such as to have parallaxes of $\frac{1}{10}$ second of arc.

[2] The method depending on photographing a star field surrounding the star in question several times at intervals of 6 months.

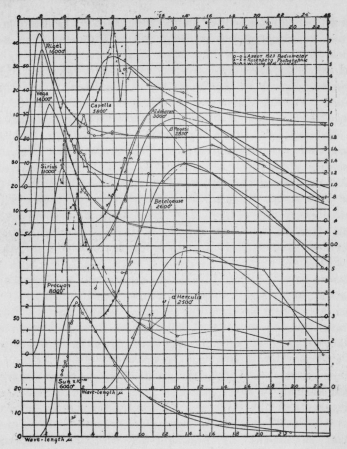

FIG. 40. THE ENERGY DISTRIBUTION IN STELLAR SPECTRA, AND TEMPERATURES CORRESPONDING.

For clearness the curves are separated in two groups, with the horizontal (wavelength) scales displaced 0.3 micron. Each star curve has its own scale of ordinates representing intensities of radiation in arbitrary units. But these several scales are all directly comparable if the numbers representing the intensities are considered. The heavy lines represent the distribution of intensity of radiation in the spectrum of the perfect radiator or "black body" at the stated temperatures. It will be seen that the fit of the star observations to these smooth curves is fairly good excepting in the ultra-violet region of wave-lengths less than 0.4 micron. This is a region of great absorption in the stellar atmospheres, and one very difficult to observe for various reasons.

special parallax methods of limited application. The future growth of our knowledge of star distances will mainly depend (1) on the wholesale parallaxes of faint stars derived from proper motions, and (2) on the numerous individual spectroscopic parallaxes. Both, however, depend for much of their foundations on the tireless, tedious, exacting labors of the "trigonometric" observers. So rapidly has this part of astronomy developed within the first quarter of the twentieth century, that what looked perfectly hopeless in 1900 is now an accomplished fact. That is, the actual motions and distances of the stars can be laid down to scale so extensively that the boundaries of our system, the main features of its migrations, and the actual diameters of some of its members are known. Before giving this picture as we may draw it now, we must explain how we know anything about the star diameters, for as everybody knows, they are all too distant to give real images in any telescope.

As we have said several times, all that we have learned about the heavenly bodies comes to us in the story told by their light. The quantity of light which a star sends us depends first on its temperature, second on its size, third on its distance. Two objects totally different in make-up, like the incandescent mercury vapor in a Cooper-Hewitt lamp on the one hand, and a solid bar of carbon on the other, if heated equally hot, would give quite unequal amounts of light. But huge balls of gas, like the stars, are nearly enough alike in character so that we may fairly suppose that if at equal temperatures their surface brightness will be roughly equal. In that case, the total light they emit will be proportional to their surface areas, or to the squares of their diameters.

How shall we take account, though, of differences associated with different temperatures? Fortunately, in the laboratory the relations of temperature and total radiating power have been determined, and also the distribution of energy in the different colors. Even in those parts of the spectrum which, invisible to the eye, lie beyond the red and beyond the violet, these relations are known. It is true that such studies have yielded exact laws only when applied to what is called the "perfect radiator," or "absolutely black body." But the distribution of energy in the spectrum of the sun and the brighter stars shows that these heavenly bodies are not widely departing from the conditions of the "perfect radiator."

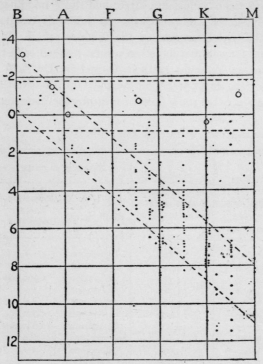

Hence, these laboratory laws are approximately applicable.

Such being the case, we are able to assign approximately the surface temperatures of the stars. Then we can observe their total output of radiation compared to that of the sun, which is known. For instance, the star Capella seems to be of a temperature of 5,800° Absolute Centigrade, compared to the sun's 6,000°, and sends us as much light on two square miles of the earth's surface as the sun does on one square centimeter (which is near the area of one's third finger nail). Knowing these facts, and the distance of Capella,

FIG. 41. GIANT AND DWARF STARS.

Russell's diagram which shows the relations between absolute magnitudes and spectral classes. Dots represent individual stars, circles mean results for groups of distant stars. It will be seen that the K and M types of red stars fall distinctly in two classes, the very bright and the very faint. This kind of distinction tends to persist also for the A, F, and G types of white, yellowish, and yellow stars, but disappears among the blue stars of type B.

we can compute from them that a "perfect radiator" at Capella's temperature, of 5,800° Absolute Centigrade, must be no less than 11,000,000 miles in diameter to equal this bright star in radiation.

As our sun is but 865,000 miles in diameter, we find here an object more than 2,000 times as great in volume as the sun.

Yet Capella is by no means unusually large, and quite middling in temperature. Applying the same methods, the following results have been found by the writer for nine of the brightest stars. In the last column is given, for comparison, some results reached earlier by Pease using an entirely different method devised by Dr. A. A. Michelson, of Chicago, the first American recipient of the Nobel prize, and the first man ever to show how to measure the diameter of a star.

STELLAR TEMPERATURES, RADIATION AND DIAMETERS

| Star | Absolute Temperature Centigrade degrees | Radiant energy Square miles of earth's surface per horse power [1] | Diameter in miles | |
|------|------|------|------|------|
| | | | Nichols Radiometer | Michelson Inter-ferometer |
| Rigel ............ | 16,000 | 6,600 | 18,000,000 | — |
| Vega............. | 14,000 | 4,500 | 1,800,000 | — |
| Sirius........... | 11,000 | 3,200 | 1,100,000 | 1,900,000 |
| Procyon.......... | 8,000 | 17,200 | 1,000,000 | — |
| Capella........... | 5,800 | 9,700 | 11,400,000 | — |
| Aldebaran........ | 3,000 | 8,400 | 61,000,000 | 35,000,000 |
| Beta Pegasi....... | 2,850 | 19,000 | 83,000,000 | 72,000,000 |
| Betelgeuse........ | 2,600 | 2,700 | 445,000,000 | 250,000,000 |
| Alpha Herculis.... | 2,500 | 5,900 | 790,000,000 | — |
| Sun.............. | 6,000 | 0.000000213 | 865,000† | — |

Dr. Michelson's method uses the interference of light. It is that property of light vibrations so beautifully seen in the colors of oil films in the streets on a rainy day, and in the colors of soap-bubbles. A long beam of structural steel was fixed to the upper end of the tube of the 100-inch telescope on Mount Wilson. On this steel beam were two light collectors (small mirrors) which could be set at any distance apart up to the length of the beam, or about 20 feet. The starlight from these two instruments was reflected

[1] Neglecting atmospheric absorption. Compare the areas with that of Massachusetts, 8,266 square miles.

† Diameter measured trigonometrically.

together and examined in an eyepiece. Alternations of bright and dark, called "fringes," resulted. But with a certain separation of the two light collectors, the fringes almost disappear. For then the bright fringe produced by light of one side of the star falls on the dark fringe due to the other side. At this position the separation of the two light collectors is measured, and the theory of the instrument shows how to calculate from it the diameter of the star.

It is too complex a subject to explain here fully, but the interesting thing is that these measurements have nothing directly to do with the temperature of the star, or any measurement of the heat it sends to us. In short, Michelson's method is totally dissimilar and independent from the other one. Yet, as may be seen above, its results show roughly the same range of star diameters as the indirect method of temperatures.

The extraordinary immensity of the giant M-type stars compared to the sun or to Sirius is striking. Here we come in by the front door of actual diameter measurements to a remarkable subject first entered upon by the back door, as one might say, of stellar magnitudes. It is the classification of the stars into the "giants" and the "dwarfs." These happily descriptive terms were chosen by Hertzsprung, who, with Russell, shares the discovery. By the latter, however, the more telling part of the work was done. Russell collected in the year 1913 all the stars, numbering between 200 and 300, whose distances were then approximately known, and calculated their absolute magnitudes.[1] He divided the stars among the spectrum classes B, A, F, G, K, M, and treating these lettered classes as if they were the six divisions of a five-part scale of length, he plotted the positions of the stars by spectrum class and absolute magnitude. The result appeared in his now celebrated diagram, Fig. 41. Every dot is for a star, and the open circles give average values for groups of stars of immense distance.

Two striking results appear:

1. In classes B and A, there are no *faint* stars.

2. There are no stars of *medium* brightness among the classes K and M. They are either very bright or very faint.

[1] The absolute magnitude is the magnitude which a star would have if it was fixed at such a distance from the earth that its parallax would be 0.1 second.

Russell's generalization was strongly confirmed when the rich spectroscopic parallax results of Adams became available. Adams' diagram for nearly two thousand stars is shown in Fig. 42. The classes B and A, to which spectroscopic results did not at first extend, are filled in by means of information of absolute magnitudes derived by Jackson and Furner from studies of double stars. That there are so few stars of the faint classes of dwarfs, K and M, is doubtless not so much due to the fact that these are absent in the sky, as that they are too faint to be readily photographed with the spectroscope.

Already when Russell found this double classification prevailing among K and M stars, it was well known by common observation, as well as by the exact work of Wilsing and Scheiner, that blue and white stars must be much hotter than red ones. Hence, it was no surprise that these stars were of smaller abso-

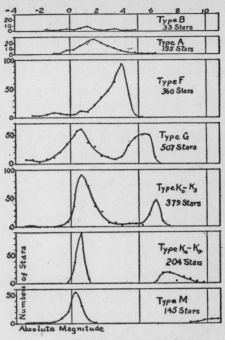

FIG. 42.   GIANT AND DWARF STARS.

These results from the studies of Adams, Jackson and Furner show very clearly for a large number of stars the same distinctions which were pointed out from much more scanty material by Russell. The complete separation into very bright and very faint groups in the red stars of types K4 to M, and the nearly complete separation in types G to K3, and the entire absence of such separation in types B and A are very evident.

lute magnitude (greater brightness) than many of the red ones. Yet one group of red stars as bright as the blue ones was found to be 10 magnitudes, or 10,000 times, brighter than another group of red stars. That no red stars lay between these extremes of brightness could only mean that two very distinct classes of stars having identical spectra must be recognized here, of which one appeared to have 10,000 times as great areas, or 100 times as great diameters as the other. If the diameters were 100 times as great and the densities equal, the giants must have 1,000,000 times the mass of the dwarfs.

But studies of double stars, as we shall directly see, cut off this possibility. Quite to the contrary, in averages of considerable numbers, the stars do not seem to differ as much as 100-fold in mass. Individually, of course, there may be a few exceptionally large and small ones. This small range of masses and immense range of volumes drives us to the final conclusion that the giant red stars must be nearly a millionfold smaller in average density than the red dwarfs. Thus, if the dwarf red stars are as dense as our earth, and surely that must be nearly the maximum possible for them, the giant red stars *must be about as rare as the gas in an old-fashioned lever vacuum pump worked to highest possible exhaustion.* In other words, the density differs more than the heaviest solid metal, platinum, differs from the lightest gas, hydrogen, at atmospheric pressure. We shall see in another chapter how these facts have changed our ideas of how the stars grow old.

We have several times said a few words about double stars, but, as our knowledge of star masses depends on it, the subject deserves more attention. If two stars bright enough to be seen with the naked eye lie close together, the probability is very great that they are really revolving about a common center in mutual gravitational control. In so enormous an area as the whole sky, containing only about 5,000 visible stars, only very seldom can two of them accidentally lie in close proximity. Of the thousands of double stars discovered by assiduous telescopic observation from Sir William Herschel's time till now, a large number have revolved through a part or the whole of an orbit since their discovery. The facts relating to these stars are carefully set forth in the great publication of the late Professor S. W. Burnham, an enthusiastic double-star observer of great reputation in this field. Still more numerous are the close double-star observations of Aitken, now Associate Director of the Lick Observatory.

Two other types of double stars not visibly separated by telescopes are even more interesting. First are the eclipsing variables. These pairs lie too close together to be distinguished separately by the telescope, but in mutual revolution they partially or wholly eclipse each other. Hence, they produce a periodic variation of the brightness of what we see as one star, which is really two. The most celebrated of these systems is Algol, or Beta Persei.

A second class of double stars is that of the spectroscopic binaries. Of these, Capella, one of the brightest stars, is an illustration. As we have said, the spectroscope measures velocities in our line of sight. Spectroscopic binaries are discerned because, owing to their mutual revolution, the line-of-sight velocity varies. Sometimes, as indeed with Capella, the two stars are so nearly equal in light that both give measurable spectra. In this case, the Fraunhofer lines cross over each other, as the two stars revolve, because first one and then the other star is revolving toward us. More often, only one spectrum is observed, but its lines shift their positions compared to laboratory spectra. Eclipsing variables are, of course, always spectroscopic binaries, unless one component is too small to produce motion detectable as line-shifting in the other by its gravitation.

Without these numerous double stars we should be at loss to know the masses of the stars. Newton's law of gravitation yields a formula connecting masses and times of revolution with the distance of separation. We may regard the earth and sun as a binary star and by applying the formula we may compare the masses of the double stars with that of the sun. Usually the only trouble in the process is in measuring the distance of the two stars apart. There is a different kind of dilemma for each of the three different kinds of double stars. Visual binaries observed by the telescope yield only angular separations. These angular values can be reduced to actual distances only if the parallax of the system is known. Such is the case with Sirius, Procyon, Alpha Centauri, Alpha Crucis, among the very bright stars, and less accurately with Rigel. There are, however, also a considerable number of fainter visual binary stars for which the parallax is well known.

Eclipsing variables yield no means of measuring the separation of the two stars. They do indicate how large each star is, compared to their distance apart, what proportion of the combined light each star gives, and how much inclined the orbit plane is to a plane at right angles to our line of sight. If we suppose that the two stars are equal in mass, we can also find their densities compared to the sun. Most of them have densities much smaller than the sun.

Spectroscopic binaries fail to indicate precisely either their distance apart or the inclinations of their orbits. They give us a quantity which depends on both. If a spectroscopic binary is also either a visual or an eclipsing binary, the whole matter is solved, for in either case we then know the inclination of the orbit, and can find the distance apart of the two stars.

All three kinds of double stars yield the length of the period of revolution. Many of the visual binaries move so slowly that we shall have to wait much longer before they will have traveled far enough in their orbits to give the period accurately. Eclipsing variables and spectroscopic binaries have such very short periods of revolution that within a few years of discovery their times are known to a very high precision. As we have said, the double stars are weighable against the sun just as soon as the period and distance apart are found. While the distance apart is not known in the cases of many of the spectroscopic binaries, we can always assign to it the minimum possible value. Furthermore, if we collect the values for a large number of orbits, it follows that because their inclinations will be distributed at random, we can estimate the average inclination, and from it the average distance of the pairs apart, and from this their average masses.

In one way or another, therefore, we have learned a great deal about star masses from double-star measurements. In the following paragraphs there is a summary of the kind of information these stars teach us.

Visual binaries, like other stars, are crowded towards the Milky Way, and this effect is more exaggerated among them than among single stars. The closer the pairs, the more numerous, relatively, they are in the Milky Way. Whether in the Milky Way or not, close pairs are far more numerous than wide pairs. Visual binaries tend to frequent the yellow and light-red classes of stars, while eclipsing and spectroscopic binaries strongly prevail among blue stars.  Of 14 visual binary systems, mainly of yellow stars, well known in the year 1918, and enumerated by Dr. Aitken, the average combined mass of the pair was 1.76 times that of our sun.  Of 32 spectroscopic binaries, nearly all blue or white stars, which he enumerates, the average minimum mass of the brighter star was 5.1 and that of the fainter 4.3 times that of our sun.  Though these latter figures are but minimum values, because the inclinations of the individual orbits were not known, they could not reasonably be more than twice as great.

Hence, we may draw the conclusion that stars in general are of about the same mass as our sun, but the blue and white ones are rather more massive, yet not often tenfold more so.  This is the sort of evidence which, with the recent results on star diameters, goes to prove that some giant stars are far rarer in their constitution than our atmosphere, while some dwarfs are several times denser than water, and not much different from our earth in that respect.

Now, to close this chapter, we come to the grandest scene that the mind can contemplate in the realm of the motions of the heavenly bodies.  The atoms with their complex maze of orbits; the solar system with its law-abiding, tireless march of the planets, satellite-attended as they are, around the sun; the double stars that ceaselessly encircle one another, some almost in contact in their nearness, others so far apart that even light itself takes full years to pass between them — all these fascinating examples of the wonders of motion are insignificant compared to the scope of the grand procession we are now about to survey.  It is no less than the orderly march of our whole starry system, in numbers twentyfold exceeding human kind, in space extended over cubic quadrillions of miles.

It is only within the last years that this tremendous spectacle could be presented.  We have remarked that when, in 1910, there appeared almost simultaneously the classical papers of Boss and Campbell, it was not yet possible to piece together the proper motions and the radial motions as so to disclose the real motions of the stars in space.  The distances of the stars were then still lacking.  This has been to a good degree supplied, partly by the

tireless labors of the trigonometrical parallax observers, partly by the
happy discovery of Adams that the measurement of star distances

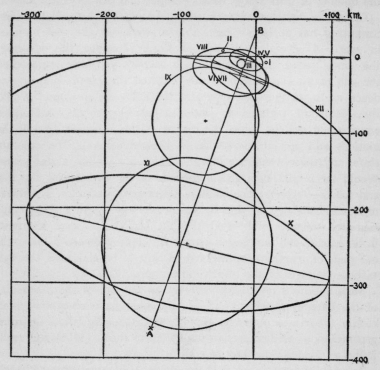

FIG. 43. THE CELESTIAL OBJECTS MOVING ALONG THE GREAT CELESTIAL
WAY. (Strömberg, Mt. Wilson Observatory.)

The elliptical figures show where and how widely the different groups of stars
and nebulæ would disperse if all should be collected at our sun and set free to
move away from him for a given time at their actual rates and directions in space.
The plane of the figure is approximately that of the Milky Way. There would be
a dispersion above and below the plane of the paper about to the extent of the
shorter axes of the ellipses. Figures I to XI relate to stars of various types. The
great circle XII whose center is $A$, relates to the spiral nebulæ. These have greatest dispersion of any celestial objects and also the greatest average motion away
from the sun.

lies within the province of that amazing instrument, the spectroscope. The two great telescopes on Mount Wilson, that of the

Dominion Observatory at Victoria, and several others now engaged in spectroscopic parallax work, have more than doubled since 1910 the number of stars whose radial motions and distances are known.

Using the distances determined by Adams and his collaborators, Strömberg has at length been able to work out the real motions in space of several thousands of stars. Imagine the suspense, the almost bated breath, with which he may well have approached the end of his computations, and collected the grand total of evidence as to whither and how fast the stars are moving! Would they be found, perhaps, to wheel majestically about some center which could well be called the capital of the universe? Would the motions add to our knowledge of the evolution of the separate stars, and show which are old and which are young in star years? Would the results even give a measure of the duration of star life, and tell us whether to count it in billions or, perchance, in trillions or quadrillions of our years? Would there come from this discussion any evidence to show whether the Universe is finite or infinite in its extent, and whether its space is simply geometrical after the old plan of length, breadth, and thickness, or embraces the fantastic curvatures of the fourth dimension?

Such questions may have occurred as the end of the assembling of the data approached, but no one could have recognized more clearly than these observers that it must take the labors of future generations of astronomers to resolve all of them. What was really found was indeed startling enough.

Imagine a great celestial thoroughfare stretching almost straight away in the general line from the sun to a point east of the bright star, Antares. It lies practically in the plane of the Milky Way. Consider the stars by groups. There will be a group of the giant blue stars of type B, another of the dwarf yellow stars of the type G, in whose class our sun belongs, and so on, enumerating all the other well-known classes of our starry system. Then we must go farther afield and think of the globular star clusters, like that famous one in Hercules, objects which lie far beyond the ordinary reach of our system. Think also of the spiral nebulæ, whose extraordinary possibilities we shall describe in another chapter. Thus classify all the celestial objects.

*All of these groups will be found on parade along the great thoroughfare we have suggested.* They have been happily compared by Adams to a lot of swarms of bees, all flying in the same direction as swarms, but flying at different rates. Like swarms of bees, however, the individuals that compose these groups are darting hither or thither, while still remaining with the swarm in its general course along the great thoroughfare.

The following little table and Fig. 43 give an idea of the average speeds of the groups along their great racing course, measuring their rates from the sun, as if it were stationary. The reader will readily see that we can no longer speak without qualification of a solar velocity compared to the stars, for the solar velocity with respect to the different groups goes through an enormous range. Moreover, the direction of it shifts steadily towards the north, as we consider it with respect to swifter and swifter moving star groups.

VELOCITIES OF CELESTIAL OBJECTS AWAY FROM SUN

| Objects | Number observed | Average velocity Km. per second |
|---|---|---|
| Giant A and F stars | 153 | 21 |
| "   G   " | 224 | 20 |
| "   K   " | 325 | 18 |
| "   M   " | 98 | 16 |
| Dwarf A and F stars | 153 | 23 |
| "   G   " | 154 | 40 |
| "   K   " | 112 | 33 |
| "   M   " | 16 | 27 |
| Globular clusters | 16 | 266 |
| Spiral Nebulæ | 43 | 401 |

Within the groups, the rates of motion hither or thither of the group individuals themselves increase, as the rate of motion grows of the group as a whole, measured from the sun.

Only less remarkable than the motion of all the divisions of the heavenly host along the great celestial highway, is the fact that nearly all of the groups of stars show greater dispersion at right angles to it than along its course. This is shown by the elliptical figures in the diagram.[1]   It was the great astronomer Kapteyn who first drew attention prominently to this wide generality of preferential motion, which he designated as the two-drift system.   Though important, it must now take a secondary place compared to the universal march along the great celestial highway.

No doubt this remarkable procession of the stars and other celestial objects has a profound bearing on the great subject of the evolution of the universe.   It is highly extraordinary, to say the least, that though we may go as far as the telescope will penetrate, to distances too great to be justly expressed or realized, even to the outlying globular clusters and spiral nebulæ themselves, yet all the host of heaven seems to bear one allegiance to and be governed by one principle of order.   Though there is infinite variety of detail, there is entire unity of organization throughout the whole visible universe.   The Universe is one.   Its mighty thoroughfare seems to be an axis of absolute character, a datum line to reckon all positions from.

[1] The line of preference for this greater dispersion lies between the opposite points in the sky marked by right ascension 90°, declination + 10°, and right ascension 270°, declination − 10°.

# Chapter XIII

## NEW STARS, VARIABLES, CLUSTERS, AND NEBULÆ

A BRILLIANT star appeared, in November 1572, in the constellation Cassiopeia, where none had ever been seen before. The famous astronomer Tycho Brahe made a careful record of it. From the eleventh day to nearly the end of November, it was brighter than any of the fixed stars, exceeded the light of Jupiter, and almost rivalled Venus in luster. Some people even saw it in daytime. Soon it began to decline, and by March, 1574, became invisible.

Kepler, Tycho's great pupil, also records a wonderful new star which was first seen on October 17, 1604, in the constellation Serpentarius. This star also, for a time, exceeded the brilliance of any of the fixed stars and planets, except Venus, but soon faded, and ceased to be visible after about a year.

In the first quarter of the twentieth century, we have seen two brilliant new stars, Nova Persei of 1901, and Nova Aquilæ of 1918. Neither was quite the equal of these famous earlier ones, but both were bright enough to rival any of the fixed stars. They were eagerly watched by skilled telescopic and spectroscopic observers, so that the history of such outbursts is now pretty well known.

Nova Persei was discovered on February 21, 1901, by Rev. T. D. Anderson, of Edinburgh, Scotland. It was then of 2.7 magnitude and shone with a bluish-white light. There was a rapid increase in brightness until, on February 23, it reached 0.0 magnitude, and was then brighter than any fixed star except Sirius and Canopus. An immediate search of the photographic plates of the Harvard College Observatory showed that on February 2, 6, 8, 18, and 19, 1901, up to within two days of Dr. Anderson's discovery there was no star there as bright as 10.5 magnitude. Later it was discovered to have been of about the fourteenth magnitude before the outburst.

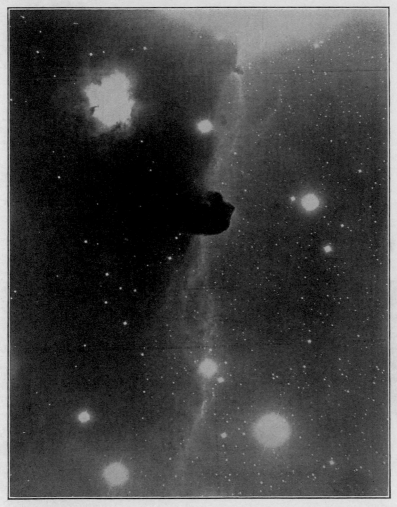

PLATE 31. A DARK NEBULOSITY NEAR ZETA ORIONIS.
(Mt. Wilson Observatory.)

Notice how completely the fainter stars are blotted out by this nonluminous gas which lies between us and them.

PLATE 32, FIG. 1. THE FINE SPIRAL NEBULA IN CANES VENATICI.
(Mt. Wilson Observatory.)

Note the two spiral arms starting opposite each other, and showing breaks
and condensations, which may indicate a galaxy of stars in the making.

PLATE 32, FIG. 2. A SPIRAL NEBULA SEEN NEARLY ON EDGE.
(Mt. Wilson Observatory.)

This object reminds us in its shape of our own galaxy, but it is probably not
yet advanced to the stage of separate stars. The dark band lying at the outside
of the spiral is probably matter of the same sort as that which lies within, but
too cool to give light of its own, and hiding by its substance the light of the
bright parts nearer the center.

After reaching its maximum on February 23, the brightness almost immediately declined, and by February 28 had reached the second magnitude. A temporary slight recovery was followed by a further decline, so that by March 18 it reached the fifth magnitude. Then began an almost periodic fluctuation, with extremes about two days apart. For instance, on March 19 and 21, the magnitudes were 6.5 and 4.7 respectively, showing a range of nearly sixfold in brightness within two days.

So the fluctuations went on, but gradually with longer intervals and decreasing brightness, until by summer the condition became fairly steady between sixth and seventh magnitude. Slow decline continued, and by July, 1903, the brightness reached the twelfth magnitude. It has fluctuated between that and the fourteenth ever since. From February 23, 1901 to July, 1903, there was a range of over 60,000-fold in brightness! The Harvard photographs showed, however, that within a few days, in February, 1901, the star's brightness rose quite as much, from the fourteenth to the second magnitude.

To the spectroscope, the changes of the star were also interesting. On the first few nights, the spectrum was that of a white star of the ordinary A type, but quickly changed to one of numerous bright and dark lines, which is typical of the new stars. On March 19 began a series of fluctuations of the spectrum, corresponding with the beginning of the wide fluctuations in brightness. The spectrum was unusual, that is different from ordinary new-star spectra, at the times when the brightness was at minimum. It would lie outside our scope to study the details of these changes.

Still another surprise was in store. In August, 1901, it was reported by French observers that a faint nebula surrounded the new star. This was soon photographed many times. The photographs showed a perfectly astonishing development. There appeared rings in the nebula which expanded in radius at a rate no less than 2 or 3 seconds of arc per day! There is no known proper motion among all the stars as much as a fiftieth part as great as this.

What could it mean? The answer depended on a measurement of the distance of Nova Persei. The parallax came out only 0.01 seconds. Hence, the star is about 300 light-years distant. A motion of two seconds of arc per day at that distance means a velocity of about 220,000 miles per second. This is about the velocity of light. The difference might easily be explained by the roughness of the observations. Astronomers believe that the apparent motion of the nebula was really the outrush of light from the star. The outburst of light, traveling 186,000 miles per second, illuminated successively more and more distant parts of nebulous surroundings, that had been dark before.

Perhaps the most impressive thing about the whole matter is that the catastrophe happened three centuries ago. To us the star was new in February, 1901. In reality, Elizabeth was Queen of England when it happened, and the Pilgrims had not yet landed at Plymouth rock. It took light, Nature's swiftest messenger, 300 years to bring us the tidings.

There are some interesting data about the new stars, as a class, which Dr. Lundmark has recently collected. In the first place, note their arrangement in the sky. Of 78 bright new stars recorded since Tycho Brahe's times, 35 were within the Milky Way, 22 within the bounds of the Great Nebula of Andromeda, 6 included by other spiral nebulæ, and 2 within nebulæ not spirals. Thus, of the whole 78, only 13 were disconnected with the Milky Way and nebulæ.

The average gain of brightness of 21 new stars over their former estate was 9.5 magnitudes, almost 10,000-fold. They all appear to return to their original brightness within a few years. They are usually very distant, probably of the order of hundreds or thousands of light years. Thus, the real moments of the flashing up of many that have been observed since Tycho Brahe's time were probably quite as long ago as the building of the pyramids.

Some novæ have apparently expanded so as to present telescopically real disks, not mere points or spurious disks like ordinary stars. It is possible that this indicates an explosion from within. The occurrence is not so rare as one might think, for we must remember that it is only when a new star becomes bright that it is noticed. Professor Bailey estimates that at least 9 novæ each year reach the tenth magnitude, or brighter. At this rate, there must be hordes of them that are still fainter. Lundmark, therefore, suggests that since the life of the stars is very long, and their numbers limited, as we have seen, there must be a fairly large percentage of stars that have the experience of becoming novæ at some time in their careers. Eddington remarks as food for thought that they are apt to be recruited from stars in some such state as our sun. If such a catastrophe should come to him, the Biblical description of the end of things on earth, "when the elements shall melt with fervent heat," would be very appropriate.

*Variable Stars.* — We have already spoken of two strongly contrasting types of stars whose light varies. They are the eclipsing double stars and the novæ. The one is perfectly regular in its periodic changes, the other has a paroxysm of brightness once for all, and then fades into an irregularly fluctuating faintness.

There is another type of variables, irregularly recurring to brightness. The typical star of this kind is Mira (Omicron Ceti). Its average period between maxima of brightness is 333 days, but individual periods differ from this over a range of 40 days either way. At minimum, the light of the star is not always the same, but ranges from eighth to ninth magnitude. Much greater differences occur at maximum. Sometimes the peak of brightness reaches the second magnitude, and sometimes does not exceed the fifth. Thus the range of brightness in some periods is as great as 300-fold, while at others it is less than 50-fold. The rate of increase from minimum to maximum is more rapid than the rate of decrease from maximum to minimum. Another star of the same type is Chi Cygni. This star has a very large range of brightness, sometimes reaching 4,000-fold. Its period is about 406 days.

Our sun exhibits some of these characteristics, but far less conspicuously and more deliberately. In the eleven year period of sun-spots, there is a range of solar brightness which differs from period to period, but is not yet known to have exceeded 3 per cent, or about 0.03 magnitudes. The sun-spots rise to maximum numbers much quicker than they decline from maximum to minimum. Their numbers at maximum are variable over two or threefold. Whether the range of the sun's actual brightness behaves as the sun-spots do, the observations are as yet not long enough continued to prove. However, the sun is certainly brighter at times of maximum sun-spots and varies irregularly.

About half way between the Mira type and the new stars is the extraordinary variable star Eta Argus. It varied irregularly, from 1750 to about the year 1832, between second and fourth magnitudes. Increasing in brightness in 1843, it was nearly equal to Sirius. By 1869, it ceased to be visible, and is now only 7.5 magnitude. Like Nova Persei, Eta Argus is surrounded by nebulosity, which is sometimes called the "Keyhole nebula."

Another type of variable star is very important for several reasons. It is called the Cepheid type, after the star Delta Cephei. The pole star is multiple, but includes a Cepheid variable. The variability in this class is of short period, ranging from eight hours to twenty days, as a rule. Many such stars have been found in the Magellanic clouds and in the globular clusters. Those of a single globular cluster must all be nearly equally distant from us, because the cluster is so distant that in comparison all its objects are near together. Hence, the apparent relative changes of brightness of cluster variables indicate truly their real relative changes. This led Miss Leavitt to a discovery, afterwards greatly expanded by Dr. Shapley, namely that the cluster variables of equal brightness have equal periods. Shapley even arranged a scale connecting periods with brightness, so that to any Cepheid whose period is known the absolute magnitude can be assigned. In short, a Cepheid variable star is regarded as a standard object whose absolute brightness is known by its period of variation. Shapley used this fact, as we shall see, to measure the distances of the star clusters.

Although the spectroscope seems to indicate that Cepheid variables are double stars, they are not so. The distance between the supposed pairs turns out to be impossibly small. They would have to be in contact, or even lying within one another. The type of spectrum changes as well as the radial velocity. Cepheid stars become redder at their minimum brightness. At this time, too, the star appears to be receding with almost maximum rapidity from us. This could not be the case if the minimum were due to an eclipse. At such a time, the two stars of an eclipsing variable would be moving at right angles to our line of sight, and there would be no relative radial motion.

It is now generally believed, as suggested by Shapley, that the variation is due to a pulsation of the star. He imagined alternate expansion and contraction to be taking place. Such a change would no doubt produce large changes of temperature, suitable to effect the changes of color and of spectral type just mentioned. Cepheid variables appear to be extremely massive. The pulsation hypothesis as to their variation is highly interesting, as we shall see, in its relation to the source of heat which sustains star radiation over such immense periods as are involved in star life.

*Star Clusters.* — Already we have noticed that stars sometimes go in groups together. The Pleiades, the Taurus stars, the Ursa Major cluster, are all examples of families of hundreds of stars that are traveling together. If we could get far enough away we should find these groups closed up, so that we should not need the tedious comparison of proper motions to convince us that they were really physically connected.

There are many star clusters, especially in the Milky Way, that are so remote that they present this clear evidence of physical connection. For instance, there is the open cluster Praesepe in the constellation Cancer, and many others. All of these clusters are found to be within our own system. The distances, the magnitudes, and the colors of the individual stars, all bear so great a similarity to those of stars surrounding them that there can be no doubt of it.

There is another story to tell of the globular star clusters. Take the Hercules cluster for example. To the naked eye but a small, faint, insignificant patch of light, hardly even noticeable indeed, a great telescope brings it out as one of the most beautiful objects in the heavens. There is a perfect host of stars, so closely packed that they resemble bees in a swarm. On a photograph of five hours exposure with the 60-inch reflector on Mount Wilson, Pease and Shapley recorded 35,000 stars of this cluster, all within an area only two-thirds the diameter of the moon.

It is not believed that this number of stars, great as it is, at all represents the real population of the Hercules star cluster. The fact is that this system lies far, very far indeed, beyond the most of the great star host of our own Galaxy. According to Shapley, the distance is 33,000 light-years. At such an immense distance, even a 5-hour exposure with the 60-inch reflector cannot take the impress of intrinsically faint stars. It is as if we should stop with the seventeenth magnitude in our own system. We may well suppose that if all the stars to the same degree of faintness could be photographed in the Hercules cluster that exist in our Galaxy, the number would run into millions.

Shapley has approached the distances of the globular star clusters in many ways. One of the best is through the Cepheid variables that occur in some of the clusters. As we saw above, by taking into account known distances of some of these Cepheid stars which are found moderately near us, he drew a curve which shows the absolute magnitude in terms of the period of variation. The curve is very well supported by all the observations, so that it seems fair to assume that all Cepheids, wherever they are, can be assigned absolute magnitudes as soon as their periods are observed. From that it is only a step to compare with the apparent magnitudes and get the distances.

With this scheme and several other independent ones, Shapley obtained closely accordant values of the distances of the globular clusters. These range for the various clusters from about 20,000 to over 200,000 light-years. We must suppose, therefore, that in these objects we see other galaxies of stars than ours. We cannot tell if any of them have equally as numerous a star population as ours, but there is no good reason to doubt that some of them may. We are seeing some of these distant star systems by light which began its journey probably long before there were men on earth. None of them began to send the light we now see as recently as the time when the first glimmerings of human history began. All the wars and empires of ancient and modern times have been carried on while these flying beams which are just arriving were yet in mid-course in the heavens.

Shapley points out some queer things about the distribution of the globular clusters in space. Though in nearly equal numbers on both sides of the plane of the Milky Way, there are none within 4,000 light-years of that plane itself. Their numbers increase as they come nearer the Milky Way up to a certain limit, and then come to a full stop. Moreover, the globular clusters are not scattered all around the ring of the Milky Way, but 48 out of the 69

known lie within one quadrant.  It is the quadrant of the great
line of preferential motion spoken of in the preceding chapter.  Not
a single globular cluster lies in the quadrant opposite to this preferred one.

Suppose we could take up our abode on some habitable cluster,
the one called "N. G. C. 7006," which Shapley puts at 220,000
light-years distance.  We should require a large telescope to make
out the brightest stars of our own Galaxy.  Probably we should
discern that it had a somewhat elliptical shape, corresponding to
the extension along the Milky Way.  Similarly, Pease and Shapley
have observed ellipticity in nearly all of the globular clusters.

In one respect we should find our own Galaxy exceptional.  It
would show no such concentration of stars in its middle portion as
some of the other clusters.  Thus in "N. G. C. 5272" Shapley
finds no less than 15,000 stars, which, seen from the earth, exceed
the 20th magnitude, all lying within 30 light-years of its center.
There are probably but four or five stars actually as bright as these
lying within 30 light-years of our sun.  The sun, however, lies quite
a long way from the center of our Galaxy.

*The Nebulæ.* — Having considered the solar system, including the
sun, planets, asteroids, moons, comets, and meteors; the stars of
our system, among whom the sun is just an average one in lustre
and size; the double stars, variables and new stars; and the great
globular clusters which seem to be remote systems comparable in
many respects to our own Galaxy; there still remains in the celestial
compass other types of objects called nebulæ.  "Cloud-like" they are
named, and justly so.  Yet they are not at all in the nature of
clouds, for they have no relation to our atmosphere, but lie among
the stars and star clusters, at tremendous distances.

There are several kinds of nebulæ, very different in appearance
and in nature.  If we photograph the group of the Pleiades, all of
the familiar bright stars will be found wrapped in nebulosity as if
in bridal veils.  The great nebula in Cygnus and the angry-looking
great nebula in the sword of Orion, which seems so like a star to
the naked eye, are other examples of these diffuse, irregularly-shaped
kinds of nebulæ.  Viewed in the spectroscope, many of the irregular
nebulæ show a discontinuous spectrum of bright lines, in contrast

to the continuous dark-lined spectra of the stars. Hydrogen is conspicuously present, but there is no counterpart in the laboratory to some of these bright nebular spectral lines. They appear to represent an unknown substance, or an unknown modification of a familiar one. It is sometimes called nebulium.

Related to these diffuse and irregular bright-line nebulæ by a similarity of spectrum, are the annular, or planetary nebulæ. They also give bright-line spectra of the type just described. In form, however, they are exceedingly different. For example, there is the Ring Nebula in Lyra, with its central star, reminding us distantly of the rings surrounding the planet Saturn.

Curtis has listed 78 planetary nebulæ visible in the northern skies, of which 56 show conspicuous central stars. Hubble concludes that all bright nebulosity may reasonably be thought to derive its light from involved or neighboring stars. He finds a remarkable relation between the light of the nebulæ and the light of their involved stars. If the spectrum of the involved star is of a type "earlier" than B1, that is of type Oe or Bo, for instance, then the associated nebula will show bright lines. If the star has a spectrum of later type, as B5 or A, for example, then the nebula will show a continuous spectrum of dark lines. None of the nebulæ are associated with yellow or red stars.

Hubble believes that the light of stars involved and associated with nebulosity is weakened to our view by this circumstance. It is the starlight itself, he thinks, which gives the nebula the power to glow, either by scattering, as our atmosphere scatters sunlight, or by absorption and re-emission. He finds only one case of a galactic nebula without a dominating star, and this may possibly be a case where the nebula itself obscures the star.

In recent years, the idea of extensive dark nebulosity has come to the fore. The late Professor Barnard photographed and listed a very large number of dark nebulæ. There are many regions, very bright in stars, where well-marked lanes or larger vacancies with very definite borders may be photographed. Such a region is the famous "Coal-sack" in the bright Milky Way region of Southern Cross. An example even more striking as a proof of the reality of dark nebulosity, obscuring for us whatever lies behind, is found south of the star Zeta Orionis. In Hubble's opinion, these dark nebulosities would be bright if there were only bright O, B, or A type stars near enough to them to excite them to glow. We may regard the presence of such nebulous matter, light or dark, as very widespread in the celestial spaces.

Let us turn now to another type of objects also called nebulæ, but differing widely both in form and spectrum from those we have been discussing. Only one of these is readily visible to the naked eye. It is the Great Spiral Nebula of Andromeda. Even to visual observation with great telescopes, the spiral and spindle nebulæ are disappointing. Photography, however, shows their fascinating structure and large number in an impressive way. Curtis, from counts made in 1918 on photographs by the Crossley reflector, estimates that there are fully 700,000 of these objects in the sky within the range of our present great reflectors.

Many of them appear as two-branched spirals. A Fourth-of-July pinwheel, sending out its showers of sparks, particularly at the last, as it slows down just before expiring, gives some impression of the form of a spiral nebula, if seen broadside on. They are flattened objects like oyster-shells, and many of them are tilted at such angles to our vision that they are much fore-shortened. They may even be seen edgewise so that their spiral character cannot be quite certain. They will never turn over to be seen differently. The ones seen on edge will always appear so, and the ones seen broadside on will never be presented edgewise.

In some cases the arms of the spirals recede rapidly, with little curvature, leaving a very open appearance. In others, as in the Great Nebula of Andromeda, they are wound up like a clock-spring into many close convolutions. It is very typical of the spiral arms, of whatever openness, that there are two arms which start from diametrically opposite sides of a central bright core. This circumstance has led many to suppose that there were forces akin to the tidal forces at work in their original formation. For, like the arms of spirals, tides occur simultaneously at opposite ends of a diameter.

By no means do all members of the class of nebulæ that we are now discussing appear spiral, nor can they be thought to be spiral, seen edgewise. A very large number of them are globular, ellipsoidal, or spindle-shaped, without any evidence of arms, excepting that some spindle-shaped nebulæ show pointed tips, as if incipient arms were in formation. We could easily imagine that a globular nebula

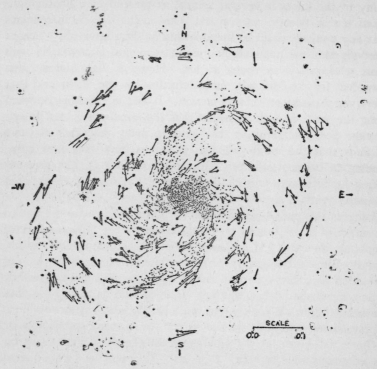

Fig. 44. Evidence of Motion along the Arms of Spiral Nebula
(Van Maanen).

The arrows show the direction, and their lengths taken with the scale show the magnitude of motions measured by Van Maanen by comparing photographs of this nebula taken about 10 years apart. The general effect is to wind up the arms so as to produce a new convolution in about 100,000 years.

might become flattened, then spindle-shaped, and finally spiral by the influence of rotation and gravitation. We shall recur to this idea in another chapter.

The spiral nebulæ almost all show their arms broken into knots and patches of various sizes. These are not sharp, pointlike objects, like stars, but some of them are sufficiently definite for accurate measurements of position. Van Maanen has seized upon this to study the motions within the spirals. He measured the positions of many of the knots in several spirals, as presented on photographs taken ten or twenty years apart. One might well be incredulous that any motions would be found within so short intervals. Longer intervals were not available because astronomical photography with great telescopes is so young an art. However, Van Maanen was rewarded for his difficult measurements by the discovery that every spiral examined showed motion. It was in the sense outward along the arms, in such a fashion that the arms would tend to coil as time goes on. Thus in the course of many thousands of years he finds that the spirals will add a coil to those they now have, tending to become less open and more convoluted. The time required for forming a new coil would be of the order of an hundred thousand years.

Long as this period is, compared to human affairs, we are apt to be surprised at its brevity as an epoch among the heavenly bodies. Doubtless the earth and sun have lasted longer than a billion years, and it seems extraordinary that anything so conspicuous as the formation of a new coil on a nebula could be accomplished within a time ten-thousand-fold shorter. It must lead us to suppose that the nebulæ grow old rapidly and must be succeeded by a continuous supply of new ones, else we should not see so many spirals now.

Our astonishment at the rapidity of the process is emphasized by the enormous scale on which it occurs. The stars, as we have seen, vary in diameter from a few hundred thousand to a few hundred million miles. Yet none of them presents a true disk to the telescope, even of the nearest of them, not 10 light-years away. But the spiral nebulæ, on the contrary, cover spaces of real angular dimensions, some even as large as that occupied by the full moon. It is not because they are nearby either. There is difficulty in measuring their parallaxes, but astronomers are agreed, at least in this, that they are very distant. The order of their distances seems to be tens or hundreds of thousands of light-years. Hubble, indeed, has observed quite a number of Cepheid variables of different periods which seem to be definitely connected with the outer regions of the Great Nebula of Andromeda. Using Shapley's method he found that these Cepheids agree well together in indicating for the Great Nebula a distance of nearly a million light-years! A spiral as wide-angled as the full moon at 10,000 light-years, would be 100 light-years across. To go completely around so enormous a circle within 300,000 years would mean a velocity of something like a million miles an hour. To sustain such a revolution as this by the influence of gravitation must mean a tremendous mass of matter contained in the central condensation, enough to compose millions of suns like ours. We shall recur to these speculations later on.

The distribution of spiral and associated forms of nebulæ with reference to the Milky Way is remarkable. Curtis has expressed this in a very striking way by printing his thesis in an arrangement similar to that which the objects he describes occupy in space. Thus:

THE FACTOR OF SPACE DISTRIBUTION

100,000 ± Spiral Nebulæ
Distance unknown[2]

.

.

.

.

The Milky Way and stellar universe
is believed to be roughly lens-shaped and
about 3,000 by 30,000 or more light-years in extent. In
this space occur nearly all the stars, nearly all the diffuse
nebulosities, nearly all the planetary nebulæ, nearly
all new stars,[1] nearly all clusters, nearly all
the variable stars, etc., but
NO SPIRAL NEBULÆ

.

.

.

.

100,000 ± Spiral Nebulæ
Distance unknown[2]

In some of the photographs of spirals there are very beautiful evidences of dark nebulæ. They lie like long streaks against the

[1] Excepting in spiral nebulæ.

[2] Hubble has since proved that several spirals are about a million light-years away. They are "Island Universes" as Sir W. Herschel aptly called them.

edges of the spirals, like the streaks of cloud which sometimes cut the sun's disk while it is setting. As we remarked in speaking of the new stars, they have seemed to be associated with spiral nebulæ in a good many instances. Of 78 new stars recorded since Tycho Brahe, 22 occurred in the limits of the Great Nebula of Andromeda. As would be expected in view of the great distances of the spirals, such new stars as seemed to lie within them were much fainter than the average seen elsewhere. Of course, there is a greater chance of observing faint novæ within spirals than elsewhere, because the spirals are more apt to be photographed and closely studied than equal areas of sky at random.

The spectroscope has had its say about the spiral nebulæ. They do not give bright-line spectra like the irregular and diffuse nebulosities or planetaries. On the contrary, their spectrum is such a spectrum as our system of stars as a whole would present if we viewed it from a habitable world in the star cluster "N. G. C. 7006." The velocity of the spiral nebulæ in the line of sight referred to the sun is very great, as we have already remarked. Measurements by Slipher, Wright, Pease and others give velocities from 300 to 1,000 kilometers per second, while stars seldom give over 100. Not only is the average speed of spiral nebulæ in our line of sight very great, but the range of speeds among themselves is even greater. This is a significant fact to which we shall recur later on.

Van Maanen's determinations of motion along the arms of spirals have confirmatory spectroscopic evidence. Pease found a variation of velocity in our line of sight at the different parts of a spiral seen on edge. This, of course, would have been the result of a rotation in the manner discovered in spirals seen broadside-on by Van Maanen.

We have dwelt quite long on these remarkable celestial objects because of the views which astronomers take as to their place in the scheme of stellar evolution. Evidently of enormous extent, and probably of enormous mass, they may well be looked upon as likely fountains of stars, if not as actually developed systems of stars, too far away to allow their separate objects to be distinguished even telescopically.[1] Their disk-like flattening and circular outline is

---

[1] Hubble, in 1924, observed the outer parts of several spiral nebulæ resolved into multitudes of faint stars.

suggestive of our own Galaxy. There are, indeed, some astronomers who believe it probable that we ourselves dwell in a spiral nebula, which if photographed from a station in the Andromeda Nebula, or some even more distant one, would have the same characteristics as the many spirals we observe. This so-called "Island Universe Theory," so called after a happy expression of Herschel's, we shall have occasion to compare with the recent views of Jeans in the next chapter.

# CHAPTER XIV

## BUILDING THE UNIVERSE

As WE saw in Chapter III, all atoms consist of two kinds of electrons. These are neither less nor more than unit charges of electricity. Here, at the very foundation of all things, begins that duality in electricity, in magnetism, in chemistry, in sex, which we remark throughout Nature. The positive charges are called protons, the negative ones simply electrons. Matter, then, is composed of electricity. Electricity is but a form of energy. The forms of motion, such as mechanical motion of bodies, heat motion of molecules, wave motion of light and radiation, and the motions of the free electrons around their nuclei, are also manifestations of energy. Fundamentally, all is energy. Matter is its passive state, the other forms, its active state.

In the atoms we see foreshadowed the systems of the stars. For as the planets revolve about the sun, and the double stars about each other in orderly orbits, so do the free electrons revolve about the nuclei of the atoms. Revolving motion holds the attracting bodies apart in atoms as in star systems. It was a triumph of the nineteenth century to show that the same atoms which compose the earth are also the material of the celestial bodies. To the twentieth century was reserved the triumphs of proving that all atoms are composed of the same constituents, and of revealing the plans of their architecture.

Without the minute study of light, the stars would be unknown. How wonderful that light also searches out for us the structure of the atom! In the intricate relations between electrons and light we discover clues that indicate what the stars are, how they are evolved, and why they continue to shine.

In order to set things in orderly array and to see how far a probable outline of the grand procedure of universal evolution can be given, we may jot down the principal and most significant facts which have been elaborated in preceding chapters.

1. We live on a non-luminous solid spheroid, over five times denser than water, that revolves, unimpeded, with other spheroids about a star, our sun, over 300,000 times as massive as the earth, and nearly 93,000,000 miles away. The sun's density is 1.4 times that of water, and his surface temperature about 6,000° Absolute Centigrade, or nearly twice the temperature required to gasify everything on earth. So the sun is probably gaseous and his high density depends partly on enormous gravitational compression, partly on including atoms of heavy metals. The sun's enormous output of energy of radiation appears to have been maintained without notable diminution for fully a billion years.

2. Our sun with the solar system finds itself at some distance from the center of a galaxy of some forty billion stars arranged in a lens-shaped space. Among them, he is of average brightness, mass, density, motion, position, spectrum, and temperature. In short, the sun follows the advice of Robinson Crusoe's father to a nicety by sticking to the middle class.

3. Ninety-nine per cent of the stars fall readily into six classes. They are distinguished by the character of their spectra as B, A, F, G, K, M, in the Harvard nomenclature. Of these, the M type is red and cool, and the B type is blue and hot. Outside of these six major classes are a few others containing relatively small numbers of stars, some as cool as M, some hotter than B. The spectral types merge by insensible gradation from B to M.

4. In the types F, G, K, and M, there is a cleavage, so that these stars are classed as giants and dwarfs in view of their wide ranges of diameter and volume. Between giants and dwarfs of the same spectral type there are some inconspicuous but highly significant differences of spectrum. Our sun appears to be a G-type dwarf.

5. From double-star observations, we learn that there is probably but a small range of mass among the stars, perhaps not over 100-fold. On the contrary, their range in volume, in density, and in total radiation exceeds 100,000,000-fold.

6. Among starry systems, fairly equal pairs of double stars are very common. Many of the companions are dark. It is not pos-

sible to observe whether other stars are attended by small cool planets, as our sun is, but there are reasons for believing such solar-like systems may be rare.

7. Catastrophes occur in the heavens. Their evidence is the sudden flaring up of a star to 10,000-fold brightness, followed by gradual return to its former state. There is reason to think such catastrophies may happen to a large proportion of stars sometime in their many billion-years long lives.

8. All of the stars are in motion. Their behavior may be likened to that of a number of swarms of bees who chanced to migrate along a common course at different speeds. Within each swarm, there is always a criss-cross flight of individuals, some going in the direction of the swarm as a whole, and others in all other directions including the opposite. Yet as a whole each swarm moves forward, despite the varying internal motions of its members. So all the stars of our Galaxy, if arranged in groups of the common spectrum classes, are found to be traveling at unequal rates as groups along a common preferential way. The separate individuals of the several groups exhibit a wide diversity in direction and velocity of motion. The common preferential way is nearly in the plane of the Milky Way and in the direction towards the constellation Sagittarius.

9. Apparently outside our Galaxy, lie about an hundred clusters of stars at immense distances. Each of them contains a multitude of stars. Some clusters may even contain millions of them, so that they approach the star-population of our own Galaxy. We may perhaps regard these populous clusters as other systems something like ours.

10. The nebulæ fall into two types. One is of gaseous nature, small density, feeble or no luminosity, and irregular or annular shape. This type is associated with the very hot stars of our Galaxy. When luminous, these nebulæ seem to derive light-giving power from associated stars. Nebulæ of another type, including globular, spindle-shaped, and spiral forms, seem to be of enormous mass and distance and to lie perhaps outside our Galaxy. These may be considered as possible reservoirs of future galaxies, if not, indeed, already composing systems of innumerable stars, too far distant to discriminate.

11. Spiral nebulæ and star clusters have very great velocities of dispersion in their own classes, and very great velocities along the preferential way, compared to a mean of all the stars of our Galaxy taken as a datum or zero of velocity.

With these facts in mind, we now take up the fascinating problem of how the stars came to be.

To begin with, we must admit that as yet we have no conception of the processes by means of which all the enormous mass of matter included in these various celestial forms came into being from electrons and protons. No one has constructed atoms, although physicists have disintegrated them in the laboratory. Possibly the constructive processes require temperatures and pressures, or other conditions, as wholly outside of our means as, so far, they are outside of our knowledge.

Having admitted that the formation of the atoms so far escapes observation, we begin with the globular, spindle-shaped and spiral nebulæ, and inquire if development might reasonably go on from thence. This inquiry is the subject of a very notable lecture by the distinguished mathematician, Dr. J. H. Jeans, which may be found in full in "Nature" of March 1, 1924. He first lays a scale of proportions whereon our earth is ultra-microscopic, our sun a microscopic speck of dust, the solar system like a threepenny piece, and the furthest star-cloud 14,000 miles away.

Jeans then draws attention to the spindle-shaped nebulæ. These are found spectroscopically to be rotating rapidly about their shortest diameters. The mathematician calculates from the laws of dynamics what shapes they must assume if, as seems likely, they are gaseous masses. From the law of constant angular momentum the rotation must grow more rapid as the gaseous mass gives off radiation and consequently condenses. Along with increasing velocity of rotation the figure flattens, and its circumferential edge sharpens. Further shrinkage and increased velocity involves the disruption of the mass, with matter going off from the sharpened edge.

If there were no other bodies in the universe, it would be impossible to say how the break would occur. But the attraction of other celestial bodies tends to raise small tides, so that there is a resultant direction where the nebula is in a trifling degree elongated in its diameter. This is the diameter from which now start to stream away armlike masses of the ejected material. Thus a spiral nebula begins to be born.

The process of shrinkage and ejection goes on from antipodal points. An even-flowing rope-shaped stream of gas is maintained in each of the opposite spiral arms. Continuing in rotation, but only with the linear velocity of the surface of the nucleus, the arms lack velocity sufficient to hold them radial. Thus, as we have seen in the results of Van Maanen, these circumstances produce the effect of winding up the arms.

Basing his computations on Van Maanen's results, Jeans computes the mass and finds the density of the gas remaining in the nucleus of some of the very long-armed nebulæ, nearly all of whose material has been ejected. It comes out smaller than the pressure in the best vacuum pumps. He says: "The small amount of gas in an ordinary electric light bulb, if spread out through St. Paul's Cathedral, would still be something like 10,000 times as dense as the nucleus of a spiral nebula."

But the arms cannot remain continuous. As a jet of water separates into drops, so, though for different reasons, nebular arms form detached knot-like aggregations under the influence of gravitation. The theory of their formation is clear, and enables the mathematician to compute what ought to be the size, mass and distance apart of the separate gas masses in the arms. When the calculations are performed, the very encouraging result comes out that the masses of single condensations must be approximately those of average stars.

Thus, the presumption is strong that here is a real step in star-evolution. Let us recapitulate. From a gaseous mass of extremest rareness, there forms a rotating figure, which assumes more and more a flattened form. At length it ejects arms, which wind up into the form of spiral nebulæ. These arms break up under gravitational force, and form separate knots of gas, each of sufficient mass to make ordinary stars. The number of stars so born from a single nebula may run to millions. It is the birth of a star cluster. Very satisfactory is the observation that star clusters and spiral nebulæ are similar in having very high migration-velocities along the great preferential way.

Such a process as this which Jeans describes reminds us of Laplace's famous nebular hypothesis of the origin of the solar system. Nevertheless that will not do for the solar system at all. One trouble is that in the solar system almost the whole mass is in the central sun. This could not be so if there had been a shrinkage from, let us say, Neptune's orbit. For the "moment of momentum" could not have been preserved constant. Jeans' scheme does not violate this principle. In the later stages the mass is very largely in the ejected portions, far out from the center.

Jeans points out another difficulty. We must recognize the immensity of spiral nebulæ, and that the sun, if it came from one, must have come from no more than a little speck, so to speak, of nebular matter. If we should suppose that a single knot of an arm of a great nebula passed along the same course of evolution as the whole had done, the laws of dynamics show that the result would be different because of the difference of scale. There would not result a solar system, but a binary star having two nearly equal masses in mutual revolution. These again may divide nearly equally if their rotation suffices, thus making a system like Epsilon Lyræ. The observed fact that fully a third of the stars are binary or multiple is then quite in harmony with what dynamics foretells. If the rotation and mass are adequate, the knot becomes a double or multiple star system. Otherwise, there result single stars.

Do all nebulæ follow this course? According to Jeans, many may not. If originally there is too little rotation, the shrinkage due to radiating and cooling will not impart sufficient acceleration of it for separation. Motionless nebulæ would remain spherical till they grew old and cold and solid, without ever becoming the parents of star systems. Further on in the progress, if one of the large condensations in the arm of a nebula lacks rotation, it, too, may grow cold without ever forming a binary or multiple system of stars.

Nowhere in all this march of events is there a path towards a solar system. The evolution of spirals leads to single and double stars, but not to suns attended by planets and satellites. Jeans, however, points to another possibility arising in stars already formed.

Though the spaces between the stars are perfectly enormous compared to the diameters of the stars themselves, nevertheless, since time is long, there may come rare cases when one star approaches another near enough to produce monstrous tides upon its gaseous material.

These tides, if they become high enough, may generate spiral arms which will break up into knots. The result is much the same as before, but with a difference. Two stars rushing by each other at celestial velocities will remain within each other's influence but a few years. The time while they are near will not suffice to cause a great proportion of the star material to be forced out into the arms. Only slightly will the central mass be diminished.

We notice, however, that there are no double planets of nearly equal masses. The earth and moon are nearest equal, and they differ by 80-fold in mass. The other planets which have moons resemble the solar system in miniature. Moreover, there are other features of similarity. Just as the sun and planets lie nearly in one plane, and all rotate and revolve almost without exception in the same sense, so the individual planets and their satellites lie nearly in the plane of rotation of the planet. In the case of the earth, its moon rotates and revolves in the same direction as the earth. From analogy we may well suppose the satellites of other planets do so too.

These similarities between solar and planetary systems lead us to think they were formed in similar ways. Jeans examines the various circumstances of the solar system, and calculates the masses of the planets and satellites on the theory that they might have been formed by tidal action of perturbing bodies and succeeding gravitational condensing effects. He finds himself constrained to conclude that many of the satellites and some of the planets were gathered together when, in cooling, the tidal arms had reached liquid or solid conditions. Only Mars, Jupiter, Saturn, and Uranus, he thinks, were born from the gaseous state.

This interesting theory of Jeans, having provided a rational interpretation of the spindle-shaped and spiral nebulæ as sources of star clusters, and individual stars in close approach as sources of solar systems, we are ready to proceed with the later stages of star life. Here we find the fruitful studies of Eddington. The matter has been popularly presented by Eddington himself in "The Scientific Monthly" for September, 1923, and more at length, with the beautiful clearness characteristic of French authors, by Bosler in "L'Evolution des Etoiles," Paris, 1923.

A star in its early stage, just condensed in the arm of a nebula, is to be regarded as a spheroid of very rare gas, hundreds of millions of miles in diameter, and many thousand times less dense than the air of the room. Not hotter, at least on its surface, than many laboratory sources of radiation, the star, a giant at birth, shines feebly with a red color. Its surface atoms are not excited sufficiently to lose electrons, and the surface temperature is even low enough to permit the existence of such compounds of atoms into molecules as titanium oxide, calcium hydride, cyanogen, and some others. The star is of the M type spectrum, and of the giant class.

These are exterior appearances. What of the interior? The temperature rises enormously towards the center of the star, reaching hundreds of thousands or millions of degrees. The pressure, also, must rise towards the center by reason of the weight of the tremendously thick mass of superincumbent gas. Yet the state of the star is purely gaseous. It is, indeed, of gas so rare that the laws of the so-called perfect gas apply. That is to say, the separate particles, some being molecules, some atoms, some electrons, and others fragments of atoms remaining after electrons are lost, shoot about in free paths very long compared to the radii of their little spheres of influence.

These are the ideal circumstances for the mathematical investigator. Not requiring to make allowances for the spaces actually occupied by the separate particles of the gaseous material, or for the mutual attractions and repulsions of them, his problem is greatly simplified. Subject to two qualifications which we shall soon name, Lane's law applies in all its simplicity. This paradoxical expression maintains that for a star in a state where the laws of the perfect gas apply, the temperatures increase proportionally as the radius decreases when the star contracts by cooling.[1]

[1] How can it be that cooling makes the star hotter?
Obviously, if the star radiates and thus loses heat, and has no supplies of heat other than its own store, it must contract at the surface by growing cooler there.

What, then, will happen to our star? If it merely radiates light and other rays, losing no gas, it will grow smaller and smaller, but hotter and hotter, until it ceases to be a perfect gas, and Lane's law ceases to apply. As it grows hotter, the color changes from deep red to light red, to yellow, to white, to blue, if the star is big enough to go through all these changes. The spectrum correspondingly passes from M type successively to K, G, F, A, and B if the star is big enough to go all the way. Many stars are not.

The relations between star mass and the hottest possible type which can evolve therefrom have been worked out by Eddington. They depend on a property which is not commonly thought of. It is the pressure of radiation. Clerke Maxwell, the great English physicist, showed theoretically, about the year 1875, that light must exercise a pressure. Dr. E. F. Nichols, whose sudden tragic death occurred while in the very act of delivering a scientific paper at the dedicatory session of the United States National Academy of Science in its new palace of science in Washington, experimentally verified Maxwell's theory a quarter of a century after its publication.

---

Lower-lying layers must supply this loss, and all of them tend to cool. Cooling produces shrinkage. Imagine that this goes on till the star loses half its diameter. Then if all corresponding depths have the same relative densities as before, each corresponding depth will come to a state of density eight times as great as originally; for the sphere is now of half the diameter and therefore eight times less in volume than at first.

How about the pressures? Since the pressure depends on the attraction of the material, which acts as if concentrated at the center, corresponding depths will by Newton's law be subjected to four times the intensity of pressure, on account of being twice as near the center. Besides this, the gas lying vertically outside of any unit of surface area of an interior sphere will be four times as much as originally over the same unit area on a corresponding sphere. This is so because all corresponding spheres have been reduced to half diameter and one-fourth surface area, so that the gas column has been compressed laterally fourfold. Thus, the pressure at corresponding points has increased fourfold from the application of Newton's law, and fourfold from lateral compression, or four times four, equals sixteenfold altogether.

In order to maintain a condition of equilibrium in a perfect gas, the product of pressure and volume must be proportional to the absolute temperature. In our supposed star the volumes have diminished eightfold, the pressures increased sixteenfold, their product has increased twofold, therefore for equilibrium the temperatures must also have increased twofold. Thus we come to an application of Lane's law. If you halve the diameter, you must double the temperature.

Consideration of light pressure modifies Lane's law. For the pressure of gravitation in a star is sustained not alone by the expansive force of gases, due to the collisions of their particles and their elastic rebounding. Light pressure helps gaseous expansion to sustain gravitational pressure. Eddington has gone through the computations. He bids us imagine a series of gaseous spheres, each ten times as massive as the one before. The first contains 10 grams, the second 100 grams, and so on. Number one weighs as much as a letter, number five as much as a man, number ten as much as an ocean liner. All the stars whose masses we know lie between numbers 33 and 35 of this scale. Nearly all are between numbers 33 and 34. This is highly interesting, for Eddington's calculations show that, until we come to sphere 33, light pressure is nearly negligible compared to gas expansion, and after we reach sphere 35, gas expansion is nearly negligible compared to light pressure.

In Eddington's quaint words, we should expect "something to happen" at this critical condition of gaseous masses, and "what happens is the stars." Masses smaller than No. 33 do not grow hot enough by virtue of Lane's law to shine. Spheres larger than No. 35 are too unstable because radiation pressure bursts them asunder. Sphere 33 is of half the mass of the sun, while sphere 35 has five times the sun's mass. Hence, we may suppose that Jeans' nebular condensations larger than five times the sun's mass will break up to form smaller stars, while those having less than half the sun's mass will never be hot enough to be visible.

There is a second possible qualification of Lane's law. We are not sure that stars lose no material. According to the present view of atomic structure, matter seems to be a passive form of energy. May it not be transmuted into the active form of radiation? This does not happen, so far as we know, on earth, but perhaps it happens in the conditions of tremendous temperature and pressure prevailing within the stars. There are, indeed, several considerations which incline us to think it may possibly be so.

At the meeting of the Royal Astronomical Society of March 14, 1924, Professor Eddington stated that the theory of the interior of those stars which obey the laws of perfect gases indicates that the luminosity is almost wholly governed by the mass. There will be, it is true, some change of luminosity with varying effective temperatures, but this is a minor influence compared to mass. The relation of luminosity to mass is expressed by a simple formula, whose unknown constant term the speaker determined by fitting in the known mass and absolute magnitude of the star Capella.

Having drawn a curve expressing the requirements of the theory as applied to Capella, Professor Eddington plotted alongside of this theoretical curve all the known observational data. The result is given in Fig. 45. It is easy to see that the curve is in almost perfect accord over its whole range with the observations, with possibly half a magnitude discrepancy for the fainter stars.

This is highly satisfactory from one point of view, but very surprising from another. For while it supports the theory splendidly, many of the fainter stars used seem not to belong there. They are not giants of rare gaseous constitution, but dwarf stars like the sun and denser. Their densities exceed that of water. It seems at first sight incredible that they can obey the laws of perfect gases.

Dr. Eddington suggested, and several of his audience supported him in an explanation. It is this. Within a star the temperature is so high that nearly all of the atoms are highly ionized. Their particles are, therefore, very much smaller on the average than the atoms or molecules of ordinary gases. Hence, a compression to a millionfold higher density, within a highly ionized star, might not carry its condition outside the applicability of the laws of a perfect gas at ordinary temperatures.

Still there remains a difficulty. Hitherto astronomers have supposed that as the stars grow older they pass from red to blue through the several stages of existence as giants and then retrace their types as dwarfs. The turning point, it has been supposed, comes when their densities pass above the range of application of the laws of perfect gases. Now that dwarfs seem to be also perfect gases to all intents, what shall we think?

In his suggested explanation, Dr. Eddington, as we say, "kills two birds with one stone." He makes the hypothesis that the passive energy of the material of the stars is being changed into the active energy of radiation, so that the stars are continually losing mass. The loss of mass, if dependent on high temperature and pressure, would be slow for the red and yellow giants, but would grow more rapid with later stages. When the losses become so great that the star can no longer retain its former high luminosity, the decline through the dwarf stage from blue to red sets in. At

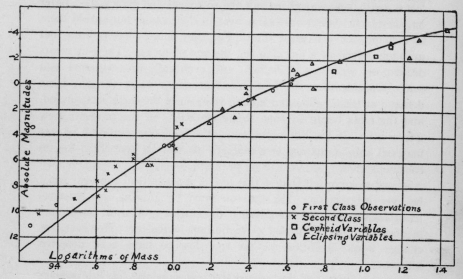

FIG. 45. THE RELATION BETWEEN MASS AND ABSOLUTE MAGNITUDE (or actual brightness) IN STARS. (After Eddington.)

The curve is theoretical entirely, and based on the supposed inner constitution of stars assuming them to be in the state of perfect gases. The curve is made to fit the data for the star Capella. All other points are pure observations, and the fact that they all lie near the curve shows that all of the stars, even the dwarfs must be in a state comparable to perfect gases. This is explained on grounds of ionization.

the same time, this hypothesis provides a source of the enormous energy of radiation which a star emits in course of its long life.

There was for a good many years a controversy, between the physicists on the one side and the geologists and zoölogists on the other, over the age of the earth. It was inspired in part by the seeming impossibility of admitting that the sun had shone over 20,000,000 years at the present average rate. The geologists and zoölogists required hundreds of millions of years for the deposition of the earth's stratified rocks, and for the evolution of species. These processes could not have been going on while the sun was cool. Yet there seemed to be but one large source of solar energy. It resided in the shrinkage of his volume, and it was insufficient to last a tenth long enough to suit the zoölogists and geologists. Later on, the physicists not only came over to their camp, but outbid them in demands on geological time. For they found that radium and uranium served as a clock to tell the age of rocks. These elements decompose, with loss of helium, and eventually are degraded into lead. Consideration of these transformations made the physicists demand at least a thousand million years since the earth was formed, and the rains began to wash to its surface. So the problem grew graver still. If Dr. Eddington's hypothesis of transmutation of star material into radiation is sustained, all will be simplified, for an enormous energy source will be provided.

It will occur to all that if this loss of mass is real, the year must be ever lengthening. For the sun must be growing less massive, its attraction must be diminishing, the earth's orbit must be gaining in diameter, and its period of revolution increasing. However, the change would doubtless be far too slow to have been detected hitherto.

Such are some of the remarkable consequences of Eddington's investigations of the interiors of stars. It would lie outside our scope to follow into the mathematical paths which lead him to these results. One other curious thing about the star interiors ought not to be omitted, however. We are accustomed to think of the store of heat which a hot body holds as being the expression of the energy of motion of its molecules or atoms. But there is another part of it, namely the energy of the radiation not yet emitted, which momentarily exists within the body. This second part of the energy is too trifling to consider in a body no hotter than the blacksmith's iron, but in a star it is perfectly immense. One thinks at first blush, of course, that the rays must rush out from the interior, and can hardly be imprisoned an instant. Not so, for the temperatures are so tremendously high that the prevailing radiations are of the minute wave-lengths which we call X-rays.

For them the star material is far from transparent. Complete absorption or scattering occurs within a path of a few inches. A ray starting from the center of a star might generate almost an infinite succession of ray-children, in the course of its absorptions and re-radiations, and a thousand years might elapse before one of them was born near enough to the surface to escape.

We have now followed in hypotheses, not proved, but not improbable, the change of spherical into spiral nebulæ, the rise of star clusters and double stars from them, and the course of evolution of the stars themselves which depends so intimately on mass. We have seen that our sun is a G-type dwarf, well past the middle age of stars. We have seen that his possessing an attending family of planets and satellites is probably an unusual condition with stars, which was very likely brought about in his case by the near approach of some other star at some time, which perhaps was several billion years ago.

It now remains to see how this scheme of things is reconcilable with the extraordinary facts relating to the motions of the nebulæ, clusters, and stars along the preferential way. Let us suppose our stars were once a cluster, and our cluster once a spiral nebula. Then, like other spiral nebulæ, it probably had a large motion in some direction as compared to the average position of all the spirals. Admit, if you please, that this motion was something like 400 miles per second along the preferential way. Becoming a star cluster, it would still have retained that motion as a whole. But the gravitational attractions, and possibly other disturbing influences, may well have modified the motions of individual members of the cluster, depending on their masses and ages in stellar conditions. Thus, the several types of stars became separated somewhat in their average velocities with respect to the center of the Galaxy. More particularly, the older and smaller stars, of which our sun is one, would long have been subjected to these influences in exceptional force. They would consequently have achieved a more extensive dispersion of velocities than the groups of younger and more massive types of stars.

All this is in accord with Strömberg's chart. How is it, though, asks some reader, that our sun is moving nearly in the preferential way, and at a higher velocity with respect to his type companions the G dwarfs, than with respect to other types like the M giants? This appears to be merely accidental. As we have said, the older dwarfs are naturally more highly dispersed in their velocities than the younger and more massive giants. Our sun, being one of them, naturally acquired a considerable velocity measured from the center of G-type dwarf-star motions. This motion had to be in some direction. It happened nearly to coincide with the great preferential way, and was *forward* with our cluster, not backward or at some wide angle to the side, as it might have happened. Had the sun's motion happened opposite to its present direction, all the giant stars would have seemed to be moving faster than the G-type dwarfs with respect to the sun, and in the opposite sense to what now seems to be their course. In that case, too, the average motion of the spiral nebulæ would have seemed more than fifty miles per second slower than it now seems, though in the same sense along the preferential way as now.

In this way most of our big facts seem to fall into a consistent whole. He would be a rash fool who would dare to maintain that this scheme of things is surely the true one. Discovery has followed discovery at such a pace of late that another decade may well find evidences of very different tenor. The problem of the evolution of the universe is too large to be exhausted in a few generations. Even if at length the foundations of its solution shall seem to be established, it will doubtless occupy a thousand years of astronomical research to fill out the noble outlines of the structure, and reveal in its full beauty the grand system of the celestial hosts.

# APPENDIX

## Appendix A

### THE TOTAL SOLAR ECLIPSE, JANUARY 24, 1925

FORTUNATELY the weather on this occasion proved highly favorable in the States of New York and Connecticut, though cloudy further west. It was a clear cold winter's morning, with a carpet of snow upon the ground, and the thermometer a little below zero Fahrenheit. The location was fortunate. Careful advance publicity by newspapers and radio had prepared the public mind. Millions of eagerly interested people watched the awe-inspiring sight.

Perhaps no event has ever tended more strongly to promote a respect and appreciation for the achievements of science. To astronomers it was too old a story to wonder at. There is, nevertheless, something very honorable to the powers of the human mind in the fact that the exact conjunction of three heavenly bodies, as far apart as the sun, the moon and the earth, all flying at high speeds in pathless space, can be foretold to within five seconds of time and a mile in place, many years before the event. This aspect of the eclipse forced itself home on the minds of multitudes on January 24, 1925.

We are so accustomed to the luxuries of recent times that we often overlook our debt to science for them. Great ingenuity of discovery and self-sacrificing lives of patient research are the foundation on which all of these things depend. Radio, for instance, did not originate even with Marconi. We trace the discoveries necessary to it back for at least a century, and none of the pioneers got financially rewarded, or had adequate means to promote their researches. The history of science abundantly proves that support to pure scientific investigation is one of the most fruitful means to promote the comfort and broaden the outlook of posterity. Something of this was forced on the minds of the millions of spectators of the total eclipse.

Dr. S. A. Mitchell, the veteran observer and chronicler of total solar eclipses, under date of February 4, 1925, has kindly furnished the following synopsis of the astronomical observations. Naturally the working up of the results had hardly begun at that date, and much more may be disclosed eventually.

"The chief results of the eclipse were:

1. Corona of sun-spot minimum type, but with long spike-like extension to the right of the vertical.

2. Extensions visible to the naked eye not so great as at minimum-type eclipse of 1900.

3. Inner corona very brilliant, the lines of coronium at 5303A and 6374A were very strong.

4. Impossible to tell anything about reflected solar light in the corona, due to slight haze in the earth's atmosphere.

5. Photographs of the flash spectrum obtained with concave grating and without slit by Anderson, Curtis and Mitchell.

6. My own flash spectra extend from wave-length 3300A to 7000A.

7. Water-vapor bands found both in the flash spectrum (taken immediately after totality) and in the coronal spectrum taken without slit.

8. Coronium lines at 5303A and 6374A are on flash-spectrum photographs taken by me, and in good strength, so that accurate wave-lengths should be available.

9. Preliminary values by Stebbins show that the total light of the corona was about equal to that of 1918.

10. Beginning of totality three seconds late. Duration of totality at Middletown three seconds greater than calculated. Southern edge of eclipse track three-quarters of a mile farther south in Central Park, New York, than expected.

11. Results from radio experiments, not yet reported.

12. Shadow bands universally observed. No preponderant direction of motion or speed. Seem to confirm the theory given on page 444 of my 'Eclipses of the Sun.'"

A new method of eclipse observing was undertaken by the United States Navy. The great dirigible balloon "Los Angeles" ascended, and occupied a station off Block Island, at an altitude of about a mile, during totality. A stiff wind was blowing, which made it necessary to drive and steer the balloon. This introduced some vibration. Nevertheless, photographs were taken by Mr. Peters of the

United States Naval Observatory, which, had ground observations failed by cloudiness, as was greatly to be feared at that season, would have given a very just impression of the form of the solar corona. Of course it was not expected that balloon observations could equal those made at fixed stations in clear weather.

Grateful acknowledgements are due the Navy for this novel expedition, designed to supplement the observing program, and give an opportunity to avoid the fatal obstacle which low-lying clouds were apt to interpose. Army airplanes also observed at much higher altitudes. These gave a still more promising chance to avoid the clouds, though they by no means offer a very favorable means of getting good eclipse photographs. Still, if the lower observatories and the balloon had all been shut out by clouds, we should have valued highly such views and eye reports as might have been brought down from an altitude of three miles and more.

## Appendix B

### THE TIDES

Possibly it may seem simpler to the reader to consider first solar tides, for we are accustomed to think of the sun as central and fixed, with the earth revolving in a mighty orbit around it. Let us recall that Newton showed that all bodies behave as if every particle attracts every other particle with a force proportional to the product of the masses of the two, and inversely as the square of their distance. He also showed that for a spherical or ellipsoidal body the attraction of the whole system of particles which compose it, acting on every particle outside, is as if the body was reduced in size to a point, containing the whole of the mass, situated at the center of figure. Recall, also, that Kepler discovered that the square of the period of revolution of a planet is proportional to the cube of its mean distance from the sun. Finally it is shown in works on mechanics that a body revolving in a curved orbit pulls away from the center with a force (called the centrifugal force) proportional to the square of the velocity divided by the radius of the orbit. In a steady state of orbital motion, the centrifugal pull is exactly balanced by the gravitational attraction toward the central body.

Before going on with the tides, we may pause to note that the effect of centrifugal force due to the earth's daily rotation is seen in the heaping up of matter at the equator. There is no centrifugal force at the poles, due to the earth's rotation, because the speed there is zero, but at the equator the centrifugal force on the water there is about 1/5 pound per cubic foot, and therefore elevates the ocean level there until the height of the column of water is such that its weight balances the centrifugal force. On this account the polar diameter of the earth is 1/297 part less than the mean equatorial diameter.

It is not necessary to take the earth's daily rotation into account to see why there is a tide-raising force, though if we should consider the actual tides produced it would be indispensable to do so.

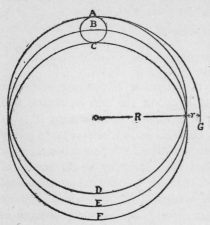

Hence, for simplicity, let us consider a spherical earth with a complete covering of ocean, and having no rotation on its axis, so that any equatorial diameter of it would point always to the same star. Referring to the figure, three equal particles at $A$, $B$, and $C$ would all be revolving with equal velocities in equal orbits $AD$, $BE$, $CF$, respectively, because all the particles are under constraint to form a part of one body, which is the supposed nonrotating earth. The centrifugal forces of the three particles would, therefore, be equal, and equal to the centrifugal force on $B$, which is equal to the attraction $\dfrac{Mm}{R^2}$. But if the particle $A$ had moved freely in an orbit $AG$ of the radius $R + r$, the centrifugal force (equal to the attraction) would have been approximately $\dfrac{Mm}{(R+r)^2} = \dfrac{Mm}{R^2\left(1+\dfrac{r}{R}\right)^2} =$

FIG. 46. TIDAL DIAGRAM.

$\dfrac{Mm}{R^2}\left(1 - \dfrac{2r}{R}\right)$. Hence, the actual centrifugal force of $A$, which we just showed was $\dfrac{Mm}{R^2}$, is too large for equilibrium by the amount $\dfrac{Mm}{R^2} - \dfrac{Mm}{R^2}\left(1 - \dfrac{2r}{R}\right)$ or $\dfrac{2Mmr}{R^3}$. This is the tide-raising force on $A$ and it is directed away from the central body. Similarly, the tide-raising force on $C$ is $\dfrac{Mm}{R^2}\left(1 + \dfrac{2r}{R}\right) - \dfrac{Mm}{R^2}$, and also approximately $\dfrac{2Mmr}{R^3}$. But it is directed towards the central body. So there are two equal tide-raising forces, oppositely directed, at the ends of the simplified earth's diameter.  In the actual earth, the shape of the land, depth of the water, physical properties of water, rotation of the earth, inclination of the ecliptic, and other factors complicate the problem so exceedingly that Lord Kelvin, despairing of solving it from first principles, introduced the other procedure of working back from the actually observed tides to determine means of predicting them.  This course is now universally adopted.

We have spoken of the solar tides as if they were simpler than lunar ones to understand.  But if we adopt the modern conception that all motion is relative, it is just as easy to understand lunar tides, for we can think of the moon as stationary, and the earth revolving about it, just as we did for the sun.  Lunar tide-raising forces are more than twice as great as solar, because although the moon's mass is only about $\dfrac{1}{81 \times 330,000}$ compared to the sun, yet the sun's distance cubed is about 60,000,000 compared to the moon's, which more than compensates.

## APPENDIX C

### PRINCIPAL DATA OF THE SOLAR SYSTEM

| Name and symbol | Number of satellites | Apparent angular diameter | Mean diameter in miles | Mass. $\oplus = 1.$ | Density. Water $= 1$ | Gravity at surface $\oplus = 1.$ |
|---|---|---|---|---|---|---|
| Sun ☉..... | — | 1891″ to 1956″ | 865,000 | 332,800 | 1.41 | 27.6 |
| Mercury ☿ . | 0 | 4.5″ to 12.5″ | 3,030 | 1/22? | 4.4? | 0.2? |
| Venus ♀... | 0 | 9.8″ to 66″ | 7,700 | 0.816 | 4.9 | 0.8 |
| Earth ⊕... | 1 | .......... | 7,918 | 1.000 | 5.525 | 1.0 |
| Mars ♂.... | 2 | 3.6″ to 26.0″ | 4,230 | 0.1073 | 3.9 | 0.4 |
| Ceres ① ... | ...... | 0.25″ to 0.5″ | 488? | 1/7000? | 3.? | 1/260? |
| Jupiter ♃.. | 9 | 32″ to 50″ | 86,500 | 317.0 | 1.3 | 2.6 |
| Saturn ♄ .. | 9 | 14″ to 20″ | 70,000 | 94.8 | 0.7 | 1.2 |
| Uranus ♅.. | 4 | 3.4″ to 3.7″ | 31,500 | 14.6 | 1.2 | 0.9 |
| Neptune ♆. | 1 | 2.7″ to 2.9″ | 34,800 | 17.0 | 1.1 | 0.9 |
| Moon ☽... | — | 1766″ to 2015″ | 2,163 | 1/81.53 | 3.4 | 1/6 |

| Name | Mean radius of orbit. Millions of miles | Ratio of aphelion to perihelion distance | Inclination of orbit to ecliptic | Sidereal period in mean solar time | |
|---|---|---|---|---|---|
| | | | | Orbital revolution | Axial rotation |
| Mercury.... | 36.0 | 1.5176 | 7°00′08″ | 87$^d$.9693 | 88d? |
| Venus....... | 67.2 | 1.0137 | 3 23 35 | 224.7008 | 1od? |
| Earth....... | 92.9 | 1.0342 | 0 00 00 | 365.2564 | 23h 56m 4.09s |
| Mars....... | 141.5 | 1.2058 | 1 51 02 | 686.9505 | 24h 37m 22.67s |
| Ceres....... | 257.1 | 1.1652 | 10 37 10 | 1681.414 | ? |
| Jupiter...... | 483.3 | 1.1013 | 1 18 41 | 4332.580 | 9h 5om to 9h 56m |
| Saturn...... | 886.0 | 1.1189 | 2 29 40 | 10759.22 | 1oh 14m to 1oh 38m |
| Uranus...... | 1781.9 | 1.0971 | 0 46 20 | 30686.82 | 1oh 5om |
| Neptune.... | 2791.6 | 1.0182 | 1 47 02 | 60181.11 | ? |
| Moon....... | 238,840 miles | 1.1162 | 5 08 40 | 27.3217 | 27d 7h 43m 11.5s |

From "The Sun" by permission of D. Appleton & Co.

## THE FIRST-MAGNITUDE STARS

| No. | Star | Mag. | Spectrum | R.A. 1900 | Dec. 1900 | Annual proper motion, $\mu$ | P.A. of $\mu$ | Parallax | Abs. mag. | Radial velocity km. | Diameter** |
|---|---|---|---|---|---|---|---|---|---|---|---|
| 1 | Achernar........ | 0.6 | B5 | 13h 34.0m | −57° 45′ | 0.094″ | 108° | +0.051″ | −0.9 | — | — |
| 2 | Aldebaran ‡..... | 1.1 | K5 | 4 30.2 | +16 18 | 0.203 | 160 | +0.056 | −0.2 | +55.1 | 35 |
| 3 | Capella † ‡..... | 0.2 | G | 5 9.3 | +45 54 | 0.437 | 168 | +0.075 | −0.5 | +30.2 | 10 |
| 4 | Rigel * †........ | 0.3 | B8 | 5 9.7 | −8 19 | 0.001 | 135 | +0.007 | −5.5 | +22.6 | 21 |
| 5 | Betelgeuse † §... | 0.6–1.2 | Ma | 5 49.8 | +7 23 | 0.029 | 74 | +0.019 | −2.7 | +21.3 | 250 |
| 6 | Canopus......... | −0.9 | F | 6 21.7 | −52 38 | 0.018 | 56 | +0.007 | −6.7 | +20.8 | — |
| 7 | Sirius *......... | −1.6 | A | 6 40.7 | −16 35 | 1.316 | 204 | +0.376 | +1.2 | −7.4 | 1.4 |
| 8 | Procyon *....... | 0.5 | F5 | 7 34.1 | +5 29 | 1.242 | 214 | +0.309 | +3.0 | −3.5 | 1.0 |
| 9 | Pollux §........ | 1.2 | K | 7 39.2 | +28 16 | 0.625 | 264 | +0.064 | +0.2 | +3.9 | — |
| 10 | Regulus ‡....... | 1.3 | B8 | 10 3.0 | +12 27 | 0.247 | 269 | +0.033 | −1.1 | −9.1 | — |
| 11 | α Crucis *....... | 1.1 | B1 | 12 21.0 | −62 33 | 0.048 | 240 | +0.047 | −0.5 | +7. | — |
| 12 | β Crucis †....... | 1.5 | B1 | 12 41.9 | −59 9 | 0.056 | 240 | +0.008 | −4.0 | +13. | — |
| 13 | Spica †......... | 1.2 | B2 | 13 19.9 | −10 38 | 0.055 | 229 | −0.012 | — | +1.6 | — |
| 14 | β Centauri †..... | 0.9 | B1 | 13 56.8 | −59 53 | 0.041 | 219 | +0.037 | −1.3 | −7. | — |
| 15 | Arcturus........ | 0.2 | K | 14 11.1 | +19 42 | 2.282 | 209 | +0.075 | −0.5 | −3.9 | — |
| 16 | α Centauri *..... | 0.3 | G | 14 32.8 | −60 25 | 3.680 | 281 | +0.759 | +4.7 | −21.6 | — |
| 17 | Antares † ‡..... | 1.2 | Ma | 16 23.3 | −26 13 | 0.034 | 192 | +0.029 | −1.5 | −3.1 | — |
| 18 | Vega §.......... | 0.1 | A | 18 33.6 | +38 41 | 0.346 | 36 | +0.091 | −0.1 | −13.8 | 2.0 |
| 19 | Altair §......... | 0.9 | A5 | 19 45.9 | +8 36 | 0.655 | 54 | +0.214 | +2.5 | −33. | — |
| 20 | Deneb §......... | 1.3 | A2 | 20 38.0 | +44 55 | 0.001 | 180 | +0.002 | −7.2 | −4. | — |
| 21 | Fomalhaut....... | 1.3 | A3 | 22 52.1 | −30 9 | 0.365 | 117 | +0.138 | +2.0 | +6.7 | — |

* Visual binary.    † Spectroscopic binary.    ‡ Pair with common proper motion.
§ Wide pair probably optical.    ** In millions of miles.

Mass relative to sun of (7) is 3.1; of (8), 1.5; of (16), 2.0.    For description of types, see page 178 or Annals of Harvard College Observatory, 28, p. 146, or more concisely 56, p. 66, and 91, p. 5.    The light ratio between successive stellar magnitudes is $\sqrt{100}$ or the number whose logarithm is 0.4000, viz., 2.512.    The absolute magnitude of a star is its magnitude reduced to a distance corresponding to 0.1″ parallax.

## Appendix E

### LIST OF THE CONSTELLATIONS

#### Northern (28)

Andromeda, Aquila, Auriga, Boötes, Camelopardus, Canes venatici, Cassiopeia, Cepheus, Coma Berenices, Corona borealis, Cygnus, Delphinus, Draco, Equuleus, Hercules, Lacerta, Leo minor, Lynx, Lyra, Ophiuchus or Serpentarius, Pegasus, Perseus, Sagitta, Serpens, Triangulum, Ursa major, Ursa minor, Vulpecula et Anser.

#### Zodiacal (12)

Aquarius, Aries, Cancer, Capricornus, Gemini, Leo, Libra, Pisces, Sagittarius, Scorpio, Taurus, Virgo.

#### Southern (49)

Antlia, Apus, Ara, Argo, Caela sculptoris, Canis major, Canis minor, Carina, Centaurus, Cetus, Chameleon, Circinus, Columba Noachi, Corona australis, Corvus, Crater, Crux, Dorado, Eridanus, Fornax chemica, Grus, Horologium, Hydra, Hydrus, Indus, Lepus, Lupus, Malus, Mons Mensæ, Microscopium, Monoceros, Musca australis, Norma, Octans, Orion, Pavo, Phoenix, Pictor, Piscis australis, Puppis, Recticulum, Sculptor, Scutum Sobieskii, Sextans, Telescopium, Tucana, Triangulum australe, Vela, Volans.

# Appendix F

*Commonly Used Astronomical Terms Simply Defined.*
*For more technical definitions see larger works.*

*Aberration of lenses* is of two kinds: *chromatic,* owing to the unequal bending or refraction of rays of different colors; *spherical,* owing to the impossibility of bringing rays inclined far from the optic axis to perfect focus. Curved *mirrors* have spherical aberration also, but not chromatic.

*Aberration of light* is the displacement of a celestial object caused by the motion of the earth in relation to that of light.

*Achromatic lens* is one corrected to avoid chromatic aberration, and thus gives no color fringe around the image.

*Albedo* of a planet is its reflecting power. The fraction of the sun's light it receives which it reflects away.

*Altazimuth,* an instrument mounted to swing about horizontal and vertical axes in altitude and azimuth like a surveyor's transit.

*Altitude* of a heavenly body is its angular distance above the horizon.

*Angular velocity* is the angle swept through by an object per unit of time.

*Anomaly of a planet* is its angular distance from perihelion or aphelion.

*Ansae of Saturn* are the extremities of the rings as they look like handles to the planet.

*Aperture of an instrument* is the opening exposed to light.

*Aphelion* of a planet is its furthest position from the sun.

*Apogee of the moon* is its farthest orbital distance from the earth.

*Appulse,* the near approach of two heavenly bodies.

*Arc,* a portion of a circle or other curve.

*Asteroid,* a minor planet.

*Astrolabe,* an ancient instrument for angular measurements among the heavenly bodies.

*Azimuth* of a heavenly body is its angular distance measured on the horizon westward from the south point.

*Base line,* in surveying, a distance accurately measured with rods or tapes, from which other distances are determined by triangulation.

*Binary star,* companion stars in mutual revolution. Binaries are *visual, telescopic* or *spectroscopic,* according to the means required to distinguish the binary character.

*Bisect* is to adjust the crosshair of the observing instrument as a diameter of an image.

*Bolometer,* an electrical thermometer used to measure the heat of rays of minute intensity. It employs the principle of Wheatstone's Bridge.

*Cassegrainian telescope* is a reflecting telescope whose object-glass has a central hole through which the rays are reflected into the eyepiece.

*Chronograph,* an electrical clock attachment, used to record intervals of time with high precision.

*Chronometer,* a large watch of high precision, principally used to determine longitude at sea.

*Circle, great,* is any circle which includes the two ends of a single diameter of a sphere.

*Circle, small,* is any circle on a sphere other than great.

*Coelostat,* an instrument for producing a fixed beam from a celestial object, having a plane mirror parallel to the earth's axis, and rotating about an axis parallel to that of the earth, at the rate of one revolution in 48 hours. Often a second mirror is employed to send the fixed beam in a desired direction. The coelostat is advantageous for simplicity, and for preserving a nonrotating field of view.

*Collimator,* an optical device to render a bundle of rays parallel.

*Colures, equinoctial* and *solstitial* are two great circles passing through the poles of the heavens. They pass through the equinox and at ninety degrees thereto, respectively.

*Conjunction* of two celestial objects occurs when they have the same longitude or right ascension.

*Conjunction of an inferior planet* with the sun is *inferior* or *superior* when it lies on the same side or on the opposite side of the sun from the earth.

*Corona,* a halo, but specifically the raylike pearly appendage of light attaching to the sun, and only visible at times of total solar eclipse.

*Crescent* is said of the moon and inferior planets when they present less than half of their disks illuminated by the sun.

*Culmination* is the passage of a heavenly body across the meridian. In the case of objects near the pole it is said to be *lower* or *upper,* according as it is beneath or above the altitude of the pole.

*Day* is *solar, mean solar,* or *sidereal* in its length according as measured to include the time interval between successive passages of the *real sun,* the *fictitious sun* (which makes uniform angular velocity in the heavens), or a *star* across the meridian.

*Declination* of a celestial object is its angular distance north or south of the celestial equator.

*Diffraction grating* is a surface of close, equally spaced, parallel lines whose joint effect on light produces a series of spectra.

*Diffraction* of *light* is the dispersion owing to the propagation of it by waves.

*Dip of the horizon* is that part of the angular distance of the visible horizon below the horizontal plane of the observer which is the geometrical consequence of elevation of the observer above the spherical surface of the earth. It is to be distinguished from atmospheric refraction.

*Disk of a heavenly body* is the flat circle which it appears to present. *Spurious disk* of a telescopic star image is the dispersion of starlight about the geometrical point to which the practically infinitely great distances of the stars reduce all their images.

*Distance, polar* is the angular distance of a celestial object from the pole. It is 90° minus the declination.

*Double star,* close companion stars, often, but not always, in mutual revolution.

*Eccentricity* of an *orbit* is the departure of it from circularity. The measure of it is technically defined in analytical geometry.

*Eclipse* is the interception of the light from a celestial object by the passage of another celestial object between it and the source of light.

*Eclipse, lunar,* is the interception of the sun's light from the moon by the earth.

*Eclipse, solar,* is the interception of the sun's light from the earth by the moon.

*Ecliptic,* is the path in which the earth revolves about the sun.

*Ecliptic, plane of,* the plane which contains the tangent to the motion of the earth's center about the sun, and also the center of the sun itself. Owing to the practically infinitely great distance of the stars compared to the solar motion, this plane may be regarded as fixed. (The same consideration applies to *Equator, Celestial.*)

*Elements* of an *orbit* comprise the six quantities required to fully define it. They are eccentricity, mean radius vector, inclination of orbit plane to plane of the ecliptic, longitude of the ascending node, period required for complete revolution, and time of passage across some definite point, as, for example, perihelion or periastron.

*Elongation,* the angular distance eastward or westward of an inferior planet from the sun, or of a satellite from its primary.

*Ephemeris,* a table of positions of celestial objects at successive times.

*Epoch,* a reference time.

*Equation of time* is the interval between mean and apparent solar time. In other words, between the times of meridian passage of the fictitious sun, which is assumed to traverse the heavens uniformly, and the real sun whose angular velocity varies.

*Equation, personal,* of an observer gives the correction to be applied to his observations on account of his habit of reading; as for instance before or after the true instant, or in advance of or behind the true position.

*Equator, celestial,* is the continuation of the plane of the terrestrial equator without limit into celestial spaces. From it astronomers reckon declination. (See remark under *Ecliptic, Plane of.*)

*Equator, terrestrial* is the great circle upon the earth midway between the poles.

*Equatorial mounting* of a telescope or other instrument is one in which two axes are employed, one parallel to the earth's axis, the other at right angles thereto. Thus the instrument moves in right ascension about the first, and in declination about the second.

*Equinox,* is the instant when the sun occupies the line in the heavens which is the intersection of the plane of the equator with the plane of the ecliptic. The name arises from the equality of night with day at such times.

*Equinox, autumnal,* the equinox which occurs in autumn, about September 21.

*Equinox, precession of,* see *Precession.*

*Equinox, vernal,* the equinox which occurs in spring, about March 21.

*Eyepiece* of an instrument is a system of small lenses adapted to present an image to the eye.

*Finder* is a small telescope attached parallel to the main one, which, since it surveys a wider angular field, promotes quicker discovery of the object sought.

*First point of Aries,* the origin from which are reckoned celestial longitudes on the ecliptic and right ascensions on the celestial equator. Now in Pisces.

*Focal length* of a *lens* or *mirror* is the distance from its center to its image of an object whose distance is very great. If f, f′, and f″ are the focal length and the respective distances of a near object and its image from the lens or mirror, $\frac{1}{f} = \frac{1}{f'} + \frac{1}{f''}$

*Focus* is the position where a lens or mirror produces its sharpest image of an object.

*Focus, principle,* is the position corresponding to an object at immense distance.

*Galactic latitude* is the angular distance of a celestial object measured from the median plane of the Milky Way.

*Galaxy,* properly speaking, the Milky Way. More broadly, our system of stars.

*Gibbous moon* or *planet* has over one-half of its disk visibly illuminated. Over "half-full" as we say.

*Gravitation,* the *force* which attracts one mass towards another. Apparently the laws of it are the same in all the heavens.

*Gravity, terrestrial,* the attractive force of the earth for masses within its scope.

*Heliocentric,* referring to the center of the sun as origin of measurement.

*Heliometer,* a telescope with divided object glass, the parts of which are moveable with a micrometric screw so as to superpose images of nearly adjacent celestial objects. Used for measuring small angular separations.

*Horizon, depressed,* is below the sensible horizon because of dip and atmospheric refraction.

*Horizon, sensible,* is bounded by a plane touching the earth at the observer's station and at right angles to the vertical.

*Horizon, true* is bounded by a plane through the earth's center at right angles to the vertical.

*Hour angle* of a celestial object is the angle between the planes of two great circles passing through the earth's poles, one of which passes through the zenith, the other bisects the object. The angle is usually expressed in hours, 15° to the hour, since this measure indicates the time to or from transit of the meridian.

*Inequality,* in mathematical astronomy a term used to mean irregularity in the motion of a planet.

*Inferior conjunction,* of an inferior planet occurs when its right ascension equals the sun's, but the planet lies between the earth and the sun.

*Inferior planet,* one whose orbit is within that of the earth.

*Latitude,* the angular distance upon the earth north or south of the equator.

*Latitude, galactic,* angular distance on the celestial sphere measured from the median plane of the Milky Way.

*Latitude, heliographic,* angular distance on the sun's sphere north or south of the sun's equator.

*Level, astronomical,* an instrument having a slightly curved closed glass tube almost full of alcohol, in which the position of the bubble indicates accurately when the base of the instrument is at right angles to the vertical, or how much it differs therefrom.

*Libration of the moon* in *latitude,* an apparent oscillation caused by the inclination of the moon's axis, and also by the inclination of the moon's orbit to the ecliptic. Owing to it we see more than half of the moon in its latitudes.

*Libration of the moon* in *longitude*, an apparent oscillation caused by the unequal velocity of revolution of the moon in its orbit, combined with its uniform velocity of rotation on its axis, and also caused by the daily rotation of the earth, bringing the observer into different positions of view at moon rising and setting. Thus we see more than half of the moon in its longitudes.

*Light-year*, the yearly distance which light travels. About 6,000,000,000,000 miles.

*Limb of the sun, planets, and satellites*. The edge of the visible disk.

*Longitude*, angular distance on the earth's surface between the planes of two great circles passing through the earth's poles, one through the observatory of Greenwich, the other through the place in question. Often reckoned in hours, 15° = 1 hour.

*Longitude, celestial*, angular distance from the first point of Aries measured on the ecliptic.

*Longitude, heliographic*, angular distance between the planes of two great circles passing through the sun's poles, one through the celestial point considered, the other through a chosen point upon the sun's equator.

*Lunation* is the period required by the moon to complete once all its phases. Otherwise termed the moon's synodic period, and the lunar month.

*Magnitude, absolute*, of a star is the brightness which would be perceived if it were removed to the distance where its parallax would be 0.1 second of arc. On this basis our sun would be of absolute magnitude about + 5, the brightest stars about − 5, and the faintest, about + 15.

*Magnitude, apparent*, is the star brightness as it actually appears. On this basis magnitudes run from − 26.7 for our sun to upwards of + 20 for the faintest stars which can be photographed by the largest telescope.

*Magnitude* of a *star* is its brightness on an adopted arbitrary geometrical scale, such that an increase of 5 magnitudes corresponds to 100-fold decrease in brightness.

*Major axis*, the larger axis of an orbit or spheroid.

*Mass*, quantity of matter contained.

*Mean distance*, the average separation of two bodies revolving about a common center.

*Meridian*, the plane of the great circle through the earth's poles and the observer's station.

*Meteor*, a small object in the solar system which, encountering the earth's atmosphere, becomes aglow by friction. Also called "shooting star."

*Meteorite*, a meteor which reaches the earth's surface as a solid of some size.

*Micrometer*, a precise instrument for measuring the angular separation of the images of two nearly adjacent objects, and also the angle between the line joining their images and a reference line.

*Minor axis*, the shorter axis of an orbit or spheroid.

*Motion, direct and retrograde*, occurs according as a celestial object advances towards the east or towards the west among the stars.

*Nadir*, the point vertically under the observer and opposite to the zenith.

*Nebula*, an object not starlike but cloudlike, existing in the distant celestial spaces.

*Nebula, bright, gaseous,* the irregularly formed type of nebula which, from its bright-line spectrum, appears to consist of gaseous material. The means of its illumination is not clear, but is thought to be associated with neighboring stars.

*Nebula, dark,* that which hides the stars in certain dark patches of the sky. Assumed to be unilluminated gaseous material.

*Nebula, planetary,* an illuminated gaseous type of nebula, with usually a ringlike form enclosing a central condensation.

*Nebulæ, spindle or spiral,* are flattened nebulous forms more or less definitely suggesting rotation. Their spectra are starlike, and not of the discontinuous, bright-line variety. Their distances are often immensely greater than those of known stars, and their extent so enormous as to suggest that they are galaxies in the making.

*New Star or Nova,* a star suddenly flaring out brightly where either none was seen before, or one excessively faint by comparison. The bright phase soon fades.

*Nodes,* of an *orbit* are the points of the orbit where the orbit plane intersects the plane of the ecliptic. The ascending node is that at which the object passes from the south to the north side of the ecliptic.

*Noon, apparent,* occurs when the real sun's center crosses the observer's meridian.

*Noon, mean,* occurs when the fictitious sun, which is assumed to march uniformly among the stars, is central on the observer's meridian.

*Nova,* see *New Star.*

*Nucleus,* of a *comet,* the roundish central part, which is all that a comet presents to view until the tail begins to form from it, at nearer approach to the sun.

*Nutation,* the wavy motion of the earth's axis, caused by the varying attractions of the sun and moon on the protuberance about the earth's equator.

*Objective or object glass,* the lens or mirror of a telescope which first receives the light of the object examined.

*Obliquity,* of the *ecliptic,* its inclination to the plane of the equator, about 23-1/2 degrees.

*Occultation,* the hiding of a star by another heavenly body, usually by the moon.

*Opposition,* of a *superior planet* occurs when its celestial longitude is 180° from the sun's, so that the planet is nearly behind the earth as viewed from the sun.

*Orbit,* the path of a heavenly body in revolution with another.

*Orientation,* the arrangement of objects.

*Parallax, solar,* the angle subtended by the earth's radius, viewed from the sun.

*Parallax, stellar,* the angle subtended by the radius of the earth's orbit, viewed from the star in question.

*Parsec,* a unit of stellar distance. The distance of a star whose parallax is one second of arc.

*Penumbra,* of a *sun-spot,* the outer part of lesser darkness.

*Periastron,* said of a companion star when nearest the principal star in its orbit.

*Perigee,* said of the moon when it is nearest to the earth in its orbit.

*Perihelion,* said of comets and planets when nearest the sun in their orbits.

*Period of orbit* is the interval required for the revolving object to pass from a given point of the orbit and return to it after one revolution.

*Perturbation*, the disturbance of an orbit by attracting masses other than the principal one.

*Phase of the moon or inferior planets* is the degree of illumination of their disk.

*Photometry*, the measuring of the intensity of light.

*Planets, inferior*, the two inner planets, Venus and Mercury.

*Planets, superior*, the five outer planets, Mars, Jupiter, Saturn, Uranus and Neptune.

*Poles of the celestial sphere*, are the points at 90° from the celestial equator.

*Poles of the Milky Way*, are the points at 90° from its median plane.

*Position angle*, of a *double star* is the angle between the line of centers of the two component stars and the great circle which passes through the larger one and the earth's poles. It is reckoned from the north point of the telescope field through east, south and west up to 360°.

*Precession of the equinoxes* is that westward march of the intersection of the planes of the equator and the ecliptic, caused by the attraction of the sun, moon and planets on the protuberant mass at the earth's equator.

*Prime Vertical* is the great circle passing through the zenith and the east and west points of the horizon.

*Quadrature*, a position of the moon or a superior planet at 90° from the sun.

*Radiometer*, a delicate instrument for measuring radiation, which operates on a similar principle to the vanes which revolve in sunlight, within partially evacuated glass bulbs, in opticians' windows.

*Radius vector* is the line joining the center of a revolving celestial object to the center of its orbit.

*Reflector*, or *reflecting telescope*, is a telescope in which the rays are received and concentrated towards a focus by means of a concave mirror.

*Refraction*, the bending of light rays as they pass from one transparent medium to another.

*Refraction, atmospheric*, the bending of rays from celestial objects which occurs within our atmosphere, because the air is more dense near the earth's surface. Atmospheric refraction elevates the sun and stars, at rising and setting, by about 1/2 degree.

*Refractor*, or *refracting telescope*, is a telescope in which the rays are received and concentrated towards a focus by means of a lens.

*Right Ascension*, the angular position of a celestial object measured eastward along the celestial equator from the point of vernal equinox called first point of Aries (now lying in the constellation Pisces) as the zero of right ascension. The angles are stated sometimes in degrees, sometimes in hours. 15° = 1 hour.

*Satellite*, or *moon*, is a small body revolving about one of the planets.

*Secular*, that which is associated with a long interval of time.

*Secular perturbation* of an *orbit* is the gradual modification in form or orientation of the orbit, due to the influence of small outside disturbing forces, and requiring many years to become conspicuous.

*Sextant*, an instrument having an arc of a sixth of a complete circle divided into 120 degrees, and used with accessories, including mirrors and a small telescope, to measure angles at sea.

*Sidereal*, pertaining to the realm of the stars as contrasted to solar, which relates to the realm of the sun.

*Siderostat*, an instrument for reflecting a beam of light from a celestial object in a fixed direction. Of two types, called polar and Foucault, of which the former is more simple. Both are inferior to the *coelostat*.

*Signs of the Zodiac*, twelve equal divisions of the Zodiac, measured from the equinoxes, and now precessed some 25° west of the constellations of the same names.

*Solar*, pertaining to the sun.

*Solstices*, the turning points in the sun's yearly apparent course northward and southward among the stars.

*Spectroscope*, a device including either one or more prisms, or else a diffraction grating, with accessories, suitably devised to disperse and separate a beam of radiation into the succession of rays of differing wave-length which compose it.

*Spherical aberration*, the departure from exact defining power of a lens or mirror, due to the divergence of the rays of the object examined from the central symmetrical line called the optic axis.

*Synodic period* of two bodies revolving about a common center is the interval between successive returns to the same situation in the orbit.

*Syzygy*, both the states of conjunction and of opposition of the moon are spoken of by this term.

*Telescopes* are *reflecting* or *refracting* according as they receive and condense the rays from the celestial object by means of a concave mirror or a lens. In the former case the mirror lies at the bottom of the tube and reflects towards the celestial object, while in the latter the lens lies at the top of the tube, and transmits the rays away from the celestial object.

*Telescope, Galilean*, of the type invented by Galileo, and still employed in opera glasses, comprises a double-convex lens, as object glass, and a double concave lens in front of the image, acting as eyepiece. The image is not inverted.

*Telescopes, reflecting*, are now usually of one of two types, called Newtonian when the image is viewed at the top of the tube, as reflected out of the tube by a flat mirror at 45°; *Cassegrainian*, when the image is viewed at the bottom of the tube, after reflection downwards from a convex mirror placed at the top of the tube, and either sending the rays through a central hole in the object mirror, or else out of the tube by reflection at 45°. Great modern reflectors are often arranged to be used in both ways.

*Thermopile*, an electrical thermometer of great delicacy used for measuring radiation.

*Time, equation of*, the difference between mean and apparent solar time.

*Transit instrument, meridian*, a telescope provided with a large accurately graduated circle and rigid pivoting, adapted to swing about an east and west horizontal axis, and therefore in the meridian. Used for observing the exact times when celestial objects cross the meridian, or "transit" as we say.

*Umbra* of *sun-spot*, the dark central part.

*Variable star* is one whose light varies in intensity, either regularly or irregularly.

*Vertex*, the highest point of a heavenly body.

*Vertical circles* are great circles passing through the observer's zenith.

*Year, anomalistic,* is equal to the interval between two successive passages of the earth through perihelion, and is nearly 5 minutes longer than the sidereal year.

*Year, mean solar,* is equal to the interval between two successive passages of the sun through the vernal or autumnal equinox. Owing to the precession of the equinoxes it is shorter by about 20 minutes than the *sidereal year.*

*Year, sidereal,* is equal to the interval between the sun's successive passages of the same star.

*Zenith,* the point vertically overhead.

*Zenith distance,* the angle between the center of a heavenly body and the zenith, or 90° minus the altitude.

*Zodiac,* the belt of the heavens containing the 12 constellations through which the sun apparently moves each year.

*Zodiacal light,* is the faint glow which may be seen after twilight is quite gone in the Zodiac. It is doubtless belonging to the solar system, not to the realm of the stars.

# INDEX